A HAWAIIAN ANTHOLOGY

Other books by Gerrit P. Judd

A

HAWAIIAN

ANTHOLOGY

EDITED BY GERRIT P. JUDD

THE MACMILLAN COMPANY

Library of Congress Catalog Card Number: 67-10888

Second Printing 1969

The Macmillan Company

Printed in the United States of America

SOURCES AND ACKNOWLEDGMENTS

Armstrong, William N. *Around the World with a King.* New York: Stokes, 1904.

Bingham, Hiram A. *A Residence of Twenty-One Years in the Sandwich Islands.* New York: Converse, 1847 (and later editions).

Bird, Isabella L. *The Hawaiian Archipelago: Six Months Among the Palm Groves, Coral Reefs and Volcanoes of the Sandwich Islands.* London: Murray, 1875 (reprinted as *Six Months in the Sandwich Islands.* Honolulu: University of Hawaii Press, 1964).

Carlyle, Thomas (ed.). *Oliver Cromwell's Letters and Speeches,* 2 vols. New York: Wiley & Putnam, 1845.

Chamberlain, Martha Ann. "Memories of the Past, Linked to Scenes of the Present, in the History of Kawaiahao Seminary" (January 24, 1889). Typescript in the possession of the Hawaiian Mission Children's Society, Honolulu. Printed with the Society's permission.

Clark, Blake. *Remember Pearl Harbor!* New York: Modern Age Books, 1942. Reprinted by permission of Blake Clark. Copyright 1942 by Blake Clark.

Coan, Titus. *Life in Hawaii: An Autobiographical Sketch of Missionary Life and Labors (1835–1881).* New York: Randolph, 1882.

Colum, Padraic. *The Bright Islands.* New Haven: Yale University Press, 1925. Reprinted by permission of the Yale University Press. Copyright 1925 by Yale University Press.

Emerson, Nathaniel B. *Unwritten Literature of Hawaii: The Sacred Songs of the Hula.* (Smithsonian Institution, Bureau of American Ethnology, Bulletin No. 38). Washington, D.C.: Government Printing Office, 1909. Reprinted by permission of the Smithsonian Institution.

Fuchida, Mitsuo. "I Led the Attack on Pearl Harbor," *United States Naval Institute Proceedings,* vol. 78, No. 9 (Sept. 1952), pp. 939–52. Reprinted from *Proceedings* by permission; copyright 1952 by U.S. Naval Institute.

Gilman, Peter. *Diamond Head.* New York: Coward-McCann, 1960. Reprinted by permission of Coward-McCann, Inc., from *Diamond Head* by Peter Gilman. Copyright © 1960 by Peter Gilman.

Gordon-Cumming, Constance F. *Fire Fountains: The Kingdom of Hawaii, Its Volcanoes and the History of Its Missions.* 2 vols. London: Blackwood, 1883.

Judd, Dr. Gerrit P. Letters to Finney, Dec. 3, 1828, and Apr. 28, 1837. Finney Papers, Oberlin College Library. Printed by permission of the Oberlin College Library.

Judd, Gerrit P. *Hawaii: An Informal History.* New York: Collier Books, 1961. Reprinted by permission of Crowell-Collier Publishing Co. Copyright © 1961 by Crowell-Collier Publishing Co.

Judd, Laura Fish. *Honolulu. Sketches of the Life, Social, Political and Religious in the Hawaiian Islands from 1828 to 1861.* New York: Randolph, 1880 (reprinted, Honolulu: *Star Bulletin,* 1928).

Krauss, Bob. *Here's Hawaii.* New York: Coward-McCann, 1960. Reprinted by permission of Coward-McCann, Inc., from *Here's Hawaii* by Bob Krauss. Copyright © 1960 by Bob Krauss.
Bob Krauss' Travel Guide to the Hawaiian Islands. New York: Coward-McCann, 1963. Reprinted by permission of Coward-McCann, Inc., from *Bob Krauss' Travel Guide to the Hawaiian Islands* by Bob Krauss. Copyright © 1963, 1964 by Bob Krauss.

Liliuokalani. *Hawaii's Story by Hawaii's Queen.* Boston: Lothrop, Lee & Shepherd, 1898 (reprinted, Rutland and Tokyo: Charles E. Tuttle, 1964).

London, Jack. "The Water Baby," in *On the Makaloa Mat.* New York: Macmillan, 1919. Reprinted by permission of Irving Shepard. Copyright 1919 by Charmian London.

Marshall, James F. B. "An Unpublished Chapter of Hawaiian History," *Harper's Magazine,* vol. 67 (1883), pp. 511–20.

Melville, Herman. *Typee.* New York: Wiley and Putnam, 1846.

Nordhoff, Charles. *Northern California, Oregon and the Sandwich Islands.* New York: Harper, 1874.

Rademaker, John A. *These Are Americans: The Japanese Americans in Hawaii in World War II.* Palo Alto, Cal.: Pacific Books, 1951. Reprinted by permission of the author. Copyright 1951 by John A. Rademaker.

Stevenson, Robert Louis. "The Bottle Imp," in *Island Nights' Entertainment.* New York: Scribner's, 1893.

Tennyson, Alfred. "Kapiolani," in *The Death of Oenone, Akbar's Dream and Other Poems.* London: Macmillan, 1892.

Toland, John. *But Not in Shame. The Six Months After Pearl Harbor.* New York: Random House, 1961. Reprinted by permission of Random House. Copyright © 1961 by John Toland.

Twain, Mark. *Following the Equator: A Journey Around the World.* 2 vols. New York: Harper, 1897.

Roughing It. Hartford: American Publishing Co., 1872.

Von Tempski, Armine. *Born in Paradise.* New York: Literary Guild of America, Inc., 1940. Reprinted by permission of Duell, Sloan & Pearce. Copyright 1940 by Armine Von Tempski.

for MSJ

CONTENTS

HAWAII'S HISTORY

HAWAIIAN TRADITIONS AND PLACES

HAWAII IN LITERATURE

IN RECENT YEARS Hawaii has acquired a glittering image, largely as a result of advertising to promote the booming tourist trade. Posters and spiels exploit Hawaii's charms in a script that any informed person may easily write for himself: a compound of year-round sunshine, bright beaches, warm blue water, surfing, lush vegetation, lovely women, throbbing music, dancing under the stars, and so forth. With so much money involved, it is only natural to go on to extol Hawaii's luxurious beachfront hotels in Honolulu's Waikiki district (on the island of Oahu) and on the major outlying islands (verdant Kauai, unspoiled Maui, the rapturous island of Hawaii, and so on)—or in softer accents and in smaller print to hint that simpler (that is, cheaper) living is also available.

This picture of Hawaii has merit, even though it is as slick and contrived as the usual Hollywood movie. Everything the glamor merchants say about the Islands is true. The climate is one of perpetual summer, the scenic beauty is exactly as portrayed, the swimming is superb, the women are lovely (well, just as lovely as anywhere else), and the hotels are as well appointed as those in Miami Beach.

It is all true, what they say about Hawaii. But it is not all of the truth. We must come down to earth now, and take a second look. There is no point in bursting into tears. For the real Hawaii, as it is and was, is much more fascinating than the caricature created by the advertising agencies.

One hundred years ago or more, Honolulu was a dusty and ramshackle frontier town, like a mid-Pacific extension of the American West. Natives and whalers caroused there, and rioted in the unpaved streets. Stern-faced missionaries of course disapproved and did what they could to make God-fearing Puritans of the "debauched" Polynesians. As in other parts of the world, fierce conflict resulted between the commercial and missionary groups.

Hawaii has known much violence. Before the coming of the white man in 1778, the native population led a far from utopian way of life. Early in the nineteenth century King Kamehameha I (the Great) unified Hawaii—by war. In 1843, a British naval squad-

ron seized the Islands. In 1893, gunfire briefly rang through Honolulu's streets in the revolution which overthrew the monarchy.
More fighting occurred in the abortive counterrevolution of 1895.
And everybody knows what happened at Pearl Harbor at 7:55 A.M.
on December 7, 1941.

Hawaii has experienced both hardship and accomplishment.
Through plain old-fashioned hard work the missionaries educated
the natives and brought public order to the Islands. Missionary
descendants and others, including laborers from Asia, spent long
and exhausting days in plantation fields. At last they discovered,
and successfully produced, two major cash crops—sugar and pineapples.

Somewhat later, in the 1930's, Hawaii came under bitter attack—
almost like an echo of the antimissionary diatribes of the past. The
Massie rape case made headlines in the American press. Military
leaders and others, from bias or ignorance or both, talked nonsense
about the "savage" Hawaiians and pointed with silly fear to
Hawaii's "un-American" Oriental population. Island residents
resented and parried such slander, and checked a strong movement
to put Hawaii under military rule. In 1959, with statehood, they won
the final victory to live on a par with all other Americans in the
federal Union.

From all this strife, confusion, and hard-won accomplishment one
central fact emerges, far more glamorous than the pretty-pretty views
of the travel posters. Hawaii has a history. People of diverse ethnic
and racial origins have come to Hawaii at various times and for
various reasons. Please, these were real people, not romantic stereo-
types. They struggled, persevered, and sometimes fought—as people
do everywhere and have since history began. And, on balance, they
have accomplished far more than they destroyed.

More than that occurred. Residents, travelers, and men of letters
recorded their impressions of the Islands. Over the years, an extraordinarily rich literature about Hawaii has arisen, some still in manuscript, and some in newspapers, periodicals, and books of all sorts.
Part of this writing is known to the general reader. The larger part
probably is not.

In making selections for this anthology, the editor has sought to
present not only some of the familiar but also, and more important,
many of the lesser known yet revealing writings about the Islands.
Selections from some prominent writers about Hawaii, for example

James Jones, do not appear here, because they are already well known and because to reprint extracts out of context might create a false impression. Some works included here have only minor literary value, for example the note by Carlyle and Tennyson's poem on Kapiolani, but appear because of associative interest. Others, for example the substantial extracts from Mark Twain and Robert Louis Stevenson, have enduring literary worth. Still others appear mainly because of their warmth and insights—and many of these pieces, it may be added, turn out to be astonishingly well written.

The editor's purpose has simply been to give a broad sample of the innumerable writings which deal with the Hawaiian experience. The first section of this book treats Hawaii's history: the missionary period (with two selections printed here for the first time), the era of the later Hawaiian monarchy, the revolution of 1893, Hawaii's annexation by the United States in 1898, the Pearl Harbor attack, and finally Hawaii as the fiftieth state. The second section deals with Hawaiian traditions and places and includes material on the *hula* and *luau* (feast) as well as descriptions of some distinctive places in the Islands which travel folders seldom mention. The third (and final) section deals with Hawaii as interpreted by some eminent men of letters.

This work has been a genuine labor of love. The editor, although not born in the Islands, belongs to a *kamaaina* (born-on-the-land, that is, born-in-Hawaii) family, descended from Dr. G. P. Judd, the missionary-physician who came to Hawaii in 1828 and served as prime minister of the Hawaiian kingdom in the years 1842 to 1853. A family tradition has it that the Judds came around Cape Horn to Hawaii and that they have been tooting their horn ever since. The editor would hestitate to give the lie to such a venerable tradition but promises the reader that in this book the horn-tooting will be muted.

G.P.J.

HAWAII'S
HISTORY

It is strange to imagine that the semitropical Hawaiian Islands, often called the Paradise of the Pacific, could have a turbulent history. Yet ever since Cook's discovery of the Islands in 1778, Hawaii has responded quickly to major historical forces. The Islands lie in the eastern sector of the North Pacific. Honolulu, on the island of Oahu, is about twenty-four hundred miles from San Francisco and about thirty-eight hundred miles from Tokyo. Because of their location, the Hawaiian Islands have served as a link between North America and Asia.

The eight main islands, with an area of 6,435 square miles, are a little bigger than Connecticut and Rhode Island combined. Volcanic in origin, and with two volcanoes still active on the Big Island (the island of Hawaii), the Islands have many mountains (some with occasional snow on their peaks) and deep valleys, along with broad plains and beaches. The climate is mild. There are no seasons, so that time seems to stand still. At sea level Hawaii's average temperature is about seventy-five degrees and varies only slightly throughout the year. Finally, Hawaii has no snakes, so that children and adults alike can romp barefooted without fear through the heavy vegetation.

Study of language and ancient remains, such as stone tools, indicates, along with other evidence, that Polynesians originated in Indonesia and that the main migration of Polynesians to Hawaii came from Tahiti about A.D. 900. The long voyage northward, some twenty-seven hundred miles in extent, across open water in open canoes, was a prodigious act of bravery and endurance. Once in Hawaii, the natives lived mainly by raising pigs and taro (for *poi*) and by fishing. But their way of life was far from idyllic. The rule of the nobility (*alii*) was often stern. The *kapu* (tabu) system was often oppressive.

In any case, early in 1778 Captain James Cook of the British Navy discovered Hawaii by accident on a voyage from Tahiti to the Pacific Northwest. After a friendly reception by the natives, Cook lost his life in a skirmish ashore in 1779 at Kealakekua Bay on the island of Hawaii. Cook's squadron departed. But many other foreigners came in increasing numbers to the Paradise of the Pacific. Contact with Western civilization had mixed results. White advisers helped King Kamehameha I (*ca.* 1759–1819) to create a unified Hawaiian kingdom by 1810. Foreigners enriched Hawaii's economy with such items as iron, cattle, horses, goats, and geese, previously unknown to the natives, along with fruit such as the mango and trees such as the algarroba (*kiawe*). But foreigners brought diseases, among them smallpox and measles, to which the natives had little immunity. Foreigners also introduced liquor, to which the natives in Hawaii, as in other Polynesian areas, proved hopelessly susceptible. The net result was predictable. The Hawaiian population dropped sharply, from about 300,000 in 1778 to about 135,000 in 1819. A drop in native morale also occurred when, in 1819, Kamehameha II abolished the *kapu* system, which had provided social order in ancient Hawaii.

Protestant American missionaries reached Hawaii in 1820. Their intentions were excellent. In accordance with the rise of liberal Calvinism in this period, they sought not only to convert the natives to Christianity but also to introduce them to the worldly improvements of Western civilization, such as schools, hospitals, and democratic government. Until the death of Kamehameha III in 1854, the American missionaries dominated Hawaii. They labored earnestly among the demoralized natives, converted them (at least formally) to Christianity, persuaded many to take the total abstinence pledge, made them almost universally literate, and provided them with a liberal government in 1840. The extent to which the missionaries helped or harmed the natives was the subject of a fierce debate at the time, and remains so. In any case, the deterioration of the native population, largely achieved in the premissionary era, continued. By 1850 the native population had fallen to about eighty-five thousand.

In the years 1854–93, the Hawaiian rulers freed themselves from missionary control and with varying degrees of success struck out on their own. Hawaii had five monarchs in this troubled era: Kamehameha IV, who ruled in the years 1854–63; his brother Kamehameha V (1863–72); Charles Lunalilo (1872–73), Hawaii's first elected king; David Kalakaua (1873–91), the Merry Monarch, celebrated for his trip around the world; and his sister, Liliuokalani (1891–93), Hawaii's last native ruler. In this period descendants of the missionaries and foreign settlers in Hawaii gradually dominated

Hawaii's economy. Whaling, previously a main source of wealth in the Islands, declined about 1860. Sugar became Hawaii's economic mainstay, especially after the signing of the Reciprocity Treaty (1875), which removed duties on Hawaii's trade with the United States. The native population continued to decline and reached a low of forty thousand in 1890. To counter a growing labor shortage, sugar planters began to import contract and other laborers. According to the census of 1890, Hawaii's population of ninety thousand included fifteen thousand Chinese, twelve thousand Japanese, and nine thousand Portuguese. At that time, Hawaii's distinctive interracial "melting pot" was well started.

In 1893, American and other foreign residents in Hawaii overthrew the monarchy and established a provisional government. They objected to Queen Liliuokalani's attempt to bring about authoritarian rule. In addition, Hawaii's commercial interests, hurt by the American tariff of 1890, which discriminated against Hawaiian sugar, hoped for annexation to the United States in order to restore prosperity to the Islands. But the annexation attempt failed, and the provisional government transformed itself into a republic. Only in 1898, in the heat of the Spanish-American War, did the United States government finally recognize the strategic importance of Hawaii as a mid-Pacific stronghold. President McKinley signed the resolution to annex Hawaii in July of that year. On August 12 the formal transfer of sovereignty took place at a ceremony in Honolulu which some old-timers still recall. Two years later Hawaii received formal organization in the Union as a territory.

In the years 1900 to 1941, Hawaii adjusted to the limited self-government of a United States Territory and met various hard problems in local administration. But on the whole the times were quiet, at least as compared to the stormy last years of the monarchy, and the era of the revolution, provisional government, and republic. Increasingly, responsible leaders in the Islands chafed at their territorial status, which gave them no vote in national elections, no representation in Congress (beyond a voteless delegate), and only limited control of their own local affairs. In addition, an extremely bad press (and threats of repressive political action) resulting from the notorious Massie rape case of 1931 and discrimination against Hawaiian sugar in the Jones-Costigan Act of 1934 convinced many thinking Islanders that, in order to have fair treatment as an "integral part" of the United States, Hawaii should become a state.

But agitation for statehood failed. Meanwhile, Hawaii's economy and population matured. Largely because of the vision and energy of James Drummond Dole, pineapples became a major crop, second only to sugar in the Islands. Hawaii's racially mixed population increased and through public education and other means became thoroughly Americanized.

The Japanese sneak attack on Pearl Harbor in Hawaii on December 7, 1941, thrust the United States into World War II and at the same time thrust Hawaii into a central position in world affairs. Thousands of troops and war workers came to Hawaii and learned about the Islands at first hand. Meanwhile, Americans of Japanese ancestry, in Hawaii as elsewhere in the United States, fought a grim battle to be permitted to fight for their country. Once in uniform they served with distinction unsurpassed in American military annals. Through unusual courage, often at the cost of their lives, they won the right, which Caucasian Americans had inherited, to stand as American citizens, first class.

After the war Hawaii prospered. Her two great cash crops, sugar and pineapples, flourished. But by 1960, income from tourism, burgeoning with the age of jet aircraft, surpassed that from both crops. Heavy federal spending continued, particularly in the military establishment. Meanwhile the drive for statehood took new vigor. After long wrangling in Congress, victory finally came. On August 21, 1959, President Eisenhower officially announced that Hawaii was the fiftieth state. Island residents of all races celebrated the news with fireworks and enormous bonfires and generally behaved as if they were guests at everybody's birthday party.

As before, Hawaii's racial groups mingled and intermarried freely. In 1960, about a third of the population of over 600,000 was Caucasian and about the same number were of Japanese descent. About one-tenth were Filipino, and about 6 per cent were Chinese. The rest (about 18 per cent) were mainly part-Hawaiian. At that time, pure-blooded Hawaiians accounted for less than 2 per cent of the population. Interracial marriage is increasing in Hawaii. Almost perfect tolerance of racial differences prevails. Island residents take pride in this happy situation. Civil Rights marchers in the American South once carried a sign which stated simply and correctly, "Hawaii Knows Integration Works."

Hiram A. Bingham

ARRIVAL OF THE FIRST MISSIONARIES

IN MARCH, 1820, the first missionaries, from the United States, reached Hawaii on the brig *Thaddeus* after an exhausting voyage from Boston around Cape Horn. Included in the first company of American missionaries was the Reverend Hiram Bingham, a staunch and uncompromising Puritan with immense conviction and immense strength of personality. In the years to follow, "King" Bingham dominated not only the mission but also the Hawaiian Kingdom. His theocratic rule brought about the formal Christianizing of Hawaii but evoked furious hostility from the sailors and merchants in the Islands.

Bingham's account of the arrival of the missionaries is a Hawaiian classic. It dramatized their hopes and uncertainties and presented in gripping detail the huge challenge involved in bringing not only Christianity but also Western civilization to a segment of Polynesia thoroughly demoralized by two generations of contact with less dedicated Americans and Europeans. It first appeared in 1847 in his long and earnest book entitled *A Residence of Twenty-One Years in the Sandwich Islands.*

TWO DAYS LATER, at early morning, March 30th, to the joy of our expecting little company, the long looked for Hawaii appeared in the West. The lofty Mauna Kea lifted its snow crowned summit above the dark and heavy clouds that begirt its waist. Our natives eagerly watching, had descried it in the night, at the distance of eight miles. As we approached, we had a fine view of about sixty miles of the N.E. coast of the island—the districts of Hilo, Hamakua, and part of Kohala; and as the sun shining in his strength dissipated the clouds, we had a more impressive view of the stupendous pyramidal Mauna Kea, having a base of some thirty miles, and a height of nearly three miles. Its several terminal peaks rise so near each other, as scarcely to be distinguished at a distance. These, resting on the shoulders of this vast Atlas of the Pacific, prove their great elevation by having their bases environed with ice, and their summits covered with snow, in this tropical region, and heighten

the grandeur and beauty of the scene, by exhibiting in miniature, a
northern winter, in contrast with the perpetual summer of the
temperate and torrid zones below the snow and ice. The shores
along this coast appeared very bold, rising almost perpendicularly,
several hundred feet, being furrowed with many ravines and
streams. From these bluffs, the country rises gradually, for a few
miles, presenting a grassy appearance, with a sprinkling of trees and
shrubs. Then, midway from the sea to the summit of the mountain,
appeared a dark forest, principally of the koa and ohia, forming a
sort of belt, some ten miles in breadth—the temperate zone of the
mountain.

As we approached the northern extremity of Hawaii, we gazed
successively, upon the verdant hills, and deep ravines, the habitations
of the islanders, the rising columns of smoke, the streams, cascades,
trees, and vestiges of volcanic agency: then, with glasses, stretching
our vision, we descried the objects of our solicitude, moving along
the shore—immortal beings, purchased with redeeming blood, and
here and there, the monuments of their superstition. Animated with
the novel and changeful scene, we longed to spring on shore, to
shake hands with the people, and commence our work by telling
them of the great salvation by Jesus Christ. As we passed round the
northern extremity of Hawaii, Maui rose on our right, at the distance of twenty-five or thirty miles.

Having gained the lee, or western side of Kohala, an officer with
Hopu and Honolii was sent by a boat, at 4 P.M., to make inquiry
of the inhabitants respecting the state of the islands, and the residence of the king. Waiting nearly three hours, we hailed their
return, eager to catch the sound of the first intelligence; and how
were our ears astonished to hear, as it were, the voice divine, pro-
claiming on their hills and plains,

> In the wilderness, prepare yet the way of the Lord,
> Make straight in the desert, a highway for our God.

How were our hearts surprised, agitated, and encouraged beyond
every expectation, to hear the report—"Kamehameha is dead—His
son Liholiho is king—the tabus are abolished—the images are destroyed—the *heiaus* [temples] of idolatrous worship are burned, and
the party that attempted to restore them by force of arms has recently been vanquished!" The hand of God! how visible in thus
beginning to answer the prayer of his people, for the Hawaiian

race! But such is the known propensity of the human heart to follow the vanities of the heathen, that even the tribes of Israel, though trained to the worship of the true God, and made to acknowledge the oft repeated and wonderful interpositions of his power and mercy, were ever ready, we remembered, to relapse into idolatry; and how much more did we fear these uninstructed heathen would do so, unless they could be speedily impressed with the claims of Christianity. Without this, there could be no security that the nation would not be scourged with atheism or anarchy, or with a species of idolatry more vile, bloody and fatal, than they had ever yet known. . . .

On the 31st of March, a considerable number of the natives came off to our vessel, from the shores of Kohala, to dispose of their little articles of barter, and to look at the strangers. Their manoeuvres in their canoes, some being propelled by short paddles and some by small sails, attracted the attention of our little group, and for a moment, gratified curiosity; but the appearance of destitution, degradation, and barbarism, among the chattering, and almost naked savages, whose heads and feet, and much of their sunburnt swarthy skins, were bare, was appalling. Some of our number, with gushing tears, turned away from the spectacle. Others with firmer nerve continued their gaze, but were ready to exclaim, "Can these be human beings! How dark and comfortless their state of mind and heart! How imminent the danger to the immortal soul, shrouded in this deep pagan gloom! Can such beings be civilized? Can they be Christianized? Can we throw ourselves upon these rude shores, and take up our abode, for life, among such a people, for the purpose of training them for heaven?" *Yes.* Though faith had to struggle for the victory, these interrogatories could all be answered decidedly in the affirmative. At sunset they returned to their dark cabins, and we passed along a little further south.

On the 1st of April, as we were abreast of Kawaihae, Kalanimoku and his wives, and Kalakua (subsequently Hoapiliwahine) and her sister Namahana (sometimes Opiia), two of the widows of the late king, came off to us with their loquacious attendants, in their double canoe. It was propelled with spirit, by eighteen or twenty athletic men. Having over their heads a huge Chinese umbrella, and the nodding *kahilis* or plumed rods of the nobility, they made a novel and imposing appearance as they drew near our becalmed Mission Barque, while we fixed on them, and their movements, our scrutinizing gaze. As they were welcomed on board, the felicitous native compliment, *aloha* (good-will, peace, affection), with shaking hands, passed between them, and each member of the mission family, Captain Blanchard and others. Their tall, portly, ponderous appearance seemed to indicate a different race from those who had visited the vessel before, or a decided superiority of the nobility over the peasantry. Their weight has I think been overrated. The younger brother of these queens, on coming to maturity, balanced in the scales two peculs of their sandal wood, 266⅔ lbs.—This was about the weight of Kalanimoku, and may be regarded as the average weight of the chiefs of the islands, male and female. Kalanimoku was distinguished from almost the whole nation, by being decently clad. His dress, put on for the occasion, consisted of a white dimity roundabout, a black silk vest, yellow Nankeen pants, shoes, and white cotton hose, plaid cravat, and fur hat. One of the bare-footed females of rank soon threw off her printed cotton gown, to which she was unused, retaining a gingham shirt, and the customary Hawaiian robe for a female of rank. This consisted of ten thicknesses of thin unwoven bark cloth, three or four yards in length, and thirty inches in breadth, laid together, and tacked by single stitches, at several places, through the upper edge. It is worn by being wrapped several times round the middle, and having the upper or stitched edge turned over a little on the hip, to confine the outer end, and keep the whole from falling off. It would be difficult to say which party was most impressed with the novelty of the objects they beheld. Kalanimoku was much attracted by the *kamalii keakea* [white children], and all were struck with the first appearance of civilized women.

Happy in so early and pleasant an introduction to personages of so much influence, we were assiduous in our efforts to impress them favorably, making them acquainted with our business, and our wish to reside in the country. But, notwithstanding our solicitude to obtain Kalanimoku's assent at once, he referred us to the king. As a token of friendship and confidence, he presented us a curiously wrought spear, a signal, we hoped, that their weapons of war were soon to be converted into implements of husbandry, and their warriors enlisted as soldiers of the Lord Jesus Christ.

Near sunset, our distinguished guests took leave and returned to the shore on their state vehicle—their double canoe, seated on a light narrow scaffolding which rested on the semi-elliptical timbers by which two large parallel canoes, each neatly carved from a tree, are yoked together, five or six feet apart. Their large canoes are two to three feet in depth, and thirty to fifty in length. The thin sides are raised by the addition of a nicely fitted waist-board. Additional pieces of thin wood, ingeniously carved, are attached at the ends, and covering a few feet as a deck and turning up some fifteen inches at the extremity, and giving the appearance of greater finish, beauty, and utility.

The favored passengers on a Hawaiian double canoe sit three or four feet above the surface of the water, while the rowers sit on a thwart in the canoe with their feet below the surface and their faces forward. The steersmen sit in the stern. Their paddles have a round handle from three to four feet long, and a thin blade from twelve to eighteen inches long and eight to twelve wide, and are grasped by one hand at the extreme end, and by the other, near the blade, and are used by main strength.

The chiefs, on this occasion, were rowed off with spirit by nine or ten athletic men in each of the coupled canoes, making regular, rapid, and effective strokes, all on one side for a while, then, changing at a signal in exact time, all on the other. Each raising his head erect, and lifting one hand high to throw the paddle blade forward beside the canoe, the rowers, dipping their blades, and bowing simultaneously and earnestly, swept their paddles back with naked muscular arms, making the brine boil, and giving great speed to their novel and serviceable sea-craft. These grandees and their ambitious rowers, gave us a pleasing indication of the physical capacity, at least, of the people whom we were desirous to enlighten, and to whose necessities we rejoiced to know the Gospel to be adapted. As they disappeared, the sun sank to his western ocean bed toward populous China, and the full orbed moon, brightly reflecting his light rose majestically from the east, over the dark Pagan mountains of Hawaii, symbolizing the approach of the mission Church, designed to be the reflector of the sun-light of Christianity upon that benighted nation. Then, ere the excitement of the chiefs' visit was over, Mr. Thurston and his yoke-fellow ascended the shrouds, and, standing upon the main-top (the mission family, captain and crew being on deck), as we gently floated along on the smooth silent sea, under the lee of Hawaii's dark shores, sang a favorite song of Zion (Melton Mowbray), which they had sung at their ordination at Goshen, and with the Park St. Church choir, at Boston, on the day of embarkation. . . .

The next morning our brig being in Kawaihae bay, I made my first visit on shore, landed on the beach near where Keoua and his companions had been murdered, and called on Kalanimoku at his thatched hut or cottage in that small uninviting village. With him, I visited Puukahola, the large heathen temple at that place, a monument of folly, superstition, and madness, which the idolatrous conqueror and his murderous priests had consecrated with human blood to the senseless deities of Pagan Hawaii. Built on a rough hill, a little way from the shore of the bay, it occupied an area about 240 feet in length, and 120 in breadth, and appeared as much like a fort as a church. On the ends and inland side of the parallelogram, the walls of loose black stone or fragments of lava, were fifteen feet high, ten feet thick at the bottom, and five at the top. On the side towards the sea, the wall consisted of several terraces on the declivity of the hill, rising from some twenty feet below the enclosed area, to a little above it. The frowning structure is so large and prominent, that it can be distinctly seen with the naked eye, from the top of Maunakea, a distance of about 32 miles. As a fortification of Satan's kingdom, its design was more for war against the human species than the worship of the Creator.

This monument of idolatry, I surveyed with mingled emotions of grief, horror, pity, regret, gratitude, and hope;—of grief and horror at the enormities which men and devils had perpetrated there before high heaven;—of pity and regret that the victims and many of the builders and worshippers, had gone to their account without the knowledge of the Gospel, which ought to have been conveyed to them; of gratitude, that this stronghold of Satan had been demolished and the spell around it broken; and of hope that soon temples to the living God would take the place of these altars of heathen abomination.

After this brief survey of this part of the field, Kalanimoku, his wives, and two of the widows of Kamehameha, embarked with us; and as we together proceeded toward Kailua, the residence of the king, we engaged in public worship, and dwelt with pleasure on the glorious theme, the design of the Messiah to establish his universal reign, and to bring the *isles* to submit to him, and rejoice in his grace, as indicated by the language of the Prophet Isaiah, "He shall not fail nor be discouraged till he have set judgment in the earth, *and the isles shall wait for his law."*

Kalakua, a widow of Kamehameha, having little sympathy with the Evangelical prophet, and shrewdly aiming to see what the *white women* could do for her temporal benefit, asked them to make a gown for her in fashion like their own. Putting her off till the Sabbath was over, apprising her that unnecessary labor was on that day prohibited to all by the great Jehovah whom we worshipped, they cheerfully plied scissors and needle the next day, and soon fitted out the rude giantess with a white cambric dress. Thus, feeble, voyage-worn, having been long without fresh provisions, and withering under a tropical sun as they crossed the equatorial regions the second time, they began before we cast anchor, to secure favor by kindness and demonstration of their ability and readiness to make themselves useful.

Dr. Gerrit P. Judd

TWO MISSIONARY LETTERS

In 1826 the handsome evangelist Charles Grandison Finney converted Dr. Gerrit Parmele Judd (the editor's great-grandfather), then twenty-three years old, at a revival in Utica, New York. Two years later Dr. Judd arrived in Hawaii as a medical missionary in the service of the American Board of Commissioners for Foreign Missions. In 1842 Dr. Judd left the mission and entered the Hawaiian government. Until 1853, in years of tempest and crisis, Dr. Judd was Hawaii's prime minister, directing almost singlehandedly the varying fortunes of the Hawaiian government.

These letters, written in 1828 and 1837, are to Finney and describe some of Dr. Judd's experiences as a missionary physician in Hawaii. Both letters, here published for the first time, are in the Oberlin College library.

SANDWICH ISLANDS
Dec. 3d. 1828

VERY DEAR SIR,

Among the number of those dear friends who present a claim for letters I enumerate you, and after so long a delay sit down to pen a few words as evidence that I have not forgotten you. I regret exceedingly, that after being joined to my Dear Laura, we were not able to set our eyes on you. But a merciful God so ordered it and I ought not to grieve, rather let us lift up the voice in grateful songs, for His mercy endureth forever.

While on the surges of the mighty deep in common with our little fraternal band L[aura] and I were happy. We had our trials and our fevers, but they are not worth accounting. In Jehovah was our strength and He kept us from all harm. Since we landed on these shores we have been happy—we have our work—though have much unfaithfulness to lament. I think a life spent among the Heathen if spent in doing good is all we ought to ask. As for inheritance Christ shall be sufficient. We suffer for none of the comforts of life. Laura minds the affairs of the house and labours like a missionary among the native women. My hands are full of my professional business, etc., yet contrive to spend a good portion of every week in attending to the study of the language and other studies preparatory to engaging more actively into missionary work. In these employments time passes swiftly by us, 14 months have glided imperceptably [sic] away, and thus no doubt will life if it is the will of God. Soon the day will come when I shall meet you my spiritual father at (as we hope) the right hand of the Captain of our Salvation, and O that although in much tribulation we may look to that day and anchor there all our hopes. You know full well what opposition is. You know that when the standard of the cross is raised there the enemy begins to fortify himself. At these Islands the wicked raise high the hand of rebellion against the Most High. Drunkness, profanity, Sabbath breaking, lewdness are with a class of those who call themselves Christians fashionable accomplishments. Whoever dares either by precept or example to condemn their conduct, must meet their curses. You have no doubt heard of their hellish rage by the publick journals and know something what wicked men will do if the restraints of law and civilization are removed from them. The natives are our best friends. If they do not favour our plans, they are unwilling to oppose us from selfish motives. The cause of religion is gaining ground among them though the novelty of the thing is partly worn away. There is however no special attention to religion at any of the Missionary Stations. Here and there a sinner is seriously enquiring what he must do to be saved. The ignorance with which most are enshrouded requires to be removed, before they can see clearly the way to flee from the wrath to come. Instances of defection among the members of the church have not as yet occurred. We however know not how soon we may be called to mourn over those who draw back into perdition. The candle of the Lord is shining about this Mission. In the midst of opposition the cause triumphs. We have our friends even among the mariners who visit these Islands. Since I have been here I have seen five sea captains who consider themselves as Christians and of whom we entertain favourable opinion.

How does the cause of religion progress at home? How is the spirit of prayer? How the cause of revivals? I long to hear from you and to know what has been the final result of all the fire and smoke and noise which was raised about the time I left. Do you and the Eastern men agree? Or are they determined to break you down? Write me soon.

Your friends here are enjoying tolerable health. Fanny is the mother of a fine son. She is just as amiable and interesting as ever. I have not seen her for 5 or 6 months but have frequent intelligence from her. Laura sends her love and wishes me to say that she intends to write Mrs. Finney before a great while.

Where is Father Nash? I intend to write him as soon as leisure shall present itself. I must now bid you farewell for the present. Wishing you every good and asking your prayers for poor weak sinners, that the grace of God may be given us to perform all our labours which we have undertaken for Jesus' sake. The Lord bless you, keep up your faith and zeal and courage and bless your preaching to the salvation of thousands. Amen.

Love to all enquiring friends.

GERRIT P. JUDD

HONOLULU
April 28, 1837

MY BELOVED BROTHER IN THE LORD,

About a fortnight ago I received a letter from you dated Nov. 6, 1836 and sent by the hand of Miss Lucia Smith, and I hope you will receive this in reply as early as August. But God must direct that. I wrote you by Mr. Richards in Dec. last I think, urging you to take the subject of a foreign mission into serious consideration,

which I hope you will receive in due time when you greet that
beloved brother and messenger to the churches.

Your proposals to visit the Sandwich Islands cannot but be
agreeable to us all, especially to those of us who have the pleasure
of knowing you, and I hope you will take passage next Nov. if not
before. Your disease, you say, is a bowel complaint. This is rather
indefinite, but if it is a chronic diarrhoea as we doctors call it,
there is no doubt but you ought ot avoid excitement and you will
find this climate very congenial. In fact nothing can be equal to
the bland, soft, and mild atmosphere of these islands, for one who
needs a southern climate. The ordinary time for acquiring the language so as to preach is six months. But I hope you will not think of
remaining only a year. You must by all means bring your Lydia and
leave the children at home, except perhaps the youngest. Should
you come, be sure to obtain a commission from the A.B.C.F.M.
either as a missionary, or a deputation to look after our welfare,
and come prepared to take our fathers by the hand, who are excellent men and have a favorable impression of you from reading
your lectures. Mr. Bingham authorizes me to tender you an invitation from him and will be glad to meet you with all his heart.
He is a cautious man. I think you will like him.

Your apprehensions respecting the spiritual state of missionaries
are doubtless well grounded, tho I think you will find good leaven
among us. As for myself, I confess the case is bad enough, tho if
any one else were to tell you so I might either deny or palliate it.
I hope to get to heaven at last, and sometimes wish it were near. I
have work enough to do and hope I do it for Christ's sake, and for
the love I bear to his cause. I think my wife is a growing Christian.
The missionaries do love one another as a body, remarkably well.
They are temperate in all things. Only a minority use tea and
coffee. Spirits and tobacco excluded, and wine except as a pres-
cribed medicine. We live comfortably as to the goods of this life.
We were promised a 100 fold, but we are not obnoxious to the
charges of ostentation or extravagance. The Jesuits who were ex-
pelled from the islands very lately returned and are now here.
Come and help confound them and pull these foreign residents out
of the fire. We are having a protracted meeting on their account
but as yet they are not broken down. The soul destroying blast of
Unitarianism has withered them and they are steeled against the
truth. The captain, second mate and five or six of the crew of the

vessel that brought our late missionaries were converted, on the way, and six made a public confession of religion. Their passage was 115 days. We have had more feeling than usual among the native children of late and some conversions. I am in hopes you may be on your way and this letter may be lost, so I will not crowd it very full. Give our united love to your wife, children, and friends.

Your affectionate brother,
G. P. JUDD

Laura F. Judd

LIFE IN THE MISSION

LAURA FISH JUDD, the wife of Dr. G. P. Judd (and the editor's great-grandmother), arrived in Honolulu in the spring of 1828 with the third missionary company a few days before her twenty-fourth birthday, after a long voyage around Cape Horn from Boston. A woman of sensitivity, strength, and charm, she had a keen eye for detail, along with a melodic prose style. Her book *Honolulu,* completed in 1861, was first published in 1880, eight years after her death. For insight, humor, and deftly turned phrases, few writers about Hawaii in the nineteenth century are her equal.

The following extracts deal with her experiences in the early days of the mission. They include descriptions of physical hardship, early conversions, and early schools, along with pointed anecdotes about such Hawaiian leaders as the pious Kaahumanu and the heroic Kapiolani. Her life in the mission was full. In addition to serving as a missionary she bore nine children. Under such circumstances it is a wonder that she found the time and strength to write at all.

HONOLULU
August, 1828

HOUSEKEEPING at last in two little rooms and a chamber, under the same roof with the Binghams! The clapboards are bare and admit quantities of dust which the trade-winds bring in such fearful clouds as to suggest the fate of Pompeii. We have three chairs, a table, a bedstead, and a nice little secretary. Dr. Judd

has converted the round-topped wooden trunk that Uncle E——
made for me into a safe for our food, by placing it on stilts set
in pans of tar water, which keeps out roaches and ants. Mrs.
Bingham kindly allows me to have one of her trained servants,
who does the washing and assists in the kitchen.

We have commenced a school for native women, which already
numbers forty-five, including Kaahumanu, Kinau, Namahana, and
several of their attendants. They are docile and very anxious to
learn. I devote two hours a day teaching them to write on paper;
Mrs. Bingham spends two hours more in giving them lessons on the
slate, and teaching them how to divide words and sentences. Their
preference is to join words together in continuous lines across
the page, without stops or marks. Miss Ward superintends the sewing department. Our school-house has no floor nor desks, the only
substitute for the latter being a long board, supported by crosstrees,
for the writers. A flag is raised to signal the hour for school; it
came from a wrecked ship, the *Superb,* and bears the name in
white letters on a red ground. "Superb school mistresses," Mr.
Bingham calls us.

I can not begin to say how happy I am to be here, and how I
love to work for this interesting people. I little thought when teaching children in the State of New York what that discipline was
preparing me for. I was but sixteen when I made my début as school-
teacher. I wonder if the little brown school-house still stands at the
place where three ways meet? . . .

Opportunities for sending letters to the United States occur only
in the fall season, when whale-ships are returning home around
Cape Horn. We have had a very hot summer, no rain, the earth
parched, and clouds of dust blowing day after day. I have emptied
quarts of it from my bed cover at night, and it pours in so thickly
that in a few minutes it is impossible to distinguish the color of
the different articles of furniture.

Our yearly supply of sugar, flour, and other stores, sent from
Boston in a whale-ship, was carried by mistake to the Japan whaling
grounds, consequently we have been on short allowance. The
drought almost produced a famine in the vegetable kingdom.
Our good queen-mother has been often absent, and we have missed
her presents of kalo [taro], fish, and other good things. The poor
cattle have almost starved, and of course our supply of milk has
failed.

One morning this week was hot and oppressive; such as occur in your "dog days." A missionary sister was with me, who had been watching all night with her sick babe, and her husband absent on an exploring tour, while mine was visiting the sick. We sat down to our little breakfast-table spread with care, and offered to our craving appetites sweet potatoes and salt beef, the latter spoiled by its long voyage around Cape Horn, and a still longer stay in the mission depository. We sent it from the table, and tried to swallow some potatoes, but they were poor, watery things, more like squash than potatoes. The effort was useless. What if I did think of the well-stored pantries and the nice little delicacies my friends in America would offer me if they could? Was it wicked? Were we like the naughty Israelites, longing for the flesh-pots of Egypt? We wiped away our tears as quickly as we could. I said to my friend: "This will never do; you must have a breakfast. I have four shillings which were in my purse when I left Boston. I will take them and send down to the beef market. I know it is against the rule, and would be thought a bad precedent; we will say nothing about it. Meanwhile, let us untie the little parcel of flour, trusting in Providence to provide more." The servant returned with about a pound and a half of fresh beef for fifty cents! We broiled it, and with our hot cake made a delicious meal, then resumed our duties with cheerfulness and gratitude.

In the afternoon of the same day our friend Captain Bunker, of the *Zone,* arrived and gave us a barrel of flour and several other articles. I do not complain. Our friends in Boston are not to blame that we are short of supplies, as they have no regular means of conveyance; and the whalers, who kindly offer to bring our stores without remuneration, can not be expected to go out of their way to land them.

The *Honqua* has arrived with letters, papers, and boxes. We are in a fever of excitement. How kind our friends are; how pleasant to have so many long letters containing assurances of love unabated; how thoughtful of our comfort to send so many nice things, just what we need! We opened the flour, the crackers, dried fruit, cheese, lard, all put up by dear father and mother Judd; and here are chairs, a whole dozen, a new bureau and book-case, and a table that will stand alone—all provided by our kind relatives and friends in Oneida County. What shall we do with so much furniture? I will make a tea-party for Mr. and Mrs. Bingham the first thing. Upai will help me to make biscuit and doughnuts and stem some dried fruit, then we will sit down together at our new table, read our letters, and talk over all the news from our dear native land. After tea we will open our boxes, and examine the treasures sent us from our friends at home. No lady shopping on Broadway with a full purse, can feel half the delight we experience in opening a box from home.

> Touched by the magic hand of those we love,
>   A trifle does of consequence appear;
> A blade of grass, a pin, a glove,
>   A scrap of paper, does become most dear.

It is but natural that with the first impulses of maternal love we should turn our thoughts more directly to native mothers and children. A few days ago we called our female church-members together, and requested those who had children to bring them. A large number assembled, our good queen-mother heading the list, although she has no children of her own. She brought little Ruth, an adopted daughter, Kinau presented her first-born, Prince David Kamehameha, a boy fine enough for any mother not of the seed royal to glory in. Close beside her sits the wife of our deacon, Ehu, with three young children. Several mothers presented their offspring, with the pride of old Roman matrons. We counted the number of those who had living children, and then requested those who had none to rise. The scene that followed I can never forget. Why are you childless? we inquired. Very few had lost children by a natural death. One woman replied in tears, holding out her hands: "These must answer the question. I have been the mother of eight children, but with these hands I buried them alive, one after another, that I might follow my pleasures, and avoid growing old. Oh, if I had but one of them back again to comfort me now! If tears and penitence could restore the dead!" She was followed by others, making the same sad confessions of burying alive, of strangling, of smothering, until sobs and tears filled the house.

"Oh," said one, "you have little idea of our heartless depravity, before we had the Word of God. We thought only of preserving our youth and beauty, following the train of our king and chiefs, singing, dancing, and being merry. When old we expected to be cast aside, and being neglected, to starve and die, and we only cared for the present pleasures. Such was our darkness."

The scene was painful. We tried to say a few words of consolation and advice, and to commend them to God in prayer. We made arrangements to meet them regularly once a month for instruction in maternal and domestic duties, and returned to our own happy Christian homes, feeling that we never before realized how much we owe to the Gospel.

After my return I related to Pali, my native woman, some of the fearful disclosures made at the meeting. "My mother had ten children," said she; "my brother, now with you, and myself, are all that escaped death at her hands. This brother was buried too, but I loved him very much, and determined to save him. As soon as she went away, I ran and dug him up. He was not dead. I ran away many miles with him, and kept him hid with some friends a long time. My mother heard of us, and tried to get us back, but I kept going from one place to another, and after a while she died. I have always taken care of him until now."

It is impossible to describe how happy we were made by a visit of the U.S. sloop-of-war *Vincennes,* Captain Finch. It brought to us again the Rev. C. S. Stewart, chaplain, who was formerly connected with this Mission, as will be remembered. He was one of the very last to whom I gave the parting hand, when we sailed out of Boston harbor, and I need not say that he received a warm welcome from us.

The visit of the *Dolphin,* Captain Percival, which did not bear the olive branch, was still fresh in the minds of the native community. The unprovoked attack upon the houses and persons of the defenceless missionaries was approved by some of the foreigners already gathered in our little metropolis, with some honorable exceptions, but, I am sorry to say, the foreign officials were not of this excepted number. They treat the magnates of the land with rudeness and indignity. They get up a tempest of words upon the slightest pretext, and threaten our timid and peace-loving rulers with vengeance and extermination.

As yet, you must know, our people have no printed code of laws, other than the Decalogue, which Kaahumanu thinks can not be improved. Public ordinances are made known by a town crier, who patrols the highways at the quiet hour of twilight, and pours forth royal edicts with stentorian voice.

The visit of Captain Finch was opportune. He brought friendly communications from his Government, which is very encouraging to the chiefs, who are anxious to do their duty, though ignorant of foreign usages.

The king gave a reception at his large grass palace, to which all the foreigners and missionaries were invited, to meet Captain Finch and his officers. The band of music from the ship was in attendance, and as the king, the chiefs, the foreign officials, and the officers, were in full uniform, there being plenty of room in the immense building, it was a fine and delightful affair. A pair of large globes, a number of books, maps, and engravings, were presented to the king, [to] Kaahumanu, and other chiefs. As Kuakini, the Governor of Hawaii, is the only one of the chiefs who reads English, he received a very handsome quarto Bible. The message from the President of the United States was cordially received and responded to, with the grateful thanks of the chiefs. The interview passed off in the most agreeable manner, and our rulers, both men and women, appeared to the best possible advantage. We were glad when it was over, as we are always a little anxious lest some blunder should be committed.

During the stay of the ship Mrs. Bingham made a tea-party for the officers and chiefs, and had quite a house full. The time passed insensibly until nine o'clock, when the feast of reason was suddenly interrupted by a sound something between a whistle and the groan of a blacksmith's bellows. It was an announcement that our queen, Kaahumanu, was tired and must go home. She arose (I never saw her look so tall), gathered up the ample folds of her black silk dress, even to the very waist, holding a portion on each arm, and exposing an undergarment of beautiful pink satin. Thus she stood in her stateliness, while we all gathered around to shake hands and bid her good-night. We laughed a little, at her expense, after she had gone, but loved her none the less for all that. . . .

HONOLULU
November, 1829

After many months of hard labor our new thatched church is completed. Several hundred men at a time have been engaged in putting on the thatch under the superintendence of Governor Boki, who has set overseers, sword in hand, at the different portions of the work. The men chatter while at work like so many meadow larks, and their voices are sufficiently confused to remind one of what the scene might have been at Babel's tower. The church has a neat pulpit, of native mahogany (koa), a glazed window behind, draped with crimson damask, furnished by Kaahumanu. Upholstering is a new business. We had some idea of festoons, but knew not how to arrange them, so as to produce the proper effect, for we were without patterns and had no one to teach us. The young king was anxious to have it as grand as possible, as it was his chapel. We did our best, and what more is required of mortals?

The king, his royal sister, and a large number of the chiefs from the other islands were present at the dedication. Kaahumanu made a very interesting address to the people, and, to the surprise of all present, the king followed with a speech and a prayer. He not only dedicated the house to the worship of the only living and true God, but solemnly, then and there, consecrated his kingdom to the Lord Jesus Christ. The princess and her maids of honor led the choir, and the chant, "O come let us sing unto the Lord," which was sung in excellent taste. Governor Boki made a great display of soldiers dressed in new suits, purchased for the occasion, augmenting the public debt some thousands of dollars. He appeared restless and ill at ease.

I record another anecdote of Kaahumanu; the incident occurred a few weeks before the dedication. Mrs. Bingham, Miss Ward, and myself were spending the day with her at her rustic country-seat in Manoa valley. As we were seated at our sewing, Kaahumanu very kindly inquired what we thought of wearing at the dedication of the new church. Without waiting for an answer, she added: "It is my wish that we dress alike; I have made a selection that pleases me, and it only waits your approval." She ordered the woman in waiting to bring in the material; it was heavy satin, striped pink, white, and blue.

She fixed her scrutinizing eyes upon us as we examined and commented upon it in our own language. As we hesitated in the approval, "What fault has it?" she hastily inquired. I replied, "No fault; it is very beautiful for you who are a queen, but we are missionaries, supported by the churches and the earnings of the poor, and such expensive material is not suitable for us." "I give it to you," she replied, "not the church, nor the poor." "Foreigners will be present," we said, "who will perhaps make ill-natured remarks." "Foreigners!" said she, "do you mean those in town who tear off calico? (meaning the salesmen in the shops). What do you care for their opinions? It does not concern them; you should not heed what they say." We declined still further the acceptance, as we should not ourselves feel comfortable in such unaccustomed attire. She looked disappointed and displeased, and ordered the woman to put it out of sight, adding, "If it is not proper for good people to wear good things, I do not know what they are made for." We were sorry to oppose her wishes, and she was taciturn all the afternoon. As we were about to take leave at evening, she resumed her cheerful manner, and asked what we would like to wear on the forthcoming occasion. We thanked her, and said we would like to make something very handsome for her, but we should prefer black silk to anything else for ourselves. She made no reply, but bade us an affectionate good-night. The next morning we received two rolls of black silk, with an order to make her dress exactly like ours.

KAAWALOA, HAWAII
[*1829*]

As the health of some of the pioneer missionaries appears to be sinking from the effects of this warm climate, the brethren in council decided to send a committee to explore the bracing regions on the slopes of these snow-clad mountains, and seek for a health station. Dr. Judd was one of that committee, so I was obliged to leave my pleasant school and home, and come to this place, the home of Mr. and Mrs. Ruggles, who are too poorly to live alone. I remain with Mrs. Ruggles and the children, while Mr. R. and Dr. Judd make their explorations, which will occupy some weeks.

We took passage from Honolulu with Captain Rice, in the whale-ship *Superior,* of New London, and were eleven days making the passage. Captain James Smith, of the *Phoenix,* was in company. We encountered a severe storm, and took three whales, one of which, captured by Captain Smith, and nearly as long as his ship, was unfortunately lost during the gale.

Kealakekua is an historical spot. I write this in sight of the very rock where the celebrated Captain Cook was killed, and I have seen the man who ate his heart. He stole it from a tree, supposing it to be a swine's heart hung there to dry, and was horrified when he discovered the truth. The Sandwich Islanders never were cannibals. This made him famous, and he is always spoken of as the man who ate Lono's heart. Here I have made the acquaintance of the old queen, Kekupuohi, wife of Kalaniopuu. She was close to Captain Cook when he fell, following her royal husband, whom the English were enticing on board the ship, to be detained as hostage until a stolen boat should be restored. She says the natives had supposed that Captain Cook was their old god Lono, returned to visit them. They paid him divine honors, which he must well have understood. Men were sent from the ship, who cut down the fences around their temple. Women visited the ship in great numbers, and husbands grew jealous, and began to distrust these new divinities. A young chief was killed by a shot from one of the ships, while passing in his canoe. There was a great uproar among the people, and when they saw their king about stepping into the boat with Captain Cook, an old warrior said, "I do not believe he is a god. I will prick him with my spear, and if he cries out I shall know he is not." He struck him in the back. Cook uttered a cry, the chief gave another thrust, and the great navigator proved to be mortal. These facts were gathered from an eye-witness, who expressed the deepest regret at the sad tragedy.

Just across the bay is the birth-place of Obookaiah, the first native convert to Christianity. He went to America in a whale-ship, was taken up and cared for by some benevolent people, who founded the Cornwall school.

It was during this residence at Kaawaloa that we visited the old "heiau," or temple, at Hoonaunau, in company with Naihe and Kapiolani. It was then surrounded by an enclosure of hideous idols carved in wood, and no woman had ever been allowed to enter its consecrated precincts. Our heroic Kapiolani led the way, and we entered the enclosure. It was a sickening scene that met our eyes. The dead bodies of chiefs were placed around the room in a sitting posture, the unsightly skeletons mostly concealed in folds of kapa, or rich silk. The blood-stained altar was there, where human victims had been immolated to idol gods. Fragments of offerings were strewed about. Kapiolani was much affected and wept, but her husband was stern and silent. I thought he was not quite rid of the old superstition in regard to women.

A few months after our visit Kaahumanu came and ordered all the bones buried, and the house and fence entirely demolished. She gave some of the timber, which was spear-wood (kauwila), to the missionaries, and told them to make it into canes and contribution boxes, to send to their friends.

When Mr. Ruggles and Dr. Judd returned, having selected a locality for the health station, Mr. and Mrs. Ruggles, Miss Ward, and ourselves embarked in canoes for Kawaihae. Here we were entertained by old John Young, an English runaway sailor, who had been many years on the islands, and had assisted Kamehameha in his conquests. He had married a native woman of rank, has a fine family of sons and daughters, and is considered a chief. He lived in a dirty adobe house, adorned with old rusty muskets, swords, bayonets, and cartridge boxes. He gave us a supper of goat's meat and fried taro, served on old pewter plates, which I was unfortunate to see his servant wipe on his red flannel shirt in lieu of a napkin. I was surprised to see how imperfectly Mr. Young spoke the native language. We were sent up a rickety flight of stairs to sleep. I was afraid, and requested Dr. Judd to look around the room carefully for concealed dangers, and he was heartless enough to laugh at me. Sleep was out of the question; I was afraid of the wind, which sometimes sweeps down the gorge of the mountain, and got up at midnight, and went down to the grass house of Mrs. Young, which was neat and comfortable. She is a noble woman. She lives in native style; one of the sons is with the king, and the daughters are in the train of the princess.

The health station is selected at Waimea, twelve miles inland from the bay. The road to it is a foot-path, rough, rugged, and ascending about two thousand feet above the level of the sea. We lodged in a dilapidated school-house, without windows or doors, for two months, while our houses were building. This work, performed by the several districts under the direction of the head-man, had been ordered by Kaahumanu. The weather was cold, and a "Scotch mist," penetrating and disagreeable, came over the hills and plains every evening. The site chosen was on the table-land, at the foot of Mauna Kea, covered with thousands of wild cattle.

Mr. Ruggles preached to the people every Sunday in a neighboring grove, while we all taught a daily school. We climbed the hills and gathered wild strawberries, which cover acres of ground, ate fresh beef, and grew strong. One day we thought we would go home with Haa, the head-man of the valley of Waipio, who was erecting one of the houses, and had often invited us. It was a long walk through a thickly tangled forest, muddy with frequent rains and the trampling of the wild cattle. A few miles brought us out of the forest, where the sun and daylight shone once more, and the valley lay before us enclosed on three sides by almost perpendicular precipices, opening only to the sea. The view was perfectly enchanting. A mountain stream at the head of the valley poured down the whole distance in a beautiful waterfall. We could see it winding its way to the ocean, looking very much like a strip of white ribbon.

The natives moving about in the valley seemed of Lilliputian size. The place of descent was covered with grass. Little sledges, made of long, green leaves fastened together, were prepared for us, and Haa said we must trust to him, if we would go down safely. Tall, strong men took sledges on both sides of us, and down we slid, clinging to the long, tough grass, to check our velocity. This was a fearful ride, and it seemed as if we must inevitably drop into a pond of water at the bottom.

When we reached the thatched hut of our host, I found my fingers much swollen in the useless effort to lessen the speed of the descent.

Haa gave us a supper of fresh fish and kalo, and we lay down on clean beds of native kapa. During the night a storm of rain, with thunder and lightning, rolled over the valley, and I thought of the slippery precipices to be climbed the next day, and wondered what induced us to commit such a folly as to go down into such a prison.

With the dawn of day we aroused our friend, and commenced the toilsome ascent. The natives led us out by a different way, by a stony path, and in an hour and a half we were up the two thousand feet and on the road to our home, a little wiser, perhaps, for the experience. Old Haa and many more of his Christian fellow-laborers have long since entered into their rest. . . .

In 1832 I had the honor of assisting some of the ladies of the mission in organizing the first school for native children. The adult portion of the population had been collected into schools by thousands, and were learning to read and write. But the children were not yet tamed, and to catch them even was considered an impossibility. Their parents said they were like the goats on the hills, and had as little idea of subjugation. The chivalrous notion prevailed in those olden times as now, that woman's influence was all-powerful, and that whatever ladies undertook was sure to be accomplished. Higher motives than the meed of human praise stimulated the already overtaxed energies of some of that number in our mission, and induced them to try.

The first effort was made with the children of the church-members, in an unfurnished building. The little urchins were not quite naked, but we did not mind the garments, if so be their skins were clean. Cotton cloth was scarce, and the people poor; but water, thank Heaven, was plenty. We brought the children together, looked into their bright faces, asked their names, sung to them, and induced them to join us. Thus we discovered that they possessed the requisites for musical culture, ear and voice. We made for them drawings in natural history, which were hung where all could see them. A description of each was taught them, in the form of questions and answers. Quick to comprehend, they repeated readily, and in concert, moral maxims, hymns, and portions of the Bible.

These exercises gained their attention, and gave them some idea of order. The singing and pictures attracted other children, and the number increased. Seated together on the mats, it was difficult to keep them quiet, for their tongues and elbows were in constant motion. Some method of seating them separately was a subject of study. Wooden seats were too expensive and not to be thought of; some one suggested rows of adobies (sun-dried bricks), with mat coverings. A bottomless soap-box served for a mold. The parents of the scholars were cheerful in the labor, and with the aid of a bright sun this substantial material was soon arranged in several long rows of seats, neatly covered with rush mats braided by the mothers. One step in the ladder of progress was gained, and we could keep them together a longer time, with less fatigue and more profit. Slates and pencils added another charm; the children were delighted with their efforts in copying the pictures that hung on the wall. It might be difficult to distinguish which was camel, elephant, sheep, or horse; but no matter, the children were busy and happy.

Native women assisted in teaching reading; and oral lessons in geography, with the aid of outline maps, were given them. The elements of arithmetic also were taught in the same simple method. As the children had never before seen a map of the world, they were quite astonished at the comparative littleness of their own islands.

It is not boasting to say that some of the best business men in the nation can be pointed out as once pupils in this first school for native children. . . .

1841

About the year 1821, as one of the pioneer missionaries was walking on the sea-shore, he saw, sitting on a rock, a large, finely proportioned native woman, saturating her dusky skin with the fragrant cocoanut oil, and basking in a tropical noon-day sun, like a seal or sea-elephant. It is difficult to believe this personage to have been our present lady-like and sensitive Kapiolani. You have seen her name in print often, as she was the heroic woman who ventured into the tabooed crater of the goddess Pele, against the remonstrances of her terror-stricken attendants, who watched her descent, expecting to see her swallowed in the fiery embrace of the incensed deity. She accompanied Mr. and Mrs. Ruggles and ourselves into the sacred enclosure at Hoohaunau, forbidden to women in the olden time; no one but Kaahumanu had been bold enough to tread the enchanted ground. Naihe, her stern and lordly husband, sometimes rebukes her audacity in tampering with ancient usages and superstitions. One reason may be that he is the guardian of those old tombs of kings and chieftains, which is an honorable and sacred trust.

The high rocky bluff, just back of their villa at Kaawaloa, where Captain Cook fell, is full of caves where a long line of warrior kings are sleeping. One bright day when Mrs. Ruggles and I were alone with Kapiolani, we sat down and watched the movements of a crazy woman who had climbed the precipice, and spent the day in passing in and out of the different caves, and in airing and throwing down those secreted treasures of centuries. We expected she would fall and be dashed in pieces, as the giddy height she attained appeared inaccessible to other than aerial beings.

What was our surprise, just after lamplight, to see her enter the door and deposit at Naihe's feet a huge bundle done up in black kapa. "Here it is," she said, "I have been busy all day airing your property." He gave her a blow with his cane, and demanded how she dared venture into such a tabu place, and bade her restore every thing as she found it, the next day.

Kapiolani watched the proceedings in silence for a few moments, and then whispered to Mrs. Ruggles and myself to interfere with the decision of her husband. "Let us see what is in the mysterious bundle," she said, "it is of no use to the dead." Naihe gave the bundle a push with his cane, adding, "Do what you like with it."

Our curiosity was greatly excited while Dr. Judd removed the wrapping of kapa. First came a hideous idol, with staring eyes and grinning teeth of white pearl shell, and a tuft of human hair on the top of the head. Then another smaller one, less hideous, of similar workmanship. These were household gods, and buried with their proprietors. "Send them to your friends in America," said Kapiolani, "and tell them such were our gods, before you sent us the Bible." There were various other articles, such as polished cocoanut shells, a canoe paddle, mats, and a variety of kapa, all supposed to be useful in the "spirit land."

Kapiolani was very much excited, and after the crazy crone was disposed of and the treasures distributed among her guests, she entertained us with stories and incidents of her childhood.

Bananas and various kinds of fish were forbidden to women under the old system. One day she resolved to taste the banana, and risk the consequences if detected. Another girl was with her of equal rank and years. They concealed the fruit as well as they could with the palm of the hand and thumb, and rushed into the sea to bathe and eat the forbidden fruit. An eagle-eyed priest discovered them; they were tried for the ungodly deed and condemned to suffer the penalty, which was poverty, loss of rank, and to remain unmarried. This they must suffer, unless suitable expiation could be made. The priest suggested the sacrifice of a little boy, a favorite page of Kapiolani's, as a suitable offering. He was immediately seized and carried to the sacred inclosure at Hoonaunau, and was seen no more. Kapiolani called for the same old priest to come and sit by her, and say what he now thought of those proceedings. "Oh," said he, "those were dark days, though we priests knew better all the time. It was power we sought over the minds of the people to influence and control them." Kapiolani asked him what he did with the boy. "He was strangled on the altar," said he. She hid her face with her hands and wept. "Oh, why did not Christians come sooner and teach us better things?"

Kapiolani is now here on a visit; she has had a cancer removed from her breast, and is rapidly improving. When the surgeons entered to perform the operation, she appeared a little fluttered and nervous, requested a few moments to go by herself and pray. She returned calm and dignified, took her seat and submitted to the surgeon's knife with unflinching fortitude and firmness. Her heart is so full of gratitude for the recovery of her health she can not be quiet a moment, and wants to enlist all hearts in a song of praise.

. . . How can I write the sad sequel? Our noble Kapiolani was attacked with erysipelas from a walk in the hot sun, and died very suddenly. Another prop removed from the nation.

Titus Coan

EARLY MISSIONARY TRAVELS

THE EARLY MISSIONARIES in Hawaii experienced much physical hardship, especially as they traveled from place to place as itinerant preachers. Conditions of travel, both by land and by sea, were rugged and dangerous. Spoiled food added to the physical distress, and loneliness created many psychological tensions. But these men had strong faith and persevered.

The following account is from the autobiography, entitled *Life in Hawaii*, of the Reverend Titus Coan, who reached the Hawaiian Islands in 1835 and was stationed on the island of Hawaii. Coan, a fervent preacher, traveled widely, often at the risk of his life, to bring Christianity to the scattered native population.

IN PASSING through the district of Hilo, the weather was sometimes fine and the rivers low, so that there was little difficulty in traveling. The path was a simple trail, winding in a serpentine line, going down and up precipices, some of which could only be descended and ascended by grasping the shrubs and grasses, and with no little weariness and difficulty and some danger.

But the streams were the most formidable obstacles. In great rains, which often occurred on my tours, when the winds rolled in the heavy clouds from the sea, and massed them in dark banks on the side of the mountain, the waters would fall in torrents at the head of the streams and along their channels, and the rush and the roar as the floods came down were like the thunder of an army charging upon the foe.

I have sometimes sat on the high bank of a streamlet, not more than fifteen to twenty feet wide, conversing with natives in the bright sunshine, when suddenly a portentous roaring, "Like the sound of many waters, or like the noise of the sea when the waves thereof roar," fell upon my ears, and looking up-stream, I have seen a column of turbid waters six feet deep coming down like the flood from a broken mill-dam. The natives would say to me, *"Awiwi! awiwi! o paa oe i ka wai"*—"Quick! quick! or the waters will stop you."

Rushing down the bank I would cross over, dry-shod, where in two minutes more there was no longer any passage for man or beast. But I rarely waited for the rivers to run by. My appointments for preaching were all sent forward in a line for thirty or sixty miles, designating the day, and usually the hours, when I would be at a given station, and by breaking one of these links the whole chain would be disturbed. It therefore seemed important that every appointment should be kept, whatever the inconvenience might be to me. In traveling, my change of raiment was all packed in one calabash, or large gourd, covered by the half of another; a little food was in a second calabash. With these gourds one may travel indefinitely in the heaviest rains while all is dry within. Faithful natives carried my little supplies.

I had several ways of crossing the streams.

1st. When the waters were low, large rocks and boulders, common in all the water-channels, were left bare, so that with a stick or pole eight or ten feet long, I leaped from rock to rock over the giddy streams and crossed dry-shod: these same poles helping me to climb up, and to let myself down steep precipices, and to leap ditches six to eight feet wide. 2d. When the streams were not too deep and too swift I waded them; and 3d, when not too deep, but too swift, I mounted upon the shoulders of a sturdy aquatic native, holding on to his bushy hair, when he moved carefully down the slippery bank of the river, leaning up-stream against a current of ten knots, and moving one foot at a time, sideways among the slimy boulders in the bottom, and then bringing the other foot carefully up. Thus slowly feeling his way across, he would land me safe with a shout and a laugh on the opposite bank. But this is a fearful way of crossing, for the cataracts are so numerous, the waters so rapid, and the uneven bottom so slippery, that the danger of falling is imminent, and the recovery from a fall often impossible, the current hurrying one swiftly over a precipice into certain destruction. Both natives and foreigners have thus lost their lives in these streams, and among them three of the members of the Hilo church who have traveled and labored and prayed with me.

I once crossed a full and powerful river in this way, not more than fifty feet above a cataract of 426 feet in height, with a basin forty feet deep below, where this little Niagara has thundered for ages. A missionary brother of another station seeing me landed safely, and knowing that this crossing would save about six miles of hard and muddy walking, followed me on the shoulders of the same bold native that took me over. But before he had reached the middle of the rushing flood, he trembled and cried out with fear. The bearer said, "Hush! hush! be still, or we perish together." The brother still trembling, the native with great difficulty managed to reach a rock in the center of the river, and on this he seated his burden, commanding him to be quiet and sit there until he was cool (he was already drenched with rain and river-spray), when he would take him off, which he did in about ten minutes and landed him safely by my side.

This mode of crossing the streams, however, was too dangerous, and I soon abandoned it.

A fourth mode was for a sufficient number of strong men to form a chain across the river. They made a line, locking hands on the bank; with heads bending up-stream entering the water carefully, and moving slowly until the head of the line reached good foothold near the opposite bank. With my hands upon the shoulders of the men I passed along this chain of bones, sinews, and muscles and arrived in safety on the other side.

The fifth and safest, and in fact the only possible way to cross some of these rivers when swollen and raging, was to throw a rope across the stream, and fasten it to trees or rocks on either side; grasping it firmly with both hands, my feet thrown down-stream, I drew myself along the line and gained the opposite bank. This I sometimes did without removing shoes or garments, then walked on to my next station, and preached in wet clothes, continuing my travels and labors until night; when in dry wrappings I slept well, and was all ready for work the next day.

I was once three hours in crossing one river. The day was cold and rainy, and I was soaked before I entered the stream. This was so wide at the only possible crossing point, that we were unable to throw a line across, even with a weight attached to the end of it. The raging, roaring, and tossing of the waters were fearful, and the sight of it made me shudder. Kind natives collected on both banks by scores, with ropes and courage to help. The fearful rapids, running probably twenty miles an hour, were before us. Fifty feet below us was a fall of some twenty feet, and about 100 yards further down was a thundering cataract, where the river was compressed within a narrow gorge with a clear plunge of about eighty feet.

Our natives tried all their skill and strength, but could not throw the line across. At length a daring man went up-stream close to a waterfall, took the end of the rope in his teeth, mounted a rock, calculated his chances of escape from the cataracts below, and leaped into the flood; down, down he went quivering and struggling till he reached the opposite shore only a few feet above the fall, over which it must have been a fatal plunge had he gone. But by his temerity, which I should have forbidden, had I known it in season, a passage was provided for me.

After years had passed, and a little had been done toward making roads, I purchased a horse, and tried to get him over these streams by swimming or hauling him over with ropes. Twice when I attempted to go over in the saddle, his foot caught between two rocks in the middle of the stream, and horse and rider were saved only by the energy and fidelity of the natives.

Once in going up a steep precipice in a narrow pass between a rocky height on one hand and a stream close on the other, my horse fell over backward and lay with his head down and his feet in the air, so wedged and so wounded that he could never have escaped from his position, had not a company of natives for whom I sent came [sic] to the rescue and extricated the poor, faithful animal from his rocky bed. I escaped instant death by sliding out of the saddle upon the narrow bank of the stream, before the back of my horse struck between the rocks. He was so hurt that I was obliged to leave him to recover.

In order to save time and escape the weariness of the road and the dangers of the rivers, I sometimes took a canoe at the end of my tours to return home by the water. This trip required six to eight hours, and was usually made in the night.

On three occasions my peril was great. One description will suffice for all; for although the difficulties and escapes were at different points along a precipitous and lofty sea-wall, yet the causes of danger were the same, viz.: stormy winds, raging billows, and want of landing-places.

About midway between our starting-place and Hilo harbor, we were met by a strong head-wind, with pouring rain and tumultuous waves in a dark midnight. We were half a mile from land, but could hear the roar and see the flashing of the white surf as it dashed against the rocky walls. We could not land, we could not sail, we could not row forward or backward. All we could do was to keep the prow of the canoe to the wind, and bail. Foaming seas dashed against our frail cockleshell, pouring in buckets of brine. Thus we lay about five hours, anxious as they "who watch for the morning." At length it dawned; we looked through the misty twilight to the rock-bound shore where "the waves dashed high." A few doors of native huts opened and men crawled out. We called, but no echo came. We made signals of distress. We were seen and numbers came down to the cliffs and gazed at us. We waved our garments for them to come off to our help. They feared, they hesitated. We were opposite the mouth of a roaring river, where the foam of breakers dashed in wild fury. At last four naked men came down from the cliff, plunged into the sea, dived under one towering wave after another, coming out to breathe between the great rolling billows, and thus reached our canoe. Ordering the crew to swim to the land, they took charge of the canoe themselves because they knew the shore. Meanwhile men stood on the high cliffs with kapa cloth in hand to signal to the boat-men when to strike for the mouth of the river. They waited long and watched the tossing waves as they rolled in and thundered upon the shore, and when at last a less furious wave came behind us, the shore men waved the signals and cried out, *"Hoi! hoi!"* and as the waves lifted the stern of our canoe, all the paddles struck the water, while the steerer kept the canoe straight on her course, and thus mounted on this crested wave as on an ocean chariot, with the feathery foam flying around us, we rode triumphantly into the mouth of the river, where we were received with shouts of gladness by the throng who had gathered to witness our escape. Then two rows of strong men waded into the surf up to their arm-pits to receive our canoe and bear it in triumph to the shore. . . .

In the early years of the mission, the trials of separation were often severe. Hawaii was not only far from all the outer world, but our islands were separated one from another by wide and windy channels, with no regular and safe packets, and no postal arrangements, or regular means of communication.

Add to this, many parts of the islands were so broken by ravines, by precipices, and dangerous streams, and so widely sundered by broad tracts of lava, without house, or pool of water to refresh the weary and thirsty traveler, and without roads withal, that social intercourse was impossible without great toil and suffering.

As to beloved friends and kindred in the far-off fatherland, it seemed like an age before we could speak to them and receive answers.

I think it was eighteen months before we received answers to our first letters sent from Hilo to the United States, a period long enough for revolutions among the nations as well as in families.

All our flour, rice, sugar, molasses, and many other articles of food, with clothing, furniture, medicines, etc., came in sailing vessels around Cape Horn, a voyage of four to six months, so that our news became old and our provisions stale before they reached us, while our stationery might be exhausted, our medicines expended, our flour mouldy and full of worms, before the new supplies arrived. Many a time have we been obliged to break up our barrel of hardened flour with an axe, or chisel and mallet.

But after all our inter-island communication was often our more severe trial. A few old schooners, leaky and slow, mostly owned by native chiefs, floated about, sometimes lying becalmed under the lee of an island for a whole week, in a burning sun, with sails lazily flapping, boom swinging from side to side, and gaff mournfully squeaking aloft.

These vessels were usually officered and manned by indolent and unskillful natives, who made dispatch, cleanliness, safety, and comfort no factors in a voyage. They would often be four and even six weeks in making a trip from Honolulu to Hilo and back, a total distance of some 600 miles. They knew nothing of the motto, "Time is money." So long as they were supplied with fish and poi, all was well. They would sometimes lash the helm while they went to eat, then lie down and sleep. We have often found our vessel in this condition at midnight, captain and all hands fast asleep, and the schooner left to the control of wind and wave, and without a lamp burning on board. In addition some vessels were without a single boat for help in the hour of peril.

The cabins being small and filthy, the missionaries slept on deck, each family providing its own food and blankets, and all exposed to wind, heat, storm, and drenching waves which often broke upon the deck. Upon a schooner of forty to sixty tons, there might be one hundred natives with their dogs and pigs, stoutly contesting deck-space with them; and often fifty members of missionary families, parents and children together. These were the families on Molokai and Maui, with, in many cases, those of the several stations on Hawaii. The crowd was distressing, and the sickness and suffering can never be told. Mothers with four or five children, including a tender nursling, would lie miserably during the hot days under a burning sun, and by night in the rain, or wet with the dashing waves, pallid and wan, with children crying for food, or retching with seasickness. I have seen some of these frail women with their pale children brought to land, exhausted, upon the backs of natives, carried to their homes on litters, and laid upon couches to be nourished till their strength returned.

Martha Ann Chamberlain

KAWAIAHAO SEMINARY

IN DOWNTOWN Honolulu, near the Public Library, stands Kawaiahao Church, sometimes called Hawaii's Westminster Abbey. Nearby are several trim early buildings, now carefully preserved by the Hawaiian Mission Children's Society, familiarly known as the Cousins' Society. Here are extensive collections of Hawaiiana in manuscript as well as in printed form.

Martha Ann Chamberlain, daughter of the mission's business manager, remembered these early buildings when they were not historical relics but centers of intense human activity. Her account of them, dated January 24, 1889, is entitled "Memories of the Past, Linked to Scenes of the Present, in the History of Kawaiahao Seminary." In decorous and delicate prose, she recorded some of her recollections. The atmosphere invoked calls to mind dried flowers pressed and brittle in old books, along with the faint scent of lavender and the shrill laughter of schoolgirls long since grown old.

The selection ends with a ludicrous account of the seminary's first day of classes. To make the incident clear, it must be explained that *uku lele* in Hawaiian means "jumping flea" and *auwe* means "alas." Somewhat later, *ukulele* became the name of the well-known Hawaiian musical instrument, presumably because the player's hand jumped like a flea.

These selections from Martha Ann Chamberlain's "Memories," from a typescript in the Hawaiian Mission Children's Society Library, are here printed for the first time.

JUST ACROSS THE STREET from my old home was a most attractive place. There stood a low-roofed, spread-out, rambling dwelling, with a small porch before the front door, on each side of which were short narrow seats, where in the cool of the day, the busy weary fathers and mothers of the mission could feel it right to take a few moments to rest and chat, while their children sported on the grass of the roomy door yard. This was before the day of our universal verandahs; and the old-fashioned New-England memory of "the front porch" was thus transplanted: for simplicity and economy, not esthetic culture, ruled the plans of our heroic fathers and mothers.

On the front door was an old-fashioned brass knocker, also a transplanted luxury, which gave an aristocratic look to this otherwise lowly dwelling.

An immense algeroba tree of the thornless variety was the prize of the garden, for in those days the algeroba was an exotic, and this was among the earliest planted, and had grown very rapidly. (What a grief it was, when a severe storm laid it low, torn up from the roots!) From its strong branches suspended a swing in which the assembled children of the neighborhood—in the visiting hours—took turns in swinging, with the utmost good-humor and generosity.

A beautiful young tamarind tree, as old, but much slower of growth than the algeroba, cast its shadow and graceful drapery over the L extension built out on the Waianae side of the house, where all the sleeping rooms of the family were.

While in the adjacent yard towards Waikiki separated by fences, were the two buildings, The Mission Printing Office, and Bindery, both places full of attractions to inquisitive intelligent children.

This was the home of Dr. G. P. Judd, the only physician then in Honolulu, and here was the Dispensary of the Mission. This was to us, a most fascinating part of the establishment, heightened in its attractions, because the place was "tabu loa" [forbidden] to our intrusion.

It was in the basement, or cellar, as we called it, of the middle building, Dr. Judd's home. For the cellar was also a New England necessity and so the missionaries all built their houses with a cellar. The house was built of coral stone, that is, the lower story, and this was all its height during Dr. and Mrs. Judd's occupancy. A second story of adobe was added in the year 1840 [1842] when Dr. Judd left the Mission to aid in forming the Government, and Rev. R. Armstrong who had been called from Wailuku to the pastorate of the Kawaiahao Church moved in, with his growing family. It is the two-story house, which is most familiar to the memory of later generations, but the memories of this paper go back to the original one-story house.

But this is a digression from the dispensary. It had a flight of steps leading down into it, and occupied the "makai" [seaward] end of the cellar directly under the parlor. Three deep casement windows were built into the coral walls of the dispensary, two towards the south, and one towards the west admitting light and air; each of these windows having a little cemented enclosure, or well of its own, on the outside; the top of the windows being level with the surrounding yard.

These little wells afforded a most tempting place—in spite of the tabu—to the most adventurous children to jump down and peek in on the sly when the crowds of half-clad, barbarous native patients were thronging the dispensary, and possibly the interesting operation of bleeding a patient going on, while even the timid girls drawn by that unknown fascination of horror, sometimes took a stolen glance down the stairs, and the sight of the bound arm, the swift sharp incision, the trickling blood into the bright basin, was photographed on memory forever, before the frightened steps sped away. One side [of] the dispensary was lined with shelves and drawers, with their display of carefully labelled drugs and medicines, and the other, occupied by rude benches for the patients in waiting, while the Dr.'s table and shelf of books filled the west end. From this outer room a door opened into an inner dark cellar of two apartments used for storage, which had small windows near the ceiling, and as the outside steps leading to the dining room had to be placed right over one of these windows the doctor had an ingenious contrivance for lighting through the steps. He bored three large circular openings in the three upright portions of the steps. And it was only when the old building was taken down (in 1887) that this old curiosity ceased to exist. This perforated door step will long live in the memory of the girls of old Kawaiahao Seminary, especially of those few, whose misfortune it was, as very naughty girls, to be locked in the dark cellar, and fed on bread and water for a while. Every part of the house was utilized during the early days of the school, and all three rooms of this cellar were used for storage purposes, the outer room for a trunk room, or even (on a pinch) for "dormitory" a few weeks. To the rear of Dr. Judd's dwelling house, were two detached cottages built of adobe, but plastered and white-washed [and] having thatched roofs. One of these was used for a few months as a school-room for the missionary children in the year 1837, shortly after the arrival of the "Great Reinforcement." Miss Marcia M. Smith (aunt of Prof. Lyons of the present faculty of Oahu College) being our teacher. Here the little Binghams, Tinkers, Judds, Chamberlains and a few other children from the town, as John O. Dominis and Newton Ladd, gained our first ideas of a regular school-room conducted as were American schools of fifty years ago! This adobe building was still standing on the present site of Kawaiahao Seminary when Miss Lydia Bingham—now Mrs. Coan—assumed the headship and forming of this now prosperous institution. Let us now in imagination go into the next yard, which has been already alluded to, and (still living in those early days of the Hawaiian mission) take a look into the Bindery, not then old and worm-eaten, but staunch and well fitted for its work.

Mounting the outside stair-case to the upper story, let us see if Mr. Henry Dimond is not too rushed today, so that he can tolerate the curious eyes, and more covetous fingers, that will ask to carry off the bright smooth shavings of red, blue, green or yellow paper, as well as white, which lie in heaps on the floor, at one end of the room where the busy Hawaiian young men are so deftly working. These paper shavings will soon be converted into lamp-lighters, or, ornaments to beautify simple doll houses. Now look around. See the piles of books stitched and trimmed, stacked up nearly to the roof, awaiting their covers; note the not unpleasant smell of poi paste, watch delightedly the several pair of huge scissors clipping and trimming in the hands of skillful apprentices, and then steal in quietly to the further back corner, where the process of making morocco covers is going on. Possibly you may pick up some scraps of leather trimmings more prized than the bright papers. Then steal down stairs again, and passing through the room on the lower floor, packed with fresh bound Bibles, hymn books and school books—finished and unfinished so that only lanes for passing around are left, go into the very back room, where a huge mangle covered with stones is used for pressure when needed. Does this not give an idea of the work going on, for the benefit of a nation wakened up from the sleep of moral darkness and turned to the marvellous light of the gospel? Now, leaving the Bindery, scamper a few rods "mauka" [inland] across the grass plot, to the Printing Office, a three-story stone building—(at least we children called it three though the upper one was only a half one, or attic). Here on the west side of the building is the main entrance up a flight of coral stone steps with ascents on three sides, similar, but on much smaller scale with the steps still seen at the front entrance of Kawaiahao Church. This leads to the main floor of the printing office, full of forms for setting types, where stand the silent Hawaiian compositors, each at his form, absorbed and busy. Don't raise your voice above a whisper, or Mr. E. O. Hall will make you scamper. But stand & watch as long as you please if you are not noisy or meddlesome. Possibly you may climb the narrow stairs with a turn in them at the top—to the attic story, just to see what is there, when they lift the heavy trap door. Oh! nothing but bales of paper. Let us go down to the basement and see the printing presses. But we must leave the account of this room for another chapter. This stone building was demolished this summer of 1888.

Our first chapter left us, children from six to twelve years old, standing near the basement of the old Printing Office and watching through the open windows, the process of printing on old fashioned hand-presses, which stood on a coral stone floor. The rollers were blacked, the frames spread with blank sheets of paper, the machines rolled and impression taken, and then the printed sheets carefully lifted off—all by hand. The workmen at the presses were all young Hawaiians who had been trained by the earlier missionaries. The first printer who did much and faithful work was Mr. Loomis who came out with the pioneers in 1820, and returned to the U.S. on account of the health of his family, in a few years. His work was done in a ruder building with thatched roof and few conveniences. He was succeeded by Mr. Stephen Sheppard, a man of lovely consecrated spirit, who carried on the work with enthusiasm and laid down his life here, dying of quick consumption. His remains lie in an unmarked grave in the south west corner of the little mission cemetery in the shadow of Kawaiahao church. He and his family resided first in the dwelling house described as Dr. Judd's, and Mrs. S. planted the large Tamarind Tree which was only cut down last year, when the old building was demolished, and which if it were still growing, would be in the centre of the present grass plot in front of the new edifice. Mr. E. O. Hall arrived at the Islands in 1835, and all the later work of mission printing was done under his supervision. In reviewing the Volumes of Missionary Heralds for dates, an accurate wood cut of the old Printing Office was found, with its square stone walls, stone outside steps, and tiers of windows, with no verandahs, no ornamental touches which afterwards relieved the building which we remember so well as part of the original Kawaiahao Seminary. The basement was partly below, and partly above ground and all the seven windows were set in the upper part of the basement wall, while the cellar foundation extended several feet beyond the building, on the east side, quite out to the dividing line of the lot bordering on S. N. Castle's present premises. This outside cellar formed a convenient door yard for the work of the office especially requiring water, and was descended into by two flights of wooden steps on the "mauka" & "makai" sides. The new school-room of Kawaiahao Seminary (completed in the summer of 1888) extends over this whole foundation, and we rejoice in the preservation of this one land mark of the past. . . .

Miss B.[ingham] commenced at once, teaching the little school in the basement of the old Printing Office, which room was also used as eating room of the few boarders, a forlorn dreary spot. The writer may perhaps be pardoned for recording one personal experience the very first day that school was taught in the basement room, as she assisted Mrs. Dr. Gulick for a few weeks before Miss Bingham's arrival in that old Press Room with its floor, half boards, half blocks of coral stone.

See arranged on the wooden half of the floor, on the "mauka" side, two long rude unpainted tables, seated round with benches without books, on which sat the eight unpolished and not too tidily attired Hawaiian girls, who were however docile, and eager to learn. The opening exercises over, and the work of assigning lessons begun, all at once, both teacher and pupils are seized with a peculiar sharp, tingling sensation of pain around the feet and ankles. The girls cannot sit still, for they are bare-footed, and dancing up and down "auwe!" "auwe!" "he uku! he uku lele"!! is the cry from one and all. Investigation reveals the feet and hands of all black with myriads of the tiniest fleas putting us in a fiery torment. Study is at an end for that day. Mrs. G. is consulted what to do. She suggests scalding water. But her kitchen fire is out, and it will take some time to kindle & get the required water hot, so resort is made to the old home across the way, where a good supply is on hand on the stove. And more fire is made up, with unlimited supplies of water. The three or four largest girls, ran back and forth across the street, carefully carrying the pails of scalding water, until the whole floor was well flooded & scrubbed. That evening coarse salt was sprinkled generously over all the cracks. The next morning all the salt was swept up and the fleas had disappeared. Peace & quiet reigned in the classes.

James F. B. Marshall

A SECRET DIPLOMATIC MISSION

In February, 1843, a British naval force under Lord George Paulet took possession of Hawaii. The seizure resulted from complaints by British residents in Hawaii, among them Alexander Simpson, that the Hawaiian government had unjustly seized the property of Richard Charlton, a British citizen. Paulet was under orders to protect British interests in Hawaii, in particular to recover Charlton's confiscated property. After consulting several advisers, the Hawaiian king ceded Hawaii provisionally to Britain, pending settlement of complex negotiations already begun in London. Until July the British flag flew over Hawaii. At that time Admiral Richard Thomas, Paulet's commanding officer, restored the Hawaiian monarchy. Thomas correctly interpreted then current British policy, which was antiimperialist. But a big "if" in history appears here. If Thomas had found Hawaii in disorder, he might have held the Islands for the time being, and the British Foreign Office might well have sanctioned their annexation. Hawaii then would be British instead of the fiftieth American state. After all, at that time British colonial policy was somewhat uncertain. Britain acquired Natal, in South Africa, rather reluctantly in 1843. It is a tribute to William Richards and Dr. Judd, former missionaries then in the service of the Hawaiian government with the support of American residents in Hawaii, that even in this time of crisis the affairs of the Hawaiian kingdom remained in order.

Meanwhile, during the temporary cession of Hawaii to Britain, the Hawaiian government made heroic and secret efforts to present its case for independence to the British Foreign Office. In an atmosphere of deep intrigue, the Hawaiian monarchy appointed a secret diplomatic agent. His name was James Fowle Baldwin Marshall, an Ameri-

can merchant in Honolulu, then in his twenty-fifth year. What follows
is Marshall's account of his accreditation and departure, originally
titled "An Unpublished Chapter of Hawaiian History," as published
in *Harper's Magazine* in 1883.

ON HIS ARRIVAL Lord Paulet, a hot-headed young nobleman,
readily lent himself to the designs of Simpson, without in-
quiring into the merits of the case, dazzled by the idea of so early
in his career making a brilliant stroke for his country, and extending
her drum-beat round the world by one more station. . . .

Lord Paulet took formal possession of the islands, installing himself as governor of her Majesty's new dominion, destroyed every
Hawaiian flag he could get hold of, and placed an embargo on
every native vessel, so that no one could go out and carry the news.

An American man-of-war, the *Boston,* Captain Long, had come
in a few days before the cession. Captain Quackenbush, late of
Norfolk, Virginia, was then a midshipman on board of her. The
Americans were very indignant. They had their guns double
shotted in hopes of an opportunity to interfere, but, being on a
cruise, could not go out of their way to carry the news, and could
only remain neutral.

Lord Paulet would thus have cruelly prevented the king from
communicating with his ambassadors who were abroad successfully working for the acknowledgment of his independence, hoping
to commit the home government to an acceptance of this "voluntary" cession at the cannon's mouth before the other side of the
story could be represented to it. His young lordship and Simpson
chuckled over the success of the stroke by which they had, as they
supposed, closed every avenue of egress for Hawaiian vessels, and
secured the arrival of their own dispatches in England in advance
of every other version of the story. Yankee shrewdness was, however, too much for his lordship's plans.

It happened that the king had chartered his own yacht *Hoikaika*
(Swift Runner), previously to the cession, to an American house
for a voyage to Mazatlan and back. Lord Paulet, anxious to get
possession of the only creditable craft at the islands in order to send
Simpson as his bearer of dispatches to England by the speediest
way, and being prevented by its charter from seizing the vessel
without the consent of the American house, offered, in case they

would relinquish their charter, to allow them to send an agent on the ship to attend to their business on the coast, and to bring down any freight on the return trip, thereby saving them the whole expense of the charter.

It must be remembered that in those days communication between the islands of the Pacific and the coast was very infrequent, depending on merchant ships that came from Boston twice a year, except for occasional chance vessels.

Lord Paulet rightly conjectured that the Yankee merchants would jump at the offer to have all their business transacted at his expense, but he little dreamed of all the use that might be made of the opportunity he was giving them.

The officers of the *Boston,* who would have been glad of an excuse for a forcible interference with his lordship's plans, not being allowed that pleasure, consoled themselves by giving a ball on board, to which the officers of the *Carysfort* were not invited.

I was then a young merchant in Honolulu, and attended the ball with many other of the American residents. At its height I was quietly invited into the cabin of the *Boston,* where I found Captain Long, Dr. Judd—previously a prominent American missionary, then acting as the king's minister—and other influential citizens and warm friends of the king. Here I was told of the king's desire to send an envoy to England to present his protest against Lord Paulet's act of violence, and his answer to the charges against him, and to demand the restitution of his sovereignty. I was informed also of the opportunity offered to the firm of Ladd and Co. of sending a messenger to the coast in the yacht.

Ladd and Co., who were warm friends of the island government, had proposed that the king should send a secret ambassador, in the character of their commercial agent, thus turning Lord Paulet's master-stroke against himself in the neatest possible way.

I was asked if I would go in this double capacity of ostensible supercargo and actual minister plenipotentiary.

Mr. Charles Brewer, who was one of the council, a noble-hearted man, with whom I was about associating myself in business—now enjoying a green old age in Boston—not only gave consent to my going, but agreed to advance for the king the necessary funds, and take his pay in *fire-wood,* all the king's other revenues having been cut off.

I readily accepted the commission. No time was to be lost. Lord Paulet had rechristened the *Hoikaika* as "her Majesty's tender *Albert*," and was fitting her out with all possible dispatch.

The king and his premier, a princess almost equal in rank, without whose signature none of his acts was valid, had left the island of Oahu immediately upon the cession, and in sullen dignity of despair buried themselves among the mountains of the adjacent island of Maui, leaving Dr. Judd, his minister, to represent and protect his interests—a man of indomitable courage, unusual ability, and unflinching devotion to his sovereign.

Those happy isles in that day did not boast a lawyer. My credentials were copied verbatim, except necessary variations, from an old Blue-book containing the credentials of John Adams as the first American minister to England. Mine were a commission as "envoy extraordinary and minister plenipotentiary to the court of St. James, from the *Native King* of the Hawaiian Islands," the title Kamehameha was allowed by Lord Paulet to retain, with some half-dozen other blank commissions signed by the king and premier, to be filled out by myself for other countries as occasion might require. These were rendered necessary by the uncertainty of my finding the king's other ambassadors, Haalileo and Richards, with whom, in case I did find them, I was to associate myself.

The papers were drawn up by Dr. Judd and a confidential clerk at midnight, in the royal tomb in Honolulu, with a king's coffin for a table. So secret was it necessary to keep the transaction that even this clerk was not trusted with the name of the ambassador, which was left to be inserted by myself after I had sailed. The papers prepared, a canoe with a picked crew of Kanakas was dispatched from a distant point to the island to summon his Majesty and his suite to a midnight council. Crossing the boisterous channel in this frail conveyance, they landed at midnight on the shores of Waikiki, a suburb of Honolulu, and in its cocoa-nut grove, by the light of torches, my credentials received the signature and seal of the king and his *kuhina-nui*—"great minister"—Kekauluohi, the "big-mouthed queen." Then, the king and his attendants returned to their mountains, without Lord Paulet having a suspicion that they had ever left them.

The American consul at Honolulu took advantage of the opportunity also to make me the bearer of his dispatches to Washington, with details of the cession, which would, of course, have momentous interest to the American government, and the protest of the American residents against the act of Lord Paulet.

All the hurried preparations being completed, "H. B. M.'s tender *Albert*" sailed on the eleventh day of March, 1843, for San Blas, commanded by a midshipman from the *Carysfort* and two old men-of-war's men, with a crew of eight Kanakas, and two passengers, one of whom was Mr. Alexander Simpson, late "deputy consul," now special bearer of dispatches to her Majesty from the "Governor of the Sandwich Islands," the other one myself.

Editor's Note

Marshall's secret mission was a success. He arrived in London in time to present the case of the Hawaiian kingdom to the British Foreign Office. A settlement favorable to the Hawaiian kingdom followed.

Herman Melville

MISSIONARIES AND THE BRITISH SEIZURE OF HAWAII

HERMAN MELVILLE, one of the greatest American novelists of the nineteenth century, left Hawaii in August, 1843, after a stay of about six months. From February to July of that year, the Hawaiian Islands were under the control of the British naval officer Lord George Paulet and technically under provisional cession to Britain until the restoration of Hawaiian independence by Admiral Richard Thomas of the British navy. The Paulet episode brought to a head the traditional hostility between the missionaries on the one hand and the trading and shipping interests on the other, a deep-seated antagonism found not only in Hawaii but also in many other colonial areas where the two groups came into contact and conflict. Such hostility was irreconcilable. The missionary interest believed, with some supporting evidence, that traders and mariners were debauching and defrauding the natives. The commercial interests condemned the attempt by the missionaries to enforce Puritan folkways in Polynesia. Probably both sides overstated their case. As so often happens, the truth may well be somewhere between the two extreme positions.

In any event, as a mariner Melville naturally opposed the missionary interest. Further, for a time he worked as a clerk in an English
firm in Honolulu, where he had ample opportunity to absorb the
English version of Paulet's seizure of the Islands. Melville reacted by
writing the following antimissionary tract as an appendix to his
Typee. He erred slightly by describing Hawaii's missionaries as
Methodists; they were nondenominational Protestants, mainly Con-
gregationalists. Nonetheless, this writing is representative of the fury
which missionaries of every denomination provoked in the nineteenth
century. The diatribe also reflects the intensity of Melville's inner life,
which many critics believe to be the mainspring of his genius.

THE AUTHOR of this volume arrived at Tahiti the very day that
the iniquitous designs of the French were consummated by
inducing the subordinate chiefs, during the absence of their queen,
to ratify an artfully-drawn treaty, by which she was virtually de-
posed. Both menaces and caresses were employed on this occasion,
and the 32-pounders which peeped out of the port-holes of the
frigate were the principal arguments adduced to quiet the scruples
of the more conscientious islanders.

And yet this piratical seizure of Tahiti, with all the woe and
desolation which resulted from it, created not half so great a sensation, at least in America, as was caused by the proceedings of the
English at the Sandwich Islands. No transaction has ever been more
grossly misrepresented than the events which occurred upon the
arrival of Lord George Paulet at Oahu. During a residence of four
months at Honolulu, the metropolis of the group, the author was
in the confidence of an Englishman who was much employed by
his lordship; and great was the author's astonishment on his arrival
at Boston, in the autumn of 1844, to read the distorted accounts and
fabrications which had produced in the United States so violent an
outbreak of indignation against the English. He deems it, therefore,
a mere act of justice towards a gallant officer briefly to state the
leading circumstances connected with the event in question.

It is needless to rehearse all the abuse that for some time previous
to the spring of 1843 had been heaped upon the British residents,
especially upon Captain Charlton, Her Britannic Majesty's consul-
general, by the native authorities of the Sandwich Islands. High in
the favour of the imbecile king at this time was one Dr. Judd, a
sanctimonious apothecary-adventurer, who, with other kindred and
influential spirits, were [*sic*] animated by an inveterate dislike to

England. The ascendancy of a junta of ignorant and designing Methodist elders in the councils of a half-civilised king, ruling with absolute sway over a nation just poised between barbarism and civilisation, and exposed by the peculiarities of its relations with foreign states to unusual difficulties, was not precisely calculated to impart a healthy tone to the policy of the government.

At last matters were brought to such an extremity, through the iniquitous maladministration of affairs, that the endurance of further insults and injuries on the part of the British consul was no longer to be borne. Captain Charlton, insultingly forbidden to leave the islands, clandestinely withdrew, and arriving at Valparaiso, conferred with Rear-Admiral Thomas, the English commander-in-chief on the Pacific station. In consequence of this communication, Lord George Paulet was despatched by the admiral in the *Carysfort* frigate, to inquire into and correct the alleged abuses. On arriving at his destination, he sent his first lieutenant ashore with a letter to the king, couched in terms of the utmost courtesy, and soliciting the honour of an audience. The messenger was denied access to His Majesty, and Paulet was cooly referred to Dr. Judd, and informed that the apothecary was invested with plenary powers to treat with him. Rejecting this insolent proposition, his lordship again addressed the king by letter, and renewed his previous request; but he encountered another repulse. Justly indignant at this treatment, he penned a third epistle, enumerating the grievances to be redressed, and demanding a compliance with his requisitions, under penalty of immediate hostilities.

The government was now obliged to act, and an artful stroke of policy was decided upon by the despicable councillors of the king to entrap the sympathies and rouse the indignation of Christendom. His Majesty was made to intimate to the British captain that he could not, as the conscientious ruler of his beloved people, comply with the arbitrary demands of his lordship, and in deprecation of the horrors of war, tendered to his acceptance the *provisional cession* of the islands, subject to the result of the negotiations then pending in London. Paulet, a bluff and straight-forward sailor, took the king at his word, and after some preliminary arrangements, entered upon the administration of Hawaiian affairs, in the same firm and benignant spirit which marked the discipline of his frigate, and which had rendered him the idol of his ship's company. He soon endeared himself to nearly all orders of the islanders; but the king and the chiefs, whose feudal sway over the common people was laboriously sought to be perpetuated by their missionary advisers, regarded all his proceedings with the most vigilant animosity. Jealous of his growing popularity, and unable to counteract it, they endeavoured to assail his reputation abroad by ostentatiously protesting against his acts, and appealing in Oriental phrase to the *wide universe* to witness and compassionate their *unparalleled wrongs.*

Heedless of their idle clamours, Lord George Paulet addressed himself to the task of reconciling the differences among the foreign residents, remedying their grievances, promoting their mercantile interests, and ameliorating, as far as lay in his power, the condition of the degraded natives. The iniquities he brought to light and instantly suppressed are too numerous to be here recorded; but one instance may be mentioned that will give some idea of the lamentable misrule to which these poor islands are subjected.

It is well known that the laws at the Sandwich Islands are subject to the most capricious alterations, which, by confounding all ideas of right and wrong in the minds of the natives, produce the most pernicious effects. In no case is this mischief more plainly discernible than in the continually shifting regulations concerning licentiousness. At one time the most innocent freedoms between the sexes are punished with fine and imprisonment; at another the revocation of the statute is followed by the most open and undisguised profligacy.

It so happened that at the period of Paulet's arrival the Connecticut blue laws had been for at least three weeks steadily enforced. In consequence of this, the fort at Honolulu was filled with a great number of young girls, who were confined there doing penance for their slips from virtue. Paulet, although at first unwilling to interfere with regulations having reference solely to the natives themselves, was eventually, by the prevalence of certain reports, induced to institute a strict inquiry into the internal administration of General Kekuanoa, governor of the island of Oahu, one of the pillars of the Hawaiian Church, and captain of the fort. He soon ascertained that numbers of the young females employed during the day at work intended for the benefit of the king, were at night smuggled over the ramparts of the fort—which on one side directly overhangs the sea—and were conveyed by stealth on board such vessels as had contracted with the General to be supplied with them. Before daybreak they returned to their quarters, and their own silence with regard to these secret excursions was purchased by a small portion of those wages of iniquity which were placed in the hands of Kekuanoa.

The vigour with which the laws concerning licentiousness were at that period enforced, enabled the General to monopolise in a great measure the detestable trade in which he was engaged, and there consequently flowed into his coffers—and some say into those of the government also—considerable sums of money. It is indeed a lamentable fact that the principal revenue of the Hawaiian government is derived from the fines levied upon, or rather the licences taken out by Vice, the prosperity of which is linked with that of the government. Were the people to become virtuous the authorities would become poor; but from present indications there is little apprehension to be entertained on that score.

Some five months after the date of the cession, the *Dublin* frigate, carrying the flag of Rear-Admiral Thomas, entered the harbour of Honolulu. The excitement that her sudden appearance produced on shore was prodigious. Three days after her arrival an English sailor hauled down the red cross which had been flying from the heights of the fort, and the Hawaiian colours were again displayed upon the same staff. At the same moment, the long 42-pounders upon Punchbowl Hill opened their iron throats in triumphant reply to the thunders of the five men-of-war in the harbour; and King Kammahammaha [*sic*] III, surrounded by a splendid group of British and American officers, unfurled the royal standard to assembled thousands of his subjects, who, attracted by the imposing military display of the foreigners, had flocked to witness the formal restoration of the islands to their ancient rulers.

The admiral Thomas, after sanctioning the proceedings of his subaltern, had brought the authorities to terms; and so removed the necessity of acting any longer under the provisional cession.

The event was made an occasion of riotous rejoicing by the king and the principal chiefs, who easily secured a display of enthusiasm from the inferior orders, by remitting for a time the accustomed severity of the laws. Royal proclamations in English and Hawaiian were placarded in the streets of Honolulu, and posted up in the more populous villages of the group, in which his Majesty announced to his loving subjects the re-establishment of his throne, and called upon them to celebrate it by breaking through all moral, legal, and religious restraint for ten consecutive days, during which time all the laws of the land were solemnly declared to be suspended.

Who that happened to be at Honolulu during those ten memorable days will ever forget them! The spectacle of universal broad-day debauchery, which was then exhibited, beggars description. The natives of the surrounding islands flocked to Honolulu by hundreds, and the crews of two frigates, opportunely let loose like so many demons to swell the heathenish uproar, gave the crowning flourish to the scene. It was a sort of Polynesian saturnalia. Deeds too atrocious to be mentioned were done at noon-day in the open street, and some of the islanders, caught in the very act of stealing from the foreigners, were, on being taken to the fort by the aggrieved party, suffered immediately to go at large and to retain the stolen property—Kekuanoa informing the white men, with a sardonic grin, that the laws were "hannapa" (tied up).

The history of these ten days reveals in their true colours the character of the Sandwich islanders, and furnishes an eloquent commentary on the results which have flowed from the labours of the missionaries. Freed from the restraint of severe penal laws, the natives almost to a man had plunged voluntarily into every species of wickedness and excess, and by their utter disregard of all decency plainly showed that, although they had been schooled into a seeming submission to the new order of things, they were in reality as depraved and vicious as ever.

Such were the events which produced in America so general an outbreak of indignation against the spirited and high-minded Paulet. He is not the first man who, in the fearless discharge of his duty, has awakened the senseless clamours of those whose narrow-minded suspicions blind them to a proper appreciation of measures which unusual exigencies may have rendered necessary.

It is almost needless to add that the British cabinet never had any idea of appropriating the islands; and it furnishes a sufficient vindication of the acts of Lord George Paulet, that he not only received the unqualified approbation of his own government, but that to this hour the great body of the Hawaiian people invoke blessings on his head, and look back with gratitude to the time when his liberal and paternal sway diffused peace and happiness among them.

Charles Nordhoff

NEW ENGLAND FOLKWAYS IN HAWAII

THE ORIGINAL INSTRUCTIONS to the American missionaries in Hawaii stated in part, "Your views are not to be limited to a low or a narrow scale; but you are to open your hearts wide, and set your mark high. You are to aim at nothing short of covering those islands with fruitful fields and pleasant dwellings, and schools and churches." In sum, in the spirit of liberal Calvinism, the missionaries were not only to Christianize the Islands but also to transplant there the folkways of distant New England.

In the opinion of Charles Nordhoff, who visited Hawaii in 1873, the missionaries had succeeded in attaining these high-flung goals. Not all observers have agreed. Some have adopted the disillusioned attitude expressed in Somerset Maugham's "Rain" and have mocked the entire missionary enterprise. In any case, Nordhoff wrote in praise of the missionaries. But his judgment was far from naïve. His account also contains some shrewd remarks about the Christianized natives. The following extracts are from his travel book *Northern California, Oregon and the Sandwich Islands,* published in 1874.

HONOLULU, being the capital of the kingdom, contains the government offices; and you will perhaps be surprised, as I was, to find an excellent public hospital, a reform school, and other proper and well-managed charities. When you have visited these and some of the numerous schools and the native churches, and have driven or ridden to Waikiki for a sea-bath, and have seen the Nuuanu Valley and the precipice called the Pali, if you are American, and familiar with New England, it will be revealed to you that the reason why all the country looks so familiar to you is that it is really a very accurate reproduction of New England country scenery. The white frame houses with green blinds, the picket-fences whitewashed until they shine, the stone walls, the small barns, the scanty pastures, the little white frame churches scattered about, the narrow "front yards," the frequent school-houses, usually with but little shade: all are New England, genuine and unadulterated; and you have only to eliminate the palms, the bananas, and

other tropical vegetation, to have before you a fine bit of Vermont
or the stonier parts of Massachusetts. The whole scene has no more
breadth nor freedom about it than a petty New England village, but
it is just as neat, trim, orderly, and silent also. There is even the
same propensity to put all the household affairs under one roof
which was born of a severe climate in Massachusetts, but has been
brought over to these milder suns by the incorrigible Puritans who
founded this bit of civilization.

In fact, the missionaries have left an indelible mark upon these
islands. You do not need to look deep to know that they were men
of force, men of the same kind as they who have left an equally deep
impress upon so large a part of our Western States; men and
women who had formed their own lives according to certain fixed
and immutable rules, who knew no better country than New England, nor any better ways than New England ways, and to whom it
never occurred to think that what was good and sufficient in
Massachusetts was not equally good and fit in any part of the world.
Patiently, and somwhat rigorously, no doubt, they sought from the
beginning to make New England men and women of these Hawaiians; and what is wonderful is that, to a large extent, they have
succeeded.

As you ride about the suburbs of Honolulu, and later as you
travel about the islands, more and more you will be impressed with
a feeling of respect and admiration for the missionaries. Whatever
of material prosperity has grown up here is built on their work,
and could not have existed but for their preceding labors; and you
see in the spirit of the people, in their often quaint habits, in their
universal education, in all that makes these islands peculiar and
what they are, the marks of the Puritans who came here but fifty
years ago to civilize a savage nation, and have done their work so
thoroughly that, even though the Hawaiian people became extinct,
it would require a century to obliterate the way-marks of that
handful of determined New England men and women.

Their patient and effective labors seem to me, now that I have
seen the results, to have been singularly undervalued at home. No
intelligent American can visit the islands and remain there even a
month, without feeling proud that the civilization which has here
been created in so marvelously short a time was the work of his
country men and women; and if you make the acquaintance of the
older missionary families, you will not leave them without deep

personal esteem for their characters, as well as admiration of their work. They did not only form a written language for the Hawaiian race, and painfully write for them school-books, a dictionary, and a translation of the Scriptures and of a hymn-book; they did not merely gather the people in churches and their children into schools; but they guided the race, slowly and with immense difficulty, toward Christian civilization; and though the Hawaiian is no more a perfect Christian than the New Yorker or Massachusetts man, and though there are still traces of old customs and superstitions, these missionaries have eradicated the grosser crimes of murder and theft so completely, that even in Honolulu people leave their houses open all day and unlocked all night, without thought of theft; and there is not a country in the world where the stranger may travel in such absolute safety as in these islands. . . .

The Hawaiian of the present day reads his Bible and newspaper, writes letters, wears clothes, owns property, serves in the legislature or Parliament, votes, teaches school, acts as justice of the peace and even as judge, is tax collector and assessor, constable and preacher. In spite of all this, or rather with it, he retains the oddest traces of the habits and customs of another age. For instance, he will labor for wages; but he will persistently and for years give away to his relations all his pay except what he needs for his actual subsistence, and if he is prosperous he is pretty sure to have quite a swarm of people to support. A lady told me that having repeatedly clothed her nurse in good apparel, and finding this liberal soul, every time, in a day or two reduced to her original somewhat shabby clothing, she at last reproached her for her folly. "What can I do?" the woman replied; "they come and ask me for the holaku [holoku, gown], or the handkerchief, or whatever I have. Suppose you say they are yours—then I will not give them away." Accordingly, the next new suit was formally declared to belong to the mistress; it was not given away. An old woman, kept chiefly for her skill in lomi-lomi [massage] by an American family, asked her master one day for ten dollars. He gave her two five-dollar gold pieces, and, to his amazement, saw her hand them over immediately, one to a little girl and one to a boy, who had evidently come to get the money—not for her use at all. A cook in my own family asked for the wages due him, which he had been saving for some time; he received forty-four dollars, and gave the whole amount at once to his father-in-law, who had come from another island on purpose to get this money. Nor was it grudged to him, so far as any of us could see. "By-and-by, if we are poor and in need, they will do as much for us," is the excuse.

As you ride along in the country, you will see your guide slyly putting a stone or a bunch of grass on a ledge near some precipice. If you look, you will see other objects of the same kind lying there. Ask him about it and he will tell you, with a laugh, that his forefathers in other times did so, and he does the same. It is, in fact, a peace offering to the local divinity of the place. Is he, then, an idolater? Not at all; not necessarily, at least. He is under the compulsion of an old custom; and he will even tell you that it is all nonsense. The same force leads him to treat with respect and veneration a chief or chiefess even if abjectly poor, though before the law the highest chief is no better than the common people. . . .

Finally, the daily life of the Hawaiian, if he lives near the seacoast and is master of his own life, is divided between fishing, taro planting, poi making, and mat weaving. All these but the last are laborious occupations; but they do not make hard work of them. Two days' labor every week will provide abundant food for a man and his family. He has from five to ten dollars a year of taxes to pay, and this money he can easily earn. The sea always supplies him with fish, sea-moss, and other food. He is fond of fussing at different things; but he also lies down on the grass a good deal— why shouldn't he?—he reads his paper, he plays at cards, he rides about a good deal, he sleeps more or less, and about midnight he gets up and eats a hearty supper. Altogether he is a very happy creature, and by no means a bad one. You need not lock your door against him; and an election and a luau occasionally, give him all the excitement he craves, and that not of an unwholesome kind.

Isabella L. Bird

GIFTS FOR A KING

In 1873 Isabella Lucy Bird, an English traveler, visited Hawaii. In 1881 she married Dr. John Bishop, an Edinburgh physician, and eleven years later she became the first female fellow of the Royal Geographical Society.

In her book *The Hawaiian Archipelago,* selections from which follow, Miss Bird reported in some detail her experiences in Hilo on the island of Hawaii, when Lunalilo, "the People's King," came there on a royal tour. From miles around the natives gathered to make a donation (*hookupu*) to their king. The lavish gifts and the atmosphere of intense veneration give clear proof of the traditional loyalty of Hawaiians for the monarchy, loyalty with its roots in old Hawaii, long before the white man came to the Islands.

AT TEN PUNCTUALLY, Lunalilo, Governor Lyman, the sheriff of Hawaii, the royal chamberlain, and the adjutant-general, walked up to the courthouse, and the king took his place, standing in the lower verandah with his suite about him. All the foreigners were either on the upper balcony, or on the stairs leading to it, on which, to get the best possible view of the spectacle, I stood for three mortal hours. The attendant gentlemen were well dressed, but wore "shocking bad hats;" and the king wore a sort of shooting suit, a short brown cut-away coat, an ash-coloured waistcoat and ash-coloured trousers with a blue stripe. He stood bareheaded. He dressed in this style in order that the natives might attend the reception in every-day dress, and not run the risk of spoiling their best clothes by Hilo torrents. The dress of the king and his attendants was almost concealed by wreaths of *ohia* blossoms and festoons of *maile,* some of them two yards long, which had been thrown over them, and which bestowed a fantastic glamour on the otherwise prosaic inelegance of their European dress. But indeed the spectacle, as a whole, was altogether poetical, as it was an ebullition of natural, national, human feeling, in which the heart had the first place. I very soon ceased to notice the incongruous elements, which were supplied chiefly by the Americans present. There were Republicans by birth and nature, destitute of traditions of loyalty or reverence for aught on earth; who bore on their faces not only republicanism, but that quintessence of puritan republicanism which hails from New England; and these were subjects of a foreign king, nay several were office-holders who had taken the oath of allegiance, and from whose lips "His Majesty, Your Majesty," flowed far more copiously than from ours which are "to the manner born."

On the king's appearance, the cheering was tremendous—regular British cheering, well led, succeeded by that which is not British, "three cheers and a tiger," but it was "Hi, hi, hi, hullah!" Every hat was off, every handkerchief in air, tears in many eyes, enthusiasm universal, for the people were come to welcome the king of their choice; the prospective restorer of the Constitution "trampled upon" by Kamehameha V., "the kind chief," who was making them welcome to his presence after the fashion of their old feudal lords. When the cheering had subsided, the eighty boys of Missionary Lyman's School, who, dressed in white linen with crimson *leis,* were grouped in a hollow square round the flagstaff, sang the Hawaiian national anthem, the music of which is the same as ours. More cheering and enthusiasm, and then the natives came through the gate across the lawn, and up to the verandah where the king stood, in one continuous procession, till 2,400 Hawaiians had enjoyed one moment of infinite and ever to be remembered satisfaction in the royal presence. Every now and then the white, pale-eyed, unpicturesque face of a foreigner passed by, but these were few, and the foreign school children were received by themselves after Mr. Lyman's boys. The Americans have introduced the villanous [*sic*] custom of shaking hands at these receptions, borrowing it, I suppose, from a presidential reception at Washington; and after the king had gone through this ceremony with each native, the present was deposited in front of the verandah, and the gratified giver took his place on the grass. Not a man, woman, or child came empty handed. Every face beamed with pride, wonder, and complacency, for here was a sovereign for whom cannon roared, and yards were manned, of their own colour, who called them his brethren.

The variety of costume was infinite. All the women wore the native dress, the sack of *holoku,* many of which were black, blue, green, or bright rose colour, some were bright yellow, a few were pure white, and others were a mixture of orange and scarlet. Some wore very pretty hats made from cane-tops, and trimmed with hibiscus blossoms or passion-flowers; others wore bright-coloured handkerchiefs, knotted lightly round their flowing hair, or wreaths of the *Microlepia tenuifolia.* Many had tied bandanas in a graceful knot over the left shoulder. All wore two, three, four, or even six beautiful *leis,* besides long festoons of the fragrant *maile. Leis* of the crimson *ohia* blossoms were universal; but besides these there were *leis* of small red and white double roses, *pohas,* yellow amaranth, sugar cane tassels like frosted silver, the orange pandanus, the delicious gardenia, and a very few of orange blossoms, and the great granadilla or passion-flower. Few if any of the women wore shoes, and none of the children had anything on their heads.

A string of 200 Chinamen passed by, "plantation hands," with boyish faces, and cunning, almond-shaped eyes. They were dressed in loose, blue, denim trousers with shirts of the same, fastening at the side over them, their front hair closely shaven, and the rest gathered into pigtails, which were wound several times round their heads. These all deposited money in the adjutant-general's hand. The dress of the Hawaiian men was more varied and singular than that of the women, every kind of dress and undress, with *leis* of *ohia* and garlands of *maile* covering all deficiencies. The poor things came up with pathetic innocence, many of them with nothing on but an old shirt, and cotton trousers rolled up to the knees. Some had red shirts and blue trousers, others considered that a shirt was an effective outer garment. Some wore highly ornamental, dandified shirts, and trousers tucked into high, rusty, mud-covered boots. A few young men were in white straw hats, white shirts, and white trousers, with crimson *leis* round their hats and throats. Some had diggers' scarves round their waists; but the most effective costume was sported by a few old men, who had tied crash towels over their shoulders.

It was often amusing and pathetic at once to see them come up. Obviously, when the critical moment arrived, they were as anxious to do the right thing as a *debutante* is to back her train successfully out of the royal presence at St. James's. Some were so agitated at last as to require much coaching from the governor as to how to present their gifts and shake hands. Some half dropped down on their knees, others passionately and with tears kissed the king's hand, or grasped it convulsively in both their own; while a few were so embarrassed by the presents they were carrying that they had no hands at all to shake, and the sovereign good-naturedly clapped them on the shoulders. Some of them, in shaking hands, adroitly slipped coins into the king's palm, so as to make sure that he received their loving tribute. There had been a *hui,* or native meeting, which had passed resolutions, afterwards presented to Lunalilo, setting forth that whereas he received a great deal of money in revenue from the *haoles,* they, his native people, would feel that he did not love them if he would not receive from their own hands contributions in silver for his support. So, in order not to wound their feelings, he accepted these rather troublesome cash donations.

One woman, sorely afflicted with quaking palsy, dragged herself slowly along. One hand hung by her side helpless, and the other grasped a live fowl so tightly that she could not loosen it to shake hands, whereupon the king raised the helpless arm, which called forth much cheering. There was one poor cripple who had only the use of his arms. His knees were doubled under him, and he trailed his body along the ground. He had dragged himself two miles "to lie for a moment at the king's feet," and even his poor arms carried a gift. He looked hardly like a human shape, as his desire was realised; and, I doubt not, would have been content then and there to die. There were ancient men, tattooed all over, who had passed their first youth when the idols were cast away, and who remembered the old days of tyranny when it was an offence, punishable with death, for a man to let his shadow fall on the king; and when none of the "swinish multitude" had any rights which they could sustain against their chiefs. These came up bewildered, trembling, almost falling on their knees, hardly daring to raise their eyes to the king's kind, encouraging face, and bathed his hand with tears while they kissed it. Numbers of little children were led up by their parents; there were babies in arms, and young-lings carried on parents' backs, and the king stooped and shook hands with all, and even pulled out the babies' hands from under their mufflings and the old people wept, and cheers rent the air.

Next in interest to this procession of beaming faces, and the blaze of colour, was the sight of the presents, and the ungrudging generosity with which they were brought. Many of the women presented live fowls tied by the legs, which were deposited, one upon another, till they formed a fainting, palpitating heap under the hot sun. Some of the men brought decorated hogs tied by one leg, which squealed so persistently in the presence of royalty, that they were removed to the rear. Hundreds carried nets of sweet potatoes, eggs, and *kalo,* artistically arranged. Men staggered along in couples with bamboos between them, supporting clusters of bananas weigh-ing nearly a hundredweight. Others brought yams, cocoanuts, oranges, onions, pumpkins, early pineapples, and even the great, delicious fruit of the large passion-flower. A few maidens presented the king with bouquets of choice flowers, and costly *leis* of the yellow feathers of the *Melithreptes Pacifica.* There were fully two tons of *kalo* and sweet potatoes in front of the courthouse, hundreds of fowls, and piles of bananas, eggs, and cocoanuts. The *hookupu* was a beautiful sight, all the more so that not one of that radiant, loving gift-offering throng came in quest of office, or for any other thing that he could obtain. It was just the old-time spirit of reverence for the man who typifies rule, blended with the extreme of personal devotion to the prince whom a united people had placed upon the throne. The feeling was genuine and pathetic in its intensity. It is said that the natives like their king better, because he was truly, "above all," the last of a proud and imperious house, which, in virtue of a pedigree of centuries, looked down upon the nobility of the Kamehamehas.

When the last gift was deposited, the lawn in front of the court-house was one densely-packed, variegated mass of excited, buzzing Hawaiians. While the king was taking a short rest, two ancient and hideous females, who looked like heathen priestesses, chanted a monotonous and heathenish-sounding chant or *male,* in eulogy of some ancient idolater. It just served to remind me that this attractive crowd was but one generation removed from slaughter-loving gods and human sacrifices.

William N. Armstrong

KING KALAKAUA IN JAPAN

In 1881 Kalakaua, who reigned from 1874 to 1891, took a trip around the world. He was the first monarch to undertake such a journey, and attracted a furor of attention as he made his various state visits. From Honolulu he went to San Francisco, thence by steamer to Japan. He next visited China, Hong Kong, Siam, Burma, and India, then Egypt and a number of European states, including Italy, Britain, Belgium, Austria, and France, before returning home by way of the United States. The entire journey was a triumph of pomp and good spirits.

Kalakaua's retinue included William N. Armstrong, Hawaii's attorney general, of a prominent missionary family, and the king's alcoholic valet, Robert, said to be a German baron. Armstrong recorded his impressions of the royal junket in a book entitled *Around the World with a King.* The following extracts from Armstrong's volume describe the king's reception in Japan.

A T EARLY DAWN on the 4th of March we steamed up the Bay of Yedo. To the westward we caught a faint glimmer of the snow-clad summit of sacred Fusyama [*sic*] rising in a truncated cone 13,000 feet from the level plain. Though in our little kingdom there were mountains of nearly the same height, with several a thousand feet higher, not one of them rose as abruptly or as symmetrically from the sea or plain. The many small fishing-villages along the coast, and the fleets of oddly rigged sampans, marked a thickly settled country.

The King hesitated to display the royal standard, for the suite advised him that if no notice was taken of it he would have voluntarily humiliated himself. For the same cautious reason we sent no notice of the royal intention to visit Japan, but had requested a fellow passenger, who was a resident of Yokohama, to secure for us lodging at one of the hotels. But the captain wished to announce the fact that he carried a distinguished person, and as the King's inclination coincided with his desire, Robert, the valet, extricated the royal standard from its canvas bag, and it was soon flying at the main truck. We did not expect that under the circumstances it would receive a salute.

While we leaned over the rail looking at the Bluffs, or foreign settlement of Yokohama, we saw a number of warships in the harbour; seven Russian, two British, one French, and three Japanese. It was an imposing line of sea-fighters, stretching for a mile before the city. They rode at their anchors in silence and without a sign of life. As our steamer crossed the bows of the first ironclad, a Russian, there was a sudden discharge of saluting guns from her batteries. At the same moment the Hawaiian flag was broken out on the mainmast. Swarms of sailors sprang aloft and manned the yards, that is, stood, in line along them, each man extending his arm to the shoulder of the next one. As if by magic the ship was dressed from stem to stern with the flags of all nations. The report of the first gun was followed slowly by a royal salute of twenty-one guns, and our royal standard was dipped in response. Within a minute we passed the bows of the next warship. From her mainmast also the Hawaiian flag was unfurled, her crew also manned the yards, the ship was dressed with flags as had been the Russian, and the slow discharges of her saluting guns swelled the volume of noise. The royal standard on the "Oceanic" was again dipped in response, and as we crossed the bows of all the warships in succession, the same ceremonies were repeated. The crews mounting and manning the yards, cheering as we passed; the roar of two hundred and seventy-three cannon; the smoke rising in clouds and rolling away in dense volumes toward the bay; the innumerable flags with which the warships were dressed, appearing and disappearing in the smoke— made an extraordinary and brilliant scene, and a startling one, because unexpected. The King stood impassive, lifting his hat as we passed each vessel, while our royal standard dipped in response.

The anchor chain of our steamer had hardly ceased its rattling when a boat from the Japanese warship "Mikado" reached the gangway. An admiral, six other naval officers, and two Imperial Commissioners, from his Imperial Majesty the Emperor of Japan, all in full uniform, boarded our steamer, and asked, with due official etiquette, to be presented to the King of Hawaii. This was done by our Chamberlain. The Imperial Commissioners stated that they had been commanded by his Imperial Majesty to receive and welcome his Majesty the King of Hawaii, and invite him to be the Emperor's guest so long as he remained in the Empire. The King towered above them with his large stature, received them easily and gracefully, and replied that it would please him to become the guest of the Emperor. After a brief conversation he was asked, with his suite, to enter the boat of a warship, and be conveyed to one of the Emperor's palaces near the city of Yokohama. He remained for a few moments to receive the calls of the admirals and commanders of the British and French warships. We were not prepared for this very splended reception; we were in the negligent clothing of travellers eagerly in search of bath-tubs, but the King stood impassive in this group of brilliantly dressed officials, making no apology for his appearance, for a king never apologises. We entered the boat of the warship; the royal standard of Hawaii was fixed in her bows, and a launch towed us to the landing. As the boat drew close to the shore we noticed great crowds on the docks, and long lines of troops in the street. When the boat touched the landing, the strains of "Hawaii Ponoi" burst from the shore. This unexpected compliment from the Emperor's military band, this music of our own country in a strange land, upset us instantly, and a snivelling monarch, with a snivelling suite, uncovered, our Japanese escort uncovering also, until the anthem ended.

Now for the first time in the history of this Empire one of the kings of Christendom was on her soil. The royal party walked a short distance between lines of troops to a public office near the landing. Many officials were presented to the King; confections and wines were served. An imperial carriage, brought from Tokio by railway, drove to the door, and the King, with his suite and the Emperor's Chamberlain, entered it. Both sides of the streets, for a mile or more, were lined with troops, and behind them were crowds of people, silent and stolid; to them it was a rare sight. Intertwined Japanese and Hawaiian flags appeared on nearly all the slight frame houses fronting on our line of march. We were slowly driven, through the thickly settled part of the city of Yokohama, to a grand house or palace on rising ground overlooking the city; built for the convenience of the Emperor's guests. It was furnished with exquisite articles of Japanese art, but European beds, chairs, sofas, and bureaus had been added for the comfort of foreign guests. A retinue of servants put us in our chambers, and we were left to ourselves. Mr. Nagasaki, the Imperial Chamberlain, was graduated at the College at Ann Arbor, Michigan, and, with a romantic faith in the future of his country, was an apostle of American ideas. The Emperor had assigned to him the duty of attending the King while he remained in the country. . . .

We were now allowed to rest during the day, after the serious business of the reception by the Emperor on the morrow had been arranged. The details were with much deference submitted by the Imperial Chamberlain to the King, and he approved of them. These arrangements were novel, for there was no precedent for the reception of a foreign monarch; but the etiquette of European courts was closely followed. The Governor of the Province of Kanagawa called in the evening, but etiquette forbade general presentations until the monarchs had exchanged visits.

The delicate subject of the exchange of speeches was disposed of by the understanding that none should be formally made; we were relieved of the dreary incident of the two sovereigns pulling manuscripts out of their pockets and reading high-sounding phrases to each other. My royal master, who was, as I have said, familiar with royal etiquette, now instructed his suite regarding their attitude and behaviour. The Chamberlain needed none, for he had been long in his Majesty's service. I, the Minister, however, was an untutored American who until lately had been denied the priceless blessings of royal associations, and, unless well instructed, there was danger that I might commit an error like that of an American

Minister to Austria, who at an imperial reception discovered an empty chair which he innocently occupied, though, as he was later informed, it had been reserved for the Emperor. The King directed me to stand at his right, and closely watch the conduct of the Prime Minister of Japan, with whom my rank was equal. As I was about to wear a sword for the first time, he warned me against allowing it to get between my legs.

I noticed that the valet, Robert, had strongly impressed the lower Japanese attendants with the dignity of his office of "Standard-Bearer," and, instead of occupying servants' quarters, was placed in a richly furnished room, with an attendant. . . .

The following morning we dressed for the imperial reception. When I put on my gorgeous trappings for the first time, with sword and cocked hat, I was as much absorbed in it as the Chinese pirate who at his execution was kindly supplied by a British officer with a pair of English boots, which so engaged his attention that he showed a culpable indifference to his own hanging.

At ten o'clock the imperial carriage with its mounted escort was at the door, and we entered it with the Emperor's Chamberlain, followed by another with the Imperial Commissioners. We took the imperial railway car at the station and arrived in Tokio in an hour. There a large number of officials received us, and led us to a room decorated with flowers, where confections and wine were served. There was the same quiet in the room, though it was filled with officials in uniform, as if the Emperor himself were present: the same respectful, and what many, who fail to understand the Japanese nature and custom, would regard as abject, service. One of the Imperial Princes now appeared, and, after his presentation to the King, declared that by order of the Emperor he was to attend his Majesty during his stay in the Empire. The King, with the Imperial Prince, now entered one of the Emperor's open carriages, while the Chamberlain and I entered another. As the carriages moved into the street they were surrounded by a large body of lancers. The railway station was decorated with Hawaiian and Japanese flags, and along the route of travel toward the Emperor's palace, a distance of four miles, these countless flags, intertwined, decorated the houses. The troops lined both sides of the streets, and behind them, as in Yokohama, the people were massed, silent, sober, and deeply interested. An ancient custom, recently forbidden by the government, required the people to prostrate themselves on the approach of the Mikado. The new order of things directed the people simply to bow respectfully. Many of them seemed to be quite uncertain as to their duty in the presence of a foreign king. All, however, bowed low, some even to the ground.

Tokio is a city of castles and moats, formerly the military encampment of the Shoguns and their great retainers. The carriages passed over many bridges spanning these moats, until, after a journey of four miles, the bugle announced our arrival at Akasaka, the palace of the Emperor. The etiquette of European courts requires a monarch to receive a visiting monarch at the threshold of his palace. The Emperor left his audience-hall and awaited the King in a room close to the entrance of the palace. The King stepped out of the carriage, and with the Imperial Prince entered this room, in the centre of which the Emperor stood alone. The suite, with officers of the imperial household, followed, and remained a few feet distant from the monarchs. They shook hands—an unusual proceeding on the part of the Emperor—and, through an interpreter, who stood in a bowing attitude behind the Emperor, conversed for several minutes. The Emperor then looked towards his own Chamberlain, and I, as the next in rank, was presented to him, and the presentation of the King's Chamberlain followed. The Emperor then turned, and with the King by his side walked briskly through several richly furnished halls to the audience-room. The Emperor walks alone when before his people; the Empress is never at his side; the belief in his divine origin permits no person in the Empire to appear to be his equal, and the Empress follows him. But for the first time in his own reign, and in those of his predecessors, he walked by the side of his kingly guest. . . .

After an interview of twenty minutes the King retired with the Emperor at his side. In the last room of the suite they shook hands again, and we entered the imperial carriage. It carried us, surrounded with a squadron of lancers, for four miles, to the palace of the Enriokwan, which had been assigned to the royal visitor. This was one of the ancient castles of the daimyos, surrounded by a wide moat, and reached by a bridge. Two years before this time it had been occupied by General Grant and his suite. In the large court-yard a battalion of troops was stationed as a guard of honour. The building contained numerous chambers, furnished with the richest Japanese and European furniture. On the table of the dressing-room we noticed, as we passed through it, the trays of confections and sweets which had been placed before us in the audience-chamber; these had been carried by swift messengers and reached the palace before we arrived. There were now in this spacious build-ing only three guests—the King and his two companions; but a score of servants stood in the parlours and at the doors of the bed-chambers. In a distant part were rooms occupied by the officials who were assigned by the Emperor to attend the King. It was assumed that we had European "habits," and spirits and champagne were tendered to us promptly; the Emperor, fortunately, did not place his royal guest under the restrictions which his government placed upon the American instructors who were employed in the Japanese schools, one of which, in a written contract, provided "that the said teacher shall not get drunk."

After we had admired the rich and delicate furniture which adorned this romantic palace, we entered the King's bedchamber. Here we found the valet, Robert, lying on one of the sofas in a tipsy sleep.

Queen Liliuokalani

HAWAII'S LAST MONARCH ABDICATES

EARLY IN 1893, an almost bloodless revolution dethroned Queen Liliuokalani, Kalakaua's sister and Hawaii's last monarch. The revo-lutionists, mainly American residents of Hawaii, objected strongly to her attempt to replace the liberal 1887 constitution with a more authoritarian government. They also hoped to bring about Hawaii's annexation by the United States, in order to end discrimination against Hawaiian sugar in the McKinley tariff of 1890, which had caused a severe depression in the Islands. The revolutionary Provisional Gov-ernment made immediate overtures to the United States, and President Benjamin Harrison sent an annexation treaty to the Senate. But Presi-dent Grover Cleveland, who took office on March 4, opposed Hawaii's annexation and withdrew the treaty. Prosperity returned to Hawaii with the Wilson-Gorman tariff of 1894, which was favorable to Hawaii's sugar interests. But annexation waited until 1898.

Meanwhile, early in January, 1895, a brief and easily repressed counterrevolution broke out in Hawaii. About two hundred of the

rebels were arrested (and ultimately pardoned), including Liliuokalani, who had prior knowledge of the uprising but did not participate
in it. In her book, *Hawaii's Story by Hawaii's Queen* (1898), a selection from which follows, she described, with understandable bitterness, how, under house arrest, she signed a document renouncing her
claim to the Hawaiian throne. A portly woman of will and pride, then
in her middle fifties, she was particularly angry at having to sign the
document with her married name (as the widow of John O. Dominis),
as if she were only a private citizen rather than of royal lineage.

FOR THE FIRST few days nothing occurred to disturb the quiet of
my apartments save the tread of the sentry. On the fourth day I
received a visit from Mr. Paul Neumann, who asked me if, in the
event that it should be decided that all the principal parties to the
revolt must pay for it with their lives, I was prepared to die? I replied to this in the affirmative, telling him I had no anxiety for myself, and felt no dread of death. He then told me that six others
besides myself had been selected to be shot for treason, but that he
would call again, and let me know further about our fate. I was in a
state of nervous prostration, as I have said, at the time of the outbreak, and naturally the strain upon my mind had much aggravated
my physical troubles; yet it was with much difficulty that I obtained
permission to have visits from my own medical attendant.

About the 22d of January a paper was handed to me by Mr.
[C. B.] Wilson, which, on examination, proved to be a purported act
of abdication for me to sign. It had been drawn out for the men in
power by their own lawyer, Mr. A. S. Hartwell, whom I had not
seen until he came with others to see me sign it. The idea of abdicat-
ing never originated with me. I knew nothing at all about such a
transaction until they sent to me, by the hands of Mr. Wilson, the
insulting proposition written in abject terms. For myself, I would
have chosen death rather than to have signed it; but it was represented to me that by my signing this paper all the persons who had
been arrested, all my people now in trouble by reason of their love
and loyalty towards me, would be immediately released. Think of
my position—sick, a lone woman in prison, scarcely knowing who
was my friend, or who listened to my words only to betray me,
without legal advice or friendly counsel, and the stream of blood
ready to flow unless it was stayed by my pen.

My persecutors have stated, and at that time compelled me to state, that this paper was signed and acknowledged by me after consultation with my friends whose names appear at the foot of it as witnesses. Not the least opportunity was given to me to confer with any one; but for the purpose of making it appear to the outside world that I was under the guidance of others, friends who had known me well in better days were brought into the place of my imprisonment, and stood around to see a signature affixed by me.

When it was sent to me to read, it was only a rough draft. After I had examined it, Mr. Wilson called, and asked me if I were willing to sign it. I simply answered that I would see when the formal or official copy was shown me. On the morning of the 24th of January the official document was handed to me, Mr. Wilson making the remark, as he gave it, that he hoped I would not retract, that is, he hoped that I would sign the official copy.

Then the following individuals witnessed my subscription of the signature which was demanded of me: William G. Irwin, H. A. Widemann, Samuel Parker, S. Kalua Kookano, Charles B. Wilson, and Paul Neumann. The form of acknowledgment was taken by W. L. Stanley, Notary Public.

So far from the presence of these persons being evidence of a voluntary act on my part, was it not an assurance to me that they, too, knew that, unless I did the will of my jailers, what Mr. Neumann had threatened would be performed, and six prominent citizens immediately put to death. I so regarded it then, and I still believe that murder was the alternative. Be this at it may, it is certainly happier for me to reflect to-day that there is not a drop of the blood of my subjects, friends or foes, upon my soul.

When it came to the act of writing, I asked what would be the form of signature; to which I was told to sign, "Liliuokalani Dominis." This sounding strange to me, I repeated the question, and was given the same reply. At this I wrote what they dictated without further demur, the more readily for the following reasons.

Before ascending the throne, for fourteen years, or since the date of my proclamation as heir apparent, my official title had been simply Liliuokalani. Thus I was proclaimed both Princess Royal and Queen. Thus it is recorded in the archives of the government to this day. The Provisional Government nor any other had enacted any change in my name. All my official acts, as well as my private letters, were issued over the signature of Liliuokalani. But when my jailers required me to sign "Liliuokalani Dominis," I did as they commanded. Their motive in this as in other actions was plainly to humiliate me before my people and before the world. I saw in a moment, what they did not, that, even were I not complying under the most severe and exacting duress, by this demand they had over-reached themselves. There is not, and never was, within the range of my knowledge, any such person as Liliuokalani Dominis.

It is a rule of common law that the acts of any person deprived of civil rights have no force nor weight, either at law or in equity; and that was my situation. Although it was written in the document that it was my free act and deed, circumstances prove that it was not; it had been impressed upon me that only by its execution could the lives of those dear to me, those beloved by the people of Hawaii, be saved, and the shedding of blood be averted. I have never expected the revolutionists of 1887 and 1893 to willingly restore the rights notoriously taken by force or intimidation; but this act, obtained under duress, should have no weight with the authorities of the United States, to whom I appealed. But it may be asked, why did I not make some protest at the time, or at least shortly thereafter, when I found my friends sentenced to death and imprisonment? I did. There are those now living who have seen my written statement of all that I have recalled here. It was made in my own handwriting, on such paper as I could get, and sent outside of the prison walls and into the hands of those to whom I wished to state the circumstances under which that fraudulent act of abdication was procured from me. This I did for my own satisfaction at the time.

After those in my place of imprisonment had all affixed their signatures, they left, with the single exception of Mr. A. S. Hartwell. As he prepared to go, he came forward, shook me by the hand, and the tears streamed down his cheeks. This was a matter of great surprise to me. After this he left the room. If he had been engaged in a righteous and honorable action, why should he be affected? Was it the consciousness of a mean act which overcame him so? Mrs. Wilson, who stood behind my chair throughout the ceremony, made the remark that those were crocodile's tears. I leave it to the reader to say what were his actual feelings in the case.

Gerrit P. Judd

THE ATTACK ON PEARL HARBOR

IT IS A common saying that Pearl Harbor put Hawaii on the map. Before the Japanese sneak attack on December 7, 1941, comparatively few Americans knew, or cared, much about the remote island chain which in 1959 became the fiftieth state of the union. Although commercial air travel to Hawaii from the mainland began before 1941, the operation was on a small scale. The relatively small number of prewar visitors to Hawaii still came mainly by steamship, on leisurely voyages lasting four to seven days. But this idyllic situation changed abruptly as a result of the "Day of Infamy." The full spotlight of national interest and fury turned on Hawaii, particularly as thousands of Americans demanded to know who was responsible for the shameful American defeat. During and after the war, amateurs and experts spoke and wrote thousands of words on this fiercely controversial topic. Meanwhile, thousands of troops and war workers entered Hawaii, for assignments there or en route to and from the war zones of the western Pacific. One result was to transform Hawaii from a dimly apprehended American semitropical outpost into a full-fledged American state, well known to millions of people throughout the world.

The following account of the attack on Pearl Harbor was first published, by the editor, in 1961, in his *Hawaii, An Informal History*. It was intended then, and may still serve, as a short summary of the main attack, along with a description of a minor phase of the fighting known affectionately in Hawaii as "The Battle of Niihau."

EVERY AMERICAN over thirty, and some younger than that, remembers Pearl Harbor. Americans in Hawaii remember it particularly well. It is an amusing parlor game, now that the war is safely won and has been for a long time, to ask members of a group where they were and what they were doing on the "Day of Infamy," as President Roosevelt so aptly called it. Some were, as Walter Lord has reported in his brilliant anecdotal book on the subject, listening to radio station WOR's broadcast of the Giant-Dodger football game at New York's Polo Grounds, when at 2:26 P.M., EST, about an hour after the Japanese attack began, an announcer interrupted with

85

the first flash-report. Others were having cocktails, doing the laundry, or engaging in a thousand other inconsequential occupations at the time, while in Hawaii many Americans were already dead or dying. Whatever the circumstances, and each person has a different story to tell, everyone remembers clearly just what he was doing when he heard the news.

At first, of course, there was much confusion and bewilderment. Except for a minority—mainly former tourists or military and naval personnel—few Americans were quite certain just where Pearl Harbor was. Many anecdotes, now remembered in tranquility, relate how so-and-so insisted that it was in the Caribbean, the Canal Zone, California, or the Philippines. It took a little while for Americans to agree that Pearl Harbor was in Hawaii, then universally pronounced "Hah-why-yuh," like a pun on "How are you."

But in any case the reaction was identical throughout the United States. Shock turned to cold fury at the sneak attack. Some men dropped what they were doing and headed for the nearest recruiting office. America's greatest defeat produced America's greatest national unification. In retrospect, although it took almost four years of fighting, Japan had lost the war just as soon as news of the attack was made public.

Instantly a spotlight of interest was turned on Hawaii. Millions of Americans learned, on December 7, 1941, what they had never known, or had once known and forgotten, that in fact the territory of Hawaii was an "integral part" of the United States.

After the attack was over, and the stable door well locked, a series of investigations began which produced thousands of pages of testimony and documents. Obviously the armed forces had blundered somehow, and the Pacific Fleet had been crippled. Much buck-passing resulted, and much of the testimony was contradictory. In some cases high military officials, preoccupied with gigantic tasks and responsibilities, were honestly vague about details of exactly what they had done in the days and hours before the outbreak of the war. The responsibility for the disaster has not been fixed, and it may never be.

Nonetheless, careful investigation has produced a hard core of reasonably well-established fact, which is worth relating in summary form. Investigation also has scotched a number of nasty rumors, and it seems worthwhile to mention a few of these, for rumors die hard, especially among the former GI's who took the brunt of the holocaust, who were therefore emotionally involved in the events more directly than most Americans, and who may not have had the opportunity to inform themselves correctly in subsequent years.

Early in 1941 leaders in the Japanese Navy began to plan the attack on Pearl Harbor, in order to destroy the American Pacific fleet should war break out between Japan and the United States. This plan matured during the summer and fall. In mid-November the Japanese task force began to assemble at Tankan (also known as Hitokappu or Shitokap) Bay of Etorofu Island in the cold and desolate Kuriles. This force left for Hawaii on November 26. It consisted of six aircraft carriers, two battleships, three cruisers, nine destroyers, three submarines, and eight tankers, under the command of Vice Admiral Chuichi Nagumo. In radio silence it proceeded eastward in waters far removed from ordinary shipping lanes. On December 2 it was told to climb Mount Niitaka, that is, to attack. A few days later it headed southeast and then south for Hawaii.

After 6:00 A.M. on December 7, when the Japanese task force was about 230 miles north of Oahu, it began to launch the first air strike. The Japanese had 432 planes—39 for air patrol, 40 in reserve, and 353 for the attack. The first attacking force consisted of 49 horizontal bombers, 51 dive bombers, 40 torpedo planes, and 43 fighters. The second consisted of 54 horizontal bombers, 80 dive bombers, and 36 fighters. The pilots, thoroughly trained and minutely briefed, had instructions to destroy the aircraft on Oahu's various military air stations and to attack the United States fleet in Pearl Harbor.

Meanwhile an advanced expeditionary force was already in Hawaiian waters. It consisted of twenty or more conventional submarines and five of the celebrated midget submarines. All five of these tiny craft were ultimately lost.

At 3:42 A.M. the American minesweeper *Condor* sighted the periscope of one of the Japanese submarines just outside Pearl Harbor. The destroyer *Ward* searched the area without success. At 6:30 A.M. the *Ward* made a second submarine contact in the area, and at 6:45 fired on the tiny craft, the first American shot to be fired in World War II. A navy PBY in the area assisted by dropping depth charges.

At 7:02 A.M. two army privates at the Opana Radar Station near Kahuku Point on northern Oahu picked up an airplane contact, which they plotted as 137 miles north and three degrees to the east. Here was well-advanced warning of the oncoming Japanese striking force. But the lieutenant in the Information Center assumed that

it was a flight of B-17's, which he had reason to believe were
scheduled to arrive from the West Coast about that time. Consequently, in this comedy of multiplied errors, he did not relay this
priceless information. Meanwhile the two privates continued to trace
the enemy force, until at 7:39 they lost it in a so-called "dead
zone" caused by the surrounding land masses. At 7:45 they left for
breakfast at Kawailoa.

Authorities in Washington also had advance indications of the
forthcoming attack. On the basis of intelligence reports and after
consultation with President Roosevelt and others, General George
Marshall, the Army Chief of Staff, sent the following message
to the commanding generals in Manila, Panama, and Hawaii:
"Japanese are presenting at 1:00 P.M. Eastern Standard Time today
what amounts to an ultimatum. Also they are under orders to
destroy their code machine immediately. Just what significance the
hour set may have we do not know but be on alert accordingly.
Inform naval authorities of this communication."

To preserve security Marshall did not use a scrambler telephone.
He did not know that because of weather conditions the Army's
radio could not establish contact with Pearl Harbor, and that the
message would be sent by commercial cable. The message was filed
in the Army Signal Center at 12:01 P.M. (6:31 A.M. Honolulu time),
and Honolulu's RCA received it at 7:33 A.M., just 22 minutes
before the attack. But the messenger boy was delayed by the fighting,
and did not reach the signal office in Fort Shafter until four hours
later. The decoded message reached Walter C. Short, the commanding general, at 2:58 P.M. By that time, of course, it was a completely
useless document.

The Japanese attack began about 7:55 A.M., Honolulu time.
Aircraft bombed and strafed Oahu's various airfields, Hickam,
Kaneohe, Wheeler, Ewa, and Bellows. The United States lost 188
aircraft, and an aditional 159 were damaged. Between 8:00 and 9:00,
Navy planes and the 11 B-17's from the mainland flew into the
center of the fighting. No Navy plane was able to take off after the
fighting started, but Army planes made 81 take-offs throughout the
day. In general the surprise was so complete that American planes
could offer little effective opposition.

At Pearl Harbor most of the damage came in the first attack,
which began at 7:55 A.M. and lasted about half an hour. A second
attack followed at 8:40 and ended about 9:45. The last Japanese

plane reached its carrier about 1:00 P.M., and half an hour later the Japanese task force headed for home.

Of the ninety-six ships in Pearl Habror, eighteen were sunk or severely damaged. The battleships *Arizona* and *Oklahoma* and the target ship *Utah* were total losses, along with the destroyers *Cassin* and *Downes*. Four ships were sunk or beached but later were salvaged: the battleships *California, Nevada,* and *West Virginia,* and the mine layer *Oglala.* Nine ships suffered major damage: the battleships *Maryland, Pennsylvania,* and *Tennessee;* the cruisers *Helena, Honolulu,* and *Raleigh;* the destroyer *Shaw;* the seaplane tender *Curtiss;* and the repair ship *Vestal.* Observers on Tantalus and other points of vantage overlooking Pearl Harbor later stated that the attack resembled the explosion of giant firecrackers.

The most serious single loss occured about 8:10 A.M., when the battleship *Arizona* took a bomb in her forward magazines and exploded. A vast cloud of smoke and fire billowed 500 feet upwards, vividly described by witnesses at the time and fully recorded for posterity in many photographs. The battered hulk of the *Arizona* still lies in Pearl Harbor as a gruesome memento of the attack and the honored grave of 1,102 sailors.

The raid killed 2,403 Americans and wounded 1,178. The Navy lost 2,008; the Army, 218; the Marine Corps, 109; and the civilian population, 68. Of the wounded, 710 were from the Navy, 364 from the Army, 69 from the Marine Corps, and 35 from the civilian population.

In addition, there were about 40 recorded explosions in the city of Honolulu, of which all but one resulted from American anti-aircraft fire. These explosions caused about $500,000 worth of damage.

In comparison, the Japanese losses were trivial. The striking force lost only 29 planes—15 dive bombers, 9 fighters, and 5 torpedo planes. The advanced expeditionary force lost 1 conventional and 5 midget submarines. The total Japanese loss in military personnel was probably less than 100 men: 55 fliers, 9 crew members of the midget submarines, and an unknown number on the conventional submarine.

Quite naturally an atmosphere of shock, near-hysteria, and rage prevailed in Honolulu. Radio station KGMB first announced the attack at 8:40 A.M., and Honolulu residents still remember well how the announcer kept insisting that it was "the Real McCoy." But under Army orders both this station and KGU went off the air at 11:42 A.M. to prevent enemy planes from navigating from their broadcast beams. Thereafter they were silent, except for occasional terse announcements. Eager residents tuned in the police radio, where they heard hundreds of garbled reports.

Under the circumstances, wild rumors multiplied. They reached such serious proportions that on December 11 Colonel (later Brigadier General) Kendall J. Fielder, assistant chief of staff to the commanding general, warned in a radio address, "It is important for you to be alert, but you must beware of unfounded rumors and fantastic flights of your imagination. Check carefully the authenticity and accuracy of the rumor you may hear. Promiscuous spreading of wild rumors will only contribute to confusion."

One of the most persistent false rumors was that Island residents of Japanese descent had helped the attack with acts of sabotage. Navy wives evacuated to the West Coast spread such nonsense far and wide. Even Frank Knox, the Secretary of the Navy, who visited Pearl Harbor shortly after the attack, stated in a press conference that Hawaii had been subjected to "the most effective fifth column work that has come out of this war except in Norway."

On January 15, 1946, Robert L. Shivers, agent in charge of the Federal Bureau of Investigation in Hawaii, stated before a Congressional committee:

"I am sure you gentlemen have heard of one hundred and one rumors that have been spread throughout this Territory and the mainland United States since the day of the attack. One of these stories was to the effect that some of the Japanese aviators who were shot down over Oahu that morning were wearing class rings of McKinley High School (of Honolulu). Another was that arrows had been cut in the cane fields by the Japanese population which pointed toward Pearl Harbor and guided the attacking force to their targets. Another was that a transmitter had been discovered in the possession of some Japanese who were transmitting information to the enemy. Another was that the sides of a milk truck at Schofield Barracks suddenly collapsed and machine guns manned by Japanese opened fire on the soldiers at the post. There were many more rumors with which you are familiar. *There was not an iota of truth in any of them.* . . . There was not one single act of sabotage committed against the war effort in the Hawaiian Islands during the course of the entire war. Nor was there any fifth-column activity in existence or in evidence here. . . . *I want to emphasize that there was no such activity in Hawaii, before, during, or after the attack on Pearl Harbor.* Consequently there was no confusion in Hawaii as a result of fifth-column activities. I was in a position to know this fact, and I speak with authority when I say that the confusion in Hawaii was in the minds of the confused, and not because of fifth-column activities. No amount of repetition before the investigating committee will alter the fact that *sabotage and fifth-column activity was never engaged in at any time prior, during, or subsequent to the attack on Pearl Harbor."*

On March 14, 1942, W. A. Gabrielson, Honolulu's chief of police, stated in a telegram, "There were no acts of sabotage committed in city and county of Honolulu December 7 nor have there been any acts of sabotage reported to police department since that date."

In March, 1943, Colonel Fielder stated, "Having been in charge of military intelligence activities since June, 1941, I am in position to know what has happened. There have been no known acts of sabotage, espionage, or fifth-column activities committed by the Japanese in Hawaii either on or subsequent to December 7, 1941."

Gwenfread Allen's authoritative book *Hawaii's War Years, 1941–1945* (Honolulu, 1950) has an illuminating analysis of the four rumors mentioned by Shivers and of many others in circulation at the time. The story about the McKinley High School rings had several variants, including rings from the University of Hawaii, the University of Oregon, and the University of Southern California. No evidence corroborates it. Besides, Japanese military discipline prohibited the wearing of rings. No arrows in the cane fields were found, although a bare spot harvested in October, 1941, in an experimental field pointed toward Pearl Harbor. The Federal Communications Commission reported, "There were no illegal radio stations operating in Hawaii on December 7 or afterwards throughout the war." Japanese voices heard over the radio came from a station in Argentina whose beam to Japan came close to Oahu. The story about the milk truck was just that—a story.

Other rumors appeared: that epidemics had spread among evacuees (undoubtedly stomach-aches from upset nerves); that Japanese in Hawaii knew about the attack in advance (pure fabrication); that commando detachments had landed (more fabrication); that plantation workers had fired on sentries (probably sentries firing on one another in the darkness); that signal lights guided ships or planes (dozens of such reports, all unverified). The otherwise staid *New York Times* in its December 8 issue mentioned unconfirmed reports that German raiders had participated in the attack. But this was mild in comparison to other rumors sweeping throughout Hawaii, among them that the Panama Canal had been bombed and that the Japanese had landed in California.

A week or so after the attack it became known that one of the Hawaiian Islands, remote Niihau, had been invaded. The story of the "Battle of Niihau" instantly caught the public fancy and in time gave rise to a saying which forever will be a part of Hawaiian lore.

About 2 P.M. on December 7 a Japanese plane made a crash landing on Niihau near the house of a Hawaiian, Hawila (Howard) Kaleohano. Instantly Kaleohano disarmed the pilot and seized his papers. As a crowd gathered, Kaleohano sent for the only two Japanese residents of the Island, Ishimatsu Shintani, an alien employed as head beekeeper for the Robinson family, and his assistant, a Nisei, Yoshio Harada, to act as interpreters.

Throughout the week the Hawaiians guarded their captive, somewhat puzzled that the regular weekly sampan from Kauai, scheduled to arrive on Monday, had not appeared. (The Army had prevented it from making the trip.)

On Friday, December 12, the Hawaiians built a huge fire as a prearranged distress signal to get help from nearby Kauai. That same day the pilot persuaded the two Japanese on Niihau to help him. After careful investigation it was established that they acted from fear rather than from loyalty to Japan. With a pistol and shotgun, taken from the Robinson house, they freed the pilot from his lone guard and began to terrorize the island.

They searched Kaleohano's house for the pilot's papers, and set up the machine guns from the plane in the village of Puuwai. The women and children fled to caves or hid throughout the night in *kiawe* forests. The three conspirators threatened to kill Mrs. Huluoulani, who was too old to hide with the others, if she would not reveal where Kaleohano was hiding. She answered that only God had control over life and death, and continued to read her Bible. The frustrated conspirators vainly searched Kaleohano's house again for the papers, and then burned it in the hope of destroying them. They then burned the plane.

Meanwhile about midnight Kaleohano and four others began to row in a whaleboat across the rough channel to Kauai. After rowing continuously for sixteen hours they reached their destination about 3 P.M. on Saturday afternoon. They returned to Niihau at 7:30 Sunday morning with Aylmer Robinson and a military detachment on board the lighthouse tender *Kukui*.

By that time the "Battle of Niihau" had ended. Shortly after 7:00 A.M. on Saturday morning, Benehakaka (Benjamin) Kanahele and his wife attacked the pilot and his ally Harada. In the scuffle the pilot shot Kanahele three times, in the thigh, groin, and stomach. "Then I got mad," Kanahele later reported. Although badly wounded he picked up the pilot by the leg and neck and beat out his brains against a stone wall. Harada then shot himself and died several hours later.

Kanahele later received the Medal of Merit and also, by special dispensation because he was a civilian, the Purple Heart. Kaleohano received the Medal of Freedom.

The "Battle of Niihau" has given rise to a classic saying, "Never shoot a Hawaiian three times (or more than twice). He will get mad at you!"

John Toland

"TORA . . . TORA . . . TORA"

BATTLE REPORTS make grim and often dull reading. The descriptions are ordinarily clear, and tell what unit fired how many units of what at which target, how much damage occurred, and how many men were killed, wounded, and missing. Anecdotal reports are much more exciting. They bring war down to a personal level; they show how the individual reacted, what he saw, thought, and finally did in the heat of crisis. So it was with the attack on Pearl Harbor. The official reports tell in general what happened, and sometimes analyze the tactics and strategy as if the whole affair were a chess maneuver. Other accounts tell the rest of the story, the human side of the story.

In his book *But Not in Shame*, part of which follows, John Toland has described the personal side of the Allied defeats in the Pacific in the six months after the Pearl Harbor attack. In gathering material, he traveled seventy-five thousand miles, interviewed over eight hundred people, and used for the first time a number of highly colorful manuscript sources.

BANKS OF CUMULUS clouds collected around the peaks of the mountain ranges east and west of Pearl Harbor on Sunday morning. But over the great naval base, lying in the valley between, were only a few scattered clouds. Visibility was good and a wind of 10 knots blew in from the north.

At 7:45 A.M. several civilian pilots were lazily circling over the area. There wasn't a single military ship visible. Eighteen planes approaching from the carrier *Enterprise* were scheduled to land at Ford Island within the hour.

The only Army Air Corps planes aloft in the vicinity were the 12 Flying Fortresses from California earmarked for MacArthur. They were due to land at Hickam Field, several miles south of Ford Island, in about an hour. But of the Oahu-based Army planes, not one was on patrol. Still on four-hour notice, they were all tightly bunched together wing tip to wing tip for security against saboteurs at Hickam, Bellows and Wheeler Fields. So were the Marine planes at Ewa.

Of all the military planes in Hawaii, only 7 Navy PBY's were on patrol. And these were many miles to the southwest. Anti-aircraft defense was almost as lax. The Pacific Fleet in the harbor had about a quarter of its 780 anti-aircraft guns manned. Of the Army's 31 anti-aircraft batteries, only 4 were in position, and these had no ready ammunition. It had been returned to depots after practice since it was "apt to disintegrate and get dusty."

About 25 miles to the northwest Japanese pilots in the leading attack planes were marvelling at the peaceful green scene below them. The entire island seemed to be lazing luxuriantly in the early sun. Not even a trace of smoke was coming up from the motionless mass of ships in Pearl Harbor.

At 7:49 A.M. Commander Fuchida from his high-level bomber gave the attack signal in Morse code, "TO . . . TO . . . TO." Four minutes later the great naval base was spread out below him like a huge relief map. It looked exactly as he had imagined. Still no fighters were climbing up to challenge; nor was there a single mushroom explosion of anti-aircraft fire. It was unbelievable. They had achieved complete surprise.

Even before a single bomb dropped he now radioed: "TORA . . . TORA . . . TORA" (Tiger). The repeated word was heard by Admiral Nagumo. It was also heard directly on board the *Nagato,* at Combined Fleet Headquarters in Japan. When the message was brought to Yamamoto he said nothing, his face betrayed no emotion. The other officers spontaneously cheered when the laconic message was read aloud. The *Nagato* was engulfed in excitement. The message decoded meant: "We have succeeded in surprise attack."

Still no bomb had fallen. Except for the roar of approaching planes all was quiet in the Honolulu area. At the RCA office, Tadao Fuchikami, one of the messengers, was checking over a handful of cables he was to deliver. One was addressed simply to "Commanding General" and was obviously for General Short at Fort Shafter. This was the same message Marshall had written so excitedly in pencil almost two hours previously, but since there was nothing on the envelope such as *Secret* or *First Priority* or even *Rush,* Fuchikami decided to make other calls first.

At that same moment, near the center of the island of Oahu, Japanese fighters and bombers began to dive on the Army's Wheeler Field, adjacent to Schofield Barracks.

Second Lieutenant Robert Overstreet, of the 696th Aviation Ordnance Company, was sleeping in the two-story wooden BOQ. He was awakened by a terrific noise. At first he thought it was an earthquake. "Looks like Jap planes," he heard someone shout. "Hell, no," said someone else. "It's just a Navy maneuver."

Overstreet's door opened and an old friend, Lieutenant Robert Skalwold, looked in. His face was white, his lips trembling. "I think Japs are attacking."

Overstreet looked out the window, saw planes circling overhead. They seemed to be olive drab. One dove on the barracks, coming so close he could see the pilot and a rear gunner. On the fuselage and wing tips were flaming red suns. He finished dressing as he ran out of the barracks and headed for his oganization. Soon he came onto a group of fighter pilots.

"We've got to get down to the line and tag some of those bastards," shouted one, Lieutenant Harry Brown. Another pilot pointed to the burning hangars and the ramp. There the closely grouped planes were already ablaze.

"Let's go to Haliewa," said Brown. This was an auxiliary field on the north coast where a few P-40's and P-36's were kept. Brown and several other pilots piled into his new Ford convertible and left. Lieutenants George Welch and Kenneth Taylor followed in the latter's car.

Hundreds were milling around in shocked confusion as bombs fell and buildings erupted. Overstreet weaved his way through the mob toward the permanent quarters area. On the Circle he saw Brigadier General Howard Davidson, the fighter commandant, and Colonel William Flood, the base commander, standing by their front doors in pajamas, staring at the sky, their faces aghast.

"Where's our Navy?" said Flood. "Where're our fighters?"

"General," shouted Overstreet, "we'd better get out of here. Those planes have tail-gunners." He ran toward the ordnance hangar. To his horror it was in flames. Inside were a million rounds of machine-gun ammunition ticketed for Midway Island. Suddenly the hangar began to explode, like an endless row of huge firecrackers.

Fifteen miles to the south, just below Pearl Harbor, Jesse Gaines and Ted Conway, aircraft mechanics at Hickam Field, were walking toward the flight line. They'd gotten up early that morning because they knew B-17's were due from the States and they had never seen a Flying Fortress.

At 7:55 A.M. a V-formation of planes suddenly appeared from the west. As they began to peel off, Conway said, "We're going to have an air show."

Gaines noticed something fall from the first plane. He guessed in alarm that it was a wheel.

"Wheel, hell, they're Japs!" cried Conway.

As Gaines said, "You're crazy," a bomb exploded among the neatly packed planes on the field. The two men began to run toward the big three-storied barracks, "Hickam Hotel." Gaines saw some gas drums and dove behind them for protection. Fighters were now diving in a strafing attack, their machine guns spitting orange flames. Gaines felt himself being kicked in the rear.

"Don't you know better than that," shouted an old sergeant. "Those damn drums are full!" Gaines scrambled to his feet and headed away from the ramp. He looked up and saw bombs falling. All seemed to be heading for him. He ran in terror first one way, then another.

Two miles to the north, right in the middle of Pearl Harbor, the first bomb was falling on the naval air station at Ford Island. Ordnanceman Third Class Donald Briggs was sitting in a PBY. He thought a plane from the *Enterprise* had spun in and crashed. Then the sky seemed to cave in as a dozen more explosions followed.

The Japanese plan was simple but efficient. First, to prevent an air counterattack, the airfields were being systematically wiped out. In the first few minutes the Navy bases, Kaneohe and Ford Island; the Army bases, Wheeler, Bellows and Hickam; and the lone Marine base, Ewa, were all but crippled.

A moment after the first bomb fell, the Pearl Harbor signal tower alerted Kimmel's headquarters by phone. Three minutes later, at 7:58 A.M., the message heard around the world was broadcast by Rear Admiral Patrick Bellinger from Ford Island:

AIR RAID, PEARL HARBOR—THIS IS NO DRILL.

Closely on its heels, at 8:00 A.M. Kimmel's headquarters radioed Washington, Admiral Hart in the Philippines and all forces at sea: AIR RAID ON PEARL HARBOR. THIS IS NO DRILL. Even as the messages were going out, torpedo planes were diving on the main target, Battleship Row.

Admiral C. C. Bloch was shaving at his quarters in the Navy Yard. He thought workmen were blasting in the nearby stone quarry. When the explosions continued he told his wife, "I'm going outside and see what that noise is." He ran out the front door. Overhead he saw a plane in flames. He went back into the house. "The Japanese are bombing us. I've got to get to the office. Don't stay down here."

At the naval housing unit adjacent to Hickam Field, First Class Metalsmith Lawrence Chappell was in bed. A plane roared overhead.

"What are those planes?" asked his wife, starting toward the window. "It's too late for the Bomber Patrol."

"Probably stragglers."

"The Rising Sun! The Rising Sun! JAPANESE!" cried Mrs. Chappell.

"You're foolish, go back to bed." Another plane roared over and Chappell went to the window. A torpedo plane swept by, so close he could see the pilot turning around, unconcerned. He hurriedly dressed and ran outside. Now he heard anti-aircraft fire and saw flames and billows of black smoke rising from Pearl Harbor.

Kimmel was watching the torpedo attack from the hill at Makalapa near his quarters. Short was standing on the *lanai* of his home near Fort Shafter watching the billows of smoke in the west and wondering what was going on at Pearl Harbor.

The smoke was rising from Battleship Row, on the east side of Ford Island where seven battleships, the heart of the Pacific Fleet, were moored. They were not protected from aerial torpedoes by nets because of Pearl Harbor's 40-foot depth. This matter had been discussed many times by Kimmel and Stark. Even the British had been consulted. Everyone agreed a minimum depth of 75 feet was necessary for torpedoes.

This unanimous conclusion was surprising since the British themselves had made a successful plane attack on the Italian fleet at Taranto the previous year with specially rigged torpedoes. The Japanese bombers diving on Battleship Row were proving as clever as the British. They were dropping torpedoes with ingeniously constructed wooden fins, specially designed for shallow water.

Not far from Battleship Row, Yeoman C. O. Lines of the oil tanker *Ramapo* was in the crew's quarters. Boatswain's Mate Graff rushed down the ladder. "The Japs are bombing Pearl Harbor!" he yelled.

The men in the room looked at him as if he were crazy.

"No fooling," he said.

Someone gave a Bronx cheer.

"No crap. Get your asses up on deck!"

Lines hurried topside to the fantail. He thought Graff was ribbing as usual. Then he heard a dull explosion and saw a plane dive toward the battleship *California.*

She was the last of the seven big vessels in Battleship Row. Two torpedoes hit her almost simultaneously. The ship took an 8-degree list and began to settle. Her fractured fuel tanks began to flood an entire lower deck. Bombs now fell and half a dozen fires flared. In minutes oil gushing from the ruptured ship burst into flame. She was surrounded by a wall of fire. The word was passed: Abandon ship.

Ahead, in tandem formation, were the *Maryland* and *Oklahoma.* A torpedo couldn't hit the *Maryland* because she was berthed inboard, next to Ford Island, and was protected by her mate. But the outboard ship, the *Oklahoma,* was hit by four torpedoes within a minute. As she listed to port, Commander Jesse Kenworthy, senior officer aboard, ordered the ship abandoned over the starboard side. He calmly walked up the ship's side over the blistered ledge and then over the bottom. Soon the ship settled, its starboard propeller out of the water. Below more than 400 men were trapped in the rapidly filling compartments.

Next in Battleship Row came another pair, the *Tennessee* and *West Virginia*. Like the *Maryland,* the *Tennessee* was inboard and safe from torpedo attack. On the *West Virginia's* battle conning tower, Lieutenant Commander T. T. Beattie, the ship's navigator, heard Captain Mervyn Bennion groan.

"I've been wounded," said the skipper, doubling up. A fragment, probably from an armor-piercing bomb that had just hit the nearby *Tennessee,* had torn into his stomach and part of his intestines were protruding. The captain sank to the deck. Beattie loosened his collar and sent a messenger for a pharmacist's mate. But the captain knew he was dying and only wanted to know how his ship was being fought. Some fires swept toward the bridge. There was no escape except by swinging hand over hand along a fire hose.

Next in line came the *Arizona.* The first torpedo planes struck at the *Arizona* and missed. A moment later high-level bombers attacked. Five bombs hit. One of these dropped through the forecastle into the second deck, starting a fire. About 1600 pounds of blackpowder, the most dangerous of all explosives, were stored here against regulations. Suddenly the blackpowder exploded, igniting hundreds of tons of smokeless powder in the forward magazines.

To those on nearby ships, the *Arizona* seemed to leap out of the water amidst a tremendous blast of fire and debris. The great 32,600-ton ship apparently broke in two and then quickly settled. Sheets of flame and clouds of black smoke swirled around the *Arizona.* It didn't seem possible that a soul could have survived.

Ahead of the *Arizona* was the leading ship in Battleship Row, the *Nevada.* She was down several feet by the head from a torpedo in her port bow and a bomb in the quarterdeck.

On the other side of Ford Island, torpedo bombers were diving on the thirty-three-year-old battleship *Utah.* Now a target ship, her decks had been stripped and covered with timber and from above she looked like a carrier. Dive bombers were swarming all over her. The first torpedo hit at 8:01. Four minutes later the *Utah* was listing to port at 40 degrees. As fighter planes swept down to strafe the tilting deck, the word was given to abandon ship. At 8:12 the tired old ship flopped over, keel sticking out of the water. There was a momentary quiet and men in a recently dug trench on Ford Island heard a faint knocking inside the ship. People in the ship's bottom were still alive.

Even by 8:10 A.M. only one ship in the entire harbor was under way. This was the destroyer *Helm* and she was trying to escape. At 27 knots she raced through the channel toward the mouth of the harbor.

Here, the anti-torpedo net, opened hours earlier for the *Condor*, was still unclosed. A Japanese midget submarine, its gyro-compass out of order, was trying to stab its way blindly into this opening and raid Pearl Harbor. The commander, Ensign Kazuo Sakamaki, surfaced to get his bearings. Through the periscope he saw columns of black smoke. He excitedly called to his aide, Second Class Petty Officer Kiyoshi Inagaki, "The air raid! Wonderful! Look at that smoke. Enemy ships burning. We must do our best too, and we will."

At 8:15 A.M. he sighted the *Helm* racing out of the harbor. It was so close he could see the white uniforms of the sailors aboard. Guessing correctly it was only a destroyer, he didn't fire. His two torpedoes were marked for bigger game, battleships. He quickly submerged and again blindly aimed at the mouth of the harbor. He hit a reef, backed away, tried again. This time he ran up on the reef and his conning tower stuck out of the water.

At 8:18 A.M. he heard a terrific explosion and figured the destroyer had seen him. The little boat shook violently. Something hit Sakamaki's head and he briefly lost consciousness. When he came to, the tiny inner chamber was filled with white smoke. He felt dizzy, sick. He reversed the motor to back off from the reef but the boat didn't budge. There was only one solution. He wormed his way on his stomach up the narrow passage to the bow and began the painful job of transferring 11-pound ballast weights to the stern. Finally to his relief he felt the submarine move.

On the surface, the *Helm* was still firing at the bobbing midget with no success. Suddenly its target slid off the coral, vanished. SMALL JAP SUB TRYING TO PENETRATE CHANNEL, radioed the destroyer.

While this new alarm was being signaled from ship to ship, another midget was slowly rising to the surface just west of Ford Island and preparing for attack. She had slipped through the open mouth of Pearl Harbor earlier that morning and hidden on the bottom.

A moment later, at 8:30 A.M. the *Breese* spotted its conning tower.

Several ships quickly opened fire. The midget launched her two torpedoes. One detonated against a dock, the other against the shore. Then the destroyer *Monaghan* slammed into the submarine. As the midget sank, depth charges from the destroyer finished the job.

By now action from the sky had slacked off momentarily. Admiral "Poco" Smith, Kimmel's chief of staff, who had been shaving in his apartment near the Royal Hawaiian Hotel when he learned about the raid, now drove up to the submarine base. Outside Kimmel's office he saw a group of Marines shooting rifles into the empty sky.

Inside Fleet Headquarters, Kimmel was calm. He was talking to Vice Admiral William Pye, commander of Battle Force. Pye, too, was calm, though covered with oil. He had just escaped from his flagship, the *California*. Smith, after some persuasion, convinced Pye and Kimmel to get in different rooms so one bomb wouldn't kill both of them.

A few minutes later, a little after 8:40 A.M., the sky above Pearl Harbor was again dark with raiders. This was Nagumo's second wave; 80 dive bombers, 54 high-level bombers and 36 fighters. This time they came from the south and east hitting Battleship Row and Drydock No. 1, where the *Pennsylvania,* the eighth battleship, was berthed. Soon 18 dive bombers from the southeast joined the attack on Battleship Row.

A principal target was the *Nevada,* moving slowly past the blazing *Arizona.* Her gun crews were shielding their ammunition from the intense heat with their own bodies. In a few minutes the *Nevada,* already suffering from one torpedo hit, drew up to the toppled *Oklahoma.* Several men stood up on the sides of that ship and cheered as the *Nevada* headed for open water.

But the attackers were finding the range. In minutes six bombs hit. The bridge and forestructure of the battleship burst into flames. The ship turned to port and, with the help of two tugs, was beached not far from the *Pennsylvania's* drydock.

The 12 Flying Fortresses from California began to arrive during this attack. The first squadron of six, under Captain Ted Landon, bewildered by the heavy traffic over Oahu, headed uncertainly for Hickam Field. Four landed safely and one was shot in half by ground troops as it touched down. The sixth plane turned north and crash-landed at Bellows.

As the second squadron of six approached Waikiki Beach, Captain Richard Carmichael, the squadron commander, was pointing out the sights to Captain Jim Twaddell. When Carmichael saw planes ahead, he figured it was some Navy maneuver. Then he saw flames leaping from Hickam Field and knew it was an attack. He called the tower, asking permission to land.

"Land from west to east," said Major Gordon Blake. "Use caution. The field is under attack."

As Carmichael lowered his wheels violent anti-aircraft fire broke out from ships in Pearl Harbor. He quickly turned north toward Wheeler. This field, too, was under heavy attack. Hangars and barracks were burning as dive bombers strafed the line.

Carmichael flew around the Koola Mountain Range. Only half an hour's fuel was left and he had to find a home quickly. He started for Bellows Field, keeping near the coast line. But Kaneohe Naval Air Station was also under attack. Suddenly he remembered Haliewa, a sod field for P-40's. He went north of the mountains and in a few minutes touched down on the short grassy fighter field. It was only 1200 feet long and by the time the big Flying Fortress skidded to a stop he had used every foot of it. All 6 of his planes landed safely: 2 at Haliewa, 1 at Kanuka Golf Course and 3 at Hickam.

On the Hickam flight line, Second Lieutenant William Welch, and other eager young pilots of the 11th Bombardment Squadron, were squabbling to see who would fly the one bomber still intact. A bomb landed 50 yards away, knocking them all flat.

"Let's go across the field," suggested an old master sergeant. Welch, eager to do anything, followed him. As they reached the parking area, three Zeros skimmed by at tree level, their machine guns spitting. Bullets sprayed over their heads into a group of pilots just standing and looking up curiously. Welch turned and fired his .45 pistol at the last plane. It was his only shot of the day.

Just then several Flying Fortresses from the States began to land. Welch ran out to disperse them. Two sprucely dressed captains stepped out of the first plane, looking shocked. "Get your ammo, load up and get ready to go," said Welch.

The captains, too surprised to move, told Welch they were in no shape for battle. All their guns were packed in cosmolene and would take hours to clean.

At Wheeler there was the same feeling of shock. The men were still groggy from the first attack when the second hit. Lieutenant

Overstreet was arguing with a sergeant from the Base Ordnance Office. Overstreet wanted rifles and pistols.

"I doubt if I'm authorized to give you any without a hand receipt," said the reluctant sergeant as bombs exploded nearby.

"Hell, man, this is war," said Overstreet angrily. He got the guns.

At Ford Island Field there was also frustration. Not a single Navy fighter had gotten into the air. By now all the planes were destroyed or inoperable. There was nothing to do. Six pilots, including Ensign Elbert Cain, were hiding behind palm trees and shooting at the invaders with their pistols.

Only about 30 Army Air Force fighters managed to get into the air that morning and these could do little to hinder the rain of bombs and torpedoes. Two pilots, Lieutenants Kenneth Taylor and George Welch, were credited with seven of the 11 Japanese planes shot down.

By 10:00 A.M. the skies above the smoke-bound harbor were suddenly empty. The second attack was over. The stink of burning oil was overwhelming. Battleship Row was a shambles. The *Arizona,* the *Oklahoma* and the *California* were sunk at their berths. The *West Virginia,* hopelessly ablaze, was sinking. The *Nevada* was aground. The other three battleships—the *Maryland, Tennessee* and drydocked *Pennsylvania*—were all damaged.

In nearby Honolulu, Takeo Yoshikawa, the lone Japanese Navy spy, was eating breakfast when windows rattled and several pictures dropped to the floor. Then he heard great explosions coming from Pearl Harbor. He ran outside in his slippers and saw Consul General Nagao Kita standing in front of his official residence. The two looked at each other but couldn't say a word. Other consular officials poured out into the courtyard, dazed and unaware of what was actually going on.

Kita and the spy went inside and tuned in Radio Tokyo. They heard "east wind, rain," repeated twice. War with America! They hurried to the consul general's office and feverishly burned code-books and secret instructions. By the time the police arrived at 8:30 A.M. everything except a half-finished sketch of Pearl Harbor had been destroyed.

Then the FBI arrived; Yoshikawa knew it was the end of the war for him. He whispered to himself, "Good-bye to the days of my youth—forever." But he had accomplished his mission. The smoke boiling up from Pearl Harbor was in great part due to the information he had gathered for $600.

There was no panic in Honolulu even though explosions had hit many parts of the city. None of these were Japanese bombs, but strays from American guns. Even so, many people had no idea what was going on a few miles away. The first radio report came just as the second attack started, but when it announced that, "A sporadic air attack has been made on Oahu," many listeners thought "sporadic" meant a mock attack.

Others in the city lived out the day as any ordinary Sunday. At the height of the attack Hawaiian girls in costume appeared as usual at the Pan American dock, arms loaded with *leis* to bid Aloha to departing Clipper passengers. They had to be told it was the end of traditional ceremony for a long, long time. They turned away bewildered and sad.

Blake Clark

BLOOD DONORS OF DECEMBER 7, 1941

THE PEARL HARBOR ATTACK, like other catastrophes, produced a wide range of responses, among them terror, bewilderment, rage, and determination. In Honolulu, transformed suddenly into a first-line field of battle, Americans fought back with what means they could muster. In the face of disaster some were genuinely heroic. But many others had scant opportunity to prove their mettle. Instead, in a hundred humble ways, they merely did what they could, said little, hoped, and waited. Their collective experience, kept alive in many anecdotes, mostly still unrecorded, is a vital part of the Pearl Harbor story.

Fortunately at least one writer paid full heed to reactions of the people at large to the Japanese attack. His name was Blake Clark, a native of Tennessee who first came to Hawaii in 1930 to teach English. In his eyewitness account *Remember Pearl Harbor,* a chapter of which is reprinted here, he described in considerable detail Honolulu's response to the urgent need for blood donors. After a frantic appeal over the radio, hundreds of people of all ages and races rushed to Queen's Hospital to donate blood. At the moment that was their only way to fight the Japanese.

One of the people mentioned in Clark's account was Sarah Wilder, aged seventy-two at the time. Aunt Sarah, or simply Sarah as she encouraged her many friends to call her, was a woman of kindness and courage. She died of a heart attack in the spring of 1961, within a few months of her ninety-second birthday, survived by her son, daughter, six grandchildren, and one great-grandson. To the last she was in the midst of life. When death overtook her, she was having lunch with friends at the beautiful Halekulani Hotel on Waikiki Beach.

WE LEARNED in Honolulu that Sunday how narrow the dividing line is between the soldier and the civilian in war time. We were inspired by the example of America's courageous soldiers and sailors, and fighting mad at the Japanese invaders for their cowardly attack. We wanted to do something. There was vitally important work to do, and civilians leaped to it.

Soon after the bombing started, a call came into the headquarters of the Hawaii Medical Association. It just said, "Pearl Harbor! Ambulances! For God's sake, hurry!"

This was the challenge that the Medical Corps had been waiting for from the day, months ago, when they first organized. And did they pick it up! Within only twenty minutes from the time the call came, the doctors and volunteer workers of the medical units had stripped the insides of over one hundred laundry trucks, lumber trucks, and delivery trucks of every description, equipped them neatly with previously prepared frames containing room for four litters each, and were speeding to the scene of action. One unit arrived early enough to receive a souvenir piece of shrapnel, flung at them by a Japanese bomb.

Another call came: "Department Surgeon King, at Tripler Hospital! Surgical teams, quick!"

Then occurred one of life's breath-taking coincidences. At that very moment virtually every surgeon in Honolulu was listening to a lecture on war surgery. It was being delivered by Colonel Moorhead, famous authority on the subject. The audience departed in a body for Tripler. In fifteen minutes, more capable surgeons stood ready at Tripler than Surgeon King could use.

By another coincidence no less fortuitous, they had with them a new surgical instrument which Colonel Moorhead had brought to Honolulu to demonstrate. Its purpose was to locate metal in the body and outline its exact location. The only instrument of its kind in existence, it proved its worth at once that morning. It saved precious hours of time that would have been spent waiting for X-ray pictures to be developed.

Colonel Moorhead, by the way, is Chief Surgeon on James M. Landis' Civilian Defense staff. He says he is telling them that "if you want to know how to organize civilian defense, come to Honolulu."

When the shooting started, Mrs. William Moir, chairman of the American Red Cross Motor Corps, was in it. She was swimming at Punaluu on the other side of the island when machine-gun bullets splashed the water around her. She looked up and saw a dogfight going on in deadly earnest directly above her. She ran ashore. As she slammed the door behind her, a plane with the Rising Sun on its wing-tips fell into the deep water offshore.

When Mrs. Moir reached town, her Motor Corps was hitting on all eight. Seventy to one hundred women were out on the road. Every available sedan, roadster, and banana wagon was carrying men to Pearl Harbor. Driving on this three-lane highway was no job for a weakling. It has been almost a bottleneck of traffic ever since travel to and from the defense areas has put such heavy demands upon it. On that memorable Sunday it was an inferno. Army trucks, official and unofficial emergency wagons, ambulances, Red Cross cars, and hundreds of taxis and Motor Corps women rushing officers and men to their battle stations literally screamed up and down the six-mile road.

The Motor Corps women were equal to the task. One member was on duty so early and rushed to the job so speedily that her car stopped a piece of shrapnel on its first trip out.

Dr. Pinkerton, making his rounds at Queen's Hospital, heard a commotion below in Emergency. He stepped to the balcony and looked down. Dozens of cases were coming in all at once—mutilations and burns. As the Doctor rushed back into the hospital to give instructions, an emergency call came from Tripler Hospital.

"Blood plasma, quick!"

In five minutes Dr. Pinkerton was at the refrigeration plant of the Hawaiian Electric Company where the local blood bank was stored. There were 210 flasks of 250 cc. (a half-pint). He rushed sixty of these to Queen's Emergency for the civilian cases coming in and sped on to Tripler with the rest.

The call came from Pearl Harbor: "Plasma!"

The precious fluid was divided and part hurried to the surgeons at the Harbor. It was going fast.

At eleven o'clock Dr. Pinkerton made a short appeal over the radio. He did not say how badly plasma was needed. He did not explain what it is, or tell how a young lieutenant's life had just been saved by its use. After getting his breath from running up three long flights of stairs at radio station KGU, all he said was, "A call for volunteer blood donors! Report immediately to Queen's Hospital!"

In half an hour five hundred people were waiting at the doors of the hospital. The staff of doctors and trained technicians, some fifteen in all, were at work at twelve tables, but they could not take the blood as fast as it was offered. Some persons stood in line for seven hours to give their blood. Most of them did not know what blood plasma is, but they knew that they were helping.

The crowd of blood donors was a thrilling mass response to the dastardly Japanese attack. This waiting line was an amazing thing. Here were Honolulu's masses, a unique amalgam in the history of the world—a people who do not communicate with each other except on the level of pidgin English, but a people emotionally united. Honolulu society women stood in line or sat on benches by the wall beside the city's great good-humored lower classes. A well-known woman painter, a wife of a corporation president, and a waterfront washwoman waited together and talked about "what a treacherous thing it was." Japanese by the hundreds were there, many of them members of the Oahu Citizens for Home Defense Committee. Some older, alien Japanese were there too, dressed in black, which they traditionally wear on occasions where respect is due. They stood in attitudes of infinite patience, waiting to register a silent protest with their blood. A Portuguese blind boy of nineteen and his blind sister three years younger were there, brought in by their mother. They had heard the call over the radio and insisted that she bring them down.

Defense workers came in their dirty work clothes, got preference in the line, gave their blood, and went back to work. Welders came with eyes red and burning. They gave their blood, and back they went to the job. Large groups of employees came straight from work in buses provided by the companies. The beds had to be draped with newspapers to save the sheets from oil, canefield dirt, and the red soil of the pineapple fields with which the workers were covered.

A bunch of huge Hawaiians came lumbering in from the Honolulu Iron Works. Dirty and oily, when they leaned against the wall, they left big smudges. They were all taken into the same room for their lettings. They laughed and joked, teasing a Puerto Rican among them who was scared. "Wait till you get that shot of brandy at the end of the line, boy. You feel numba one swell!" they told him. The average extraction was about 400 cc., or something less than a pint. Several of these Hawaiians gave 750 cc. and went back to their job at the Iron Works.

A Dutch ship was in port for only a few hours. The entire crew came up to give their blood. Numbers of passengers came, too. Six big husky Dutch women came in a body. They were very welcome, for one of the things the doctors discovered was that a pint of woman's blood gives more plasma than a pint of man's. The Dutch sextet yielded generous quantities of plasma-rich blood.

Whole families came at once. The preferable age limits were from eighteen to fifty, but young boys lied and old men asserted their rights in order to be included in the line. The Hon. Walter F. Frear, former Governor of the Territory, and Mrs. Frear went down. He is seventy-eight and she is seventy-two. When it was suggested that they might be too old, Mrs. Frear said, "It ought to be very good blood. It has lasted us a long time!" "I should say so," said Mrs. Sarah Wilder, grandmother of grown men. "My blood is better than that of half of these young squirts!"

To the hospital came a letter by special messenger from a woman of eighty-one. It said in effect: "I realize that I am eighty-one, and that the request was for younger people. I am strong and healthy. However, I am very heavy and cannot stand long at a time without great fatigue. It will save me two trips to the hospital if you will permit me to make an appointment. My daughter will bring me down." And she added, "I may say that from what I have seen of this war so far, it is nothing like as bad as Custer's was in '76."

There was one Hawaiian woman who was so big that the doctors had to give up. In the depths of fat they could not find her vein. One seaman's wife had veins too small, and was rejected. Corps of Honolulu police and firemen made up for these, swelling the bank with averages well over 600 cc. each.

At the end of the line each donor who wanted it was given a generous shot of good brandy. The policemen accused each other of coming in because of the finishing draught. The beach boys pretended to be quite faint and were given long generous draughts to revive them.

A surprising number of girls who are following Sadie Thompson's footsteps in the South Seas showed up in the line. And four of them, after donating their blood, asked to help further. They got a job washing tubing, the dirtiest, smelliest, meanest of all laboratory jobs. They worked hard and stayed at it as long as anyone.

Many donors came back. One second-class seaman was recognized by a nurse.

"You shouldn't come back so soon," she warned him.

"My brother was killed," he said. "I want to do something."

That's what everyone in Hawaii is saying—"I want to do something."

Mitsuo Fuchida

I LED THE AIR ATTACK
ON PEARL HARBOR

AMONG THE many reports, anecdotal or analytical, about the Pearl Harbor disaster, one remains unique: the account by Captain Mitsuo Fuchida of the Imperial Japanese Navy, who led the attack. Fuchida has described with graphic detail the secret preparations, the departure of the Japanese task force from the Kuriles, the careful evaluation of intelligence reports on the location of the United States Pacific Fleet, and the launching of aircraft from Japanese carriers before dawn on December 7, 1941. He continued with an even more detailed narrative of the attack itself, including at the last minute a mix-up in signals which caused considerable confusion among the Japanese pilots.

Fuchida served for twenty-five years in the Japanese Navy and was a captain at the end of World War II. He was wounded at the battle of Midway in June, 1942, and later served as air operations officer of the Japanese Combined Fleet. His account, which follows, of the

attack on Pearl Harbor, as edited by Lt. Roger Pineau, USNR, first
appeared in the September, 1952, issue of the *United States Naval
Institute Proceedings*. To speed the narrative, some technical information has been removed.

I N SEPTEMBER, 1941, I was transferred from the staff of the Third
Carrier Division to aircraft carrier *Akagi,* a position I had left just
one year earlier. Shortly after joining my old comrades in *Akagi,*
I was given additional duty as commander of all air groups of the
First Air Fleet. This was an assignment beyond all my dreams. I
felt that something big must be afoot.

It was at Kagoshima on the southern tip of Kyushu that I first
learned the magnitude of events in store for me. My good friend
Commander Genda, air operations officer on the staff of the First
Air Fleet, came to see me at the air base and said, "Now don't be
alarmed, Fuchida, but we want you to lead our air force in the event
that we attack Pearl Harbor!"

Don't be alarmed? It was all I could do to catch my breath, and
almost before I had done so we were on our way out to board
Akagi, then anchored in Ariake Bay, for a conference with First
Air Fleet commander, Vice Admiral Chuichi Nagumo, and his
staff, including Chief of Staff, Rear Admiral Ryunosuke Kusaka.

The more I heard about the plan the more astonishing it seemed.
Genda kept urging that torpedoes be used against ships in Pearl
Harbor; a feat that seemed next to impossible in view of the water
depth of only twelve meters, and the harbor being not more than
five hundred meters in width. When I pointed this out, Genda
merely grew more aggressive, insisting that if we could launch torpedoes, they would not be expected, it would add to the surprise of
the attack and multiply their effectiveness. This line of argument
won me over, and, despite the technical difficulties that would have
to be overcome, I agreed to include torpedoes in our attack plans.

Shallow-water torpedo launching was not the only difficult problem I had to cope with. From ordinary fleet practice we had to
shift our energies to specific training for this all-important mission
calling for vast and intensive preparations; and, what is more, everything had to be done in haste. It was already late September, and
the attack plan called for execution in December!

There was no time to lose. Our fliers had to work at the hardest
kind of training. An added handicap to our efforts lay in the fact

that, for security reasons, the pilots could not be told about the plans. Our progress was slow, especially with the problem of launching torpedoes in shallow water. Against my will I had to demand more and more of every man, yet none complained. They seemed to sense the intensification of the international situation and gave of themselves unquestioningly.

It was not until early November that the torpedo problem was finally solved by fixing additional fins to the torpedoes, and then my greatest worry was over. I was indeed proud of my men and felt honored to be their commander and participate in this great attack. . . .

At 0600* on the dark and cloudy morning of 26 November our 28-ship task force weighed anchor and sailed out into the waters of the North Pacific Ocean. The sortie was cloaked in complete secrecy. A patrol boat guarding the bay entrance flashed a message, "Good luck on your mission." But even that boat was unaware of our assignment. *Akagi* signalled, "Thanks," and passed by, her ensign fluttering in the morning breeze. It would not be long before this ensign was replaced by a combat flag.

But this did not mean that the arrow had already gone from the bow. "In case negotiations with the U. S. reach a successful conclusion," Nagumo had been instructed, "the task force will put about immediately and return to the homeland." Unaware of this, however, the crews shouted "Banzai!" as they took what might be their last look at Japan.

On *Akagi's* bridge Commander Gishiro Miura, the navigation officer, was concentrating all his energies on control of the ship. Whether we reached the scheduled launching point successfully rested entirely upon his shoulders. So tense was his appearance that it made us feel he was a completely different man. His usual jovial attitude had disappeared. He now wore shoes instead of his usual slippers, and he was neatly dressed, a decided change from his customary dirty, worn-out uniform. Captain Hasegawa, the skipper of the ship, stood beside him. Sitting at the flight desk control post under the bridge, I watched the gradually receding mountains of the Kuriles.

Young boys of the flying crews were boiling over with fighting

*East Longitude dates, Tokyo time (Zone minus 9) used primarily here; with West Longitude dates, Hawaiian time (Zone plus 10½) given in parentheses, where helpful.

spirit. Hard nights and days of training had been followed by hasty preparations, and now the sortie, which meant that they were going to war.

I felt their keen enthusiasm and was reassured. Still I could not help doubting whether Japan had the proper confidence for carrying out a war. At the same time, however, I fully realized my duty as a warrior to fight and win victory for my country. . . .

Since our departure from Tankan Bay, a strict alert had been kept against U. S. submarines. Our course was chosen to pass between the Aleutians and Midway Island so as to keep out of range of air patrols, some of which were supposed to extend 600 miles. Another concern during the cruise was how to avoid a chance meeting with foreign merchant ships. The three submarines sent ahead of the fleet were to report any ships sighted to the fleet, which would then alter course to avoid them.

If an enemy fleet was sighted before X-2 day, our force was to reverse course immediately and abandon the operation. On the other hand, if it was one day before X day, whether to reverse course or launch the attack was left to the discretion of the task force commander.

Meanwhile, deceptive measures were being taken elsewhere to cover up our movements. On 5, 6, and 7 December sailors of the Yokosuka Naval Barracks were sent to Tokyo on a sightseeing tour. In early December *Tatsuta Maru* of the N.Y.K. Line had even left Yokohama heading for Honolulu, and she reversed course only upon receipt of the news that hostilities had begun.

Since leaving Tankan Bay we had maintained our eastward course in complete secrecy, thanks to thick, low-hanging clouds. Moreover, on 30 November, 6 and 7 December, the sea, which we feared might be rough, was calm enough for easy fueling. The not-too-rough sea also made it easy to maintain and prepare planes, and gave the men, especially the flying crews, a much needed chance to relax.

The fleet observed strict radio silence, but concentrated on listening for broadcasts from Tokyo or Honolulu. Our predominant concern was to catch any word about the outbreak of war.

In Tokyo a liaison conference between the Government and the High Command was held every day from 27 to 30 November to discuss the U. S. proposal of the 26th. It was concluded that the proposal was an ultimatum tending to subjugate Japan and making war inevitable. At the liaison conference of the 30th the decision was made to go to war. This conference also concluded that a message declaring the end of negotiations be sent to the U. S., but that efforts be continued to the last moment. The final decision for war was made at an Imperial Conference on 1 December.

Next day the General Staff issued the long-awaited order and our task force received the Combined Fleet dispatch of 1730 which said, "X Day will be 8 December."

Now the die was cast and our duty was clear. The fleet drove headlong to the east.

Why was 8 December chosen as X day? That was 7 December and Sunday, a day of rest, in Hawaii. Was this merely a bright idea to hit the U. S. Fleet off duty? No, it was not so simple as that. This day for the opening of hostilities had been coordinated with the time of the Malayan operations, where air raids and landings were scheduled for dawn. Favorable moonlight was a major consideration, three or four days after the full moon being the most desirable time, and on 8 December the moon was 19 days old.

There was another reason for choosing 8 December. Our information indicated that the fleet returned to harbor on weekends after training periods at sea, so there was great likelihood that it would be in Pearl Harbor on Sunday morning. All things considered, 8 December was the logical day for the attack. . . .

On 6 December after fueling Cardiv 2 and the Screening Force, the 2nd Tanker Train broke off from the task force. On the next day the 1st Tanker Train fueled the Screen again and departed. Our force then increased speed to 24 knots and raced toward Pearl Harbor. On the carrier decks planes were lined up wing to wing for their final check. Maintenance crews and flying crews worked assiduously to complete final preparation of their planes.

About this time we received Admiral Yamamoto's message for going to war: "The rise or fall of the Empire depends upon this battle; everyone will do his duty with utmost efforts." The message was immediately relayed to all hands, and the "Z" flag was hoisted on *Akagi*'s mast. This was the same signal flag that was run up in *Mikasa* almost thirty years before in the Straits of Tsushima.

At 1225 on the 7th (1725, 6 December in Honolulu) a message came in from submarine *I-72:* "American Fleet is not in Lahaina Anchorage."

This anchorage was used for training because it was open and deep. If the Pacific Fleet was there, it would have offered our best chance for success, and we had hoped accordingly. Receipt of the negative information, however, blasted our hopes for such an opportunity.

It was now obvious that the warships were either in Pearl Harbor or at sea. Admiral Nagumo was thumbing through the message log to check on battleships reported to be in Pearl Harbor. Completing the count, he looked up and said to the staff members, "All of their battleships are now in. Will any of them leave today?"

The Intelligence Officer, Lieutenant Commander Ono, was first to reply: "Since five of their eight battleships reached port on the 29th, and two others left that day returning on the 6th, there is one more which has remained in harbor all this time, supposedly under repair, or perhaps in drydock. The five ships which arrived on the 29th have been there eight days, and it is time for them to leave. I suspect they may go out today."

"Today is Saturday, 6 December," said Chief of Staff Kusaka. "Their general practice is to leave on Tuesday, which would be the 9th."

"It is most regrettable," said Genda, the Operations Officer, "that no carriers are in."

"On 29 November," Ono explained, *Enterprise* left harbor accompanied by two battleships, two heavy cruisers and twelve destroyers. The two battleships returned on the 6th, but the rest have not yet come back. *Lexington* came in on the 29th and left with five heavy cruisers on the 6th. Thus, *Enterprise* ought to return today. *Saratoga* is under repair at San Diego, and *Wasp* is in the Atlantic. But *Yorktown* and *Hornet* belonging to the Pacific Fleet must be out here. They may have arrived with *Enterprise* today."

"If that happens," said Genda, "I don't care if all eight of the battleships are away."

"As an air man," remarked Oishi, "you naturally place much importance on carriers. Of course it would be good if we could get three of them, but I think it would be better if we get all eight of the battleships."

Chief of Staff Kusaka, who had always been strong for statistical studies of the U. S. Pacific Fleet, now spoke, "There is only a slight chance that carriers may enter the harbor on Saturday, and it seems unlikely that the battleships would leave on Saturday or Sunday. We may take it for granted that all eight battleships will be in the harbor tomorrow. We can't do anything about carriers that are not there. I think we should attack Pearl Harbor tomorrow."

Thus he set the stage for the decision of the task force commander, which was made known in the evening of the 7th when Admiral Nagumo gave his appraisal of the enemy situation:

1. Enemy strength in the Hawaiian area consists of eight battleships, two carriers, about ten heavy and six light cruisers. The carriers and heavy cruisers seem to be at sea, but the others are in the harbor. Those operating at sea are most likely in the training area south of Maui; they are not in Lahaina.

2. Unless an unforeseen situation develops tonight, our attack will be launched upon Pearl Harbor.

3. So far there is no indication that the enemy has been alerted, but that is no reason to relax our security.

At 0530, 7 December,* *Chikuma* and *Tone* each catapulted a "Zero" float plane for a pre-attack reconnaissance of Pearl Harbor. On carrier flight decks readied fighter and attack planes were lined up. The flying crews, also primed for the operation, were gathered in the briefing room. The ships pitched and rolled in the rough sea, kicking up white surf from the pre-dawn blackness of the water. At times wave spray came over the flight deck, and crews clung desperately to their planes to keep them from going into the sea.

In my flying togs I entered the operation room and reported to the Commander in Chief, "I am ready for the mission." Nagumo stood up, grasped my hand firmly and said, "I have confidence in you." He followed me to the dimly lit briefing room where *Akagi's* Captain was waiting with the pilots. The room was not large enough for all of the men, some of whom had to stand out in the passageway. On a blackboard were written the positions of ships in Pearl Harbor as of 0600, 7 December. We were 230 miles due north of Oahu.

Calling the men to attention, I saluted Captain Hasegawa, who spoke a brief final order, "Take off according to plan."

The crews went out hurriedly to their waiting planes. Last to leave, I climbed to the flight deck command post where Genda put his hand on my shoulder. We smiled without speaking, knowing well each other's thoughts.

*West Longitude date and Hawaiian (Zone plus 10½) time used hereinafter.

Turning to me, Air Officer Masuda said, "There is a heavy pitch and roll. What do you think about taking off in the dark?" The sea was rough, and there was a strong wind blowing. The sky was completely dark, and as yet the horizon was not visible.

"The pitch is greater than the roll," I replied. "Were this a training flight, the take-off would be delayed until dawn. But if we coordinate the take-offs with the pitching we can launch successfully." I saluted the officers and went to my plane, the tail of which was striped with red and yellow to distinguish it as the commander's.

The senior petty officer of the maintenance gang handed me a white *hachimaki* (cloth headband) saying, "This is a present from the maintenance crews. May I ask that you take it along to Pearl Harbor?" I nodded and fastened the gift to my flying cap.

The carrier turned to port and headed into the northerly wind. The battle flag was now added to the "Z" flag flying at the masthead. Lighted flying lamps shivered with the vibration of engines as planes completed their warm-up.

On the flight deck a green lamp was waved in a circle to signal "Take off!" The engine of the foremost fighter plane began to roar. With the ship still pitching and rolling, the plane started its run, slowly at first but with steadily increasing speed. Men lining the flight deck held their breath as the first plane took off successfully just before the ship took a downward pitch. The next plane was already moving forward. There were loud cheers as each plane rose into the air.

Thus did the first wave of 183 fighters, bombers, and torpedo planes take off from the six carriers. Within fifteen minutes they had all been launched and were forming up in the still-dark sky, guided only by signal lights of the lead planes. After one great circling over the fleet formation, the planes set course due south for Oahu Island and Pearl Harbor. It was 0615.

Under my direct command were 49 level bombers. About 500 meters to my right and slightly below me were 40 torpedo planes. The same distance to my left, but about 200 meters above me, were 51 dive bombers, and flying cover for the formation there were 43 fighters. These other three groups were led by Lieutenant Commanders Murata, Takahashi, and Itaya, respectively.

We flew through and over the thick clouds which were at 2000 meters, up to where day was ready to dawn. And the clouds began gradually to brighten below us after the brilliant sun burst into the eastern sky. I opened the cockpit canopy and looked back at the large formation of planes. The wings glittered in the bright morning sunlight.

The speedometer indicated 125 knots and we were favored by a tail wind. At 0700 I figured that we should reach Oahu in less than an hour. But flying over the clouds we could not see the surface of the water, and, consequently, had no check on our drift. I switched on the radio-direction finder to tune in the Honolulu radio station and soon picked up some light music. By turning the antenna I found the exact direction from which the broadcast was coming and corrected our course, which had been five degrees off.

Continuing to listen to the program, I was wondering how to get below the clouds after reaching Oahu. If the island was covered by thick clouds like those below us, the level bombing would be difficult; and we had not yet had reports from the reconnaissance planes.

In tuning the radio a little finer I heard, along with the music, what seemed to be a weather report. Holding my breath, I adjusted the dial and listened intently. Then I heard it come through a second time, slowly and distinctly: "Averaging partly cloudy, with clouds mostly over the mountains. Cloud base at 3500 feet. Visibility good. Wind north, 10 knots."

What a windfall for us! No matter how careful the planning, a more favorable situation could not have been imagined. Weather conditions over Pearl Harbor had been worrying me greatly, but now with this information I could turn my attention to other problems. Since Honolulu was only partly cloudy, there must be breaks in the clouds over the island. But since the clouds over the mountains were at 1000 meters altitude, it would not be wise to attack from the northeast, flying over the eastern mountains, as previously planned. The wind was north and visibility good. It would be better to pass to the west of the island and make our approach from the south.

At 0730 we had been in the air for about an hour and a half. It was time that we were seeing land, but there was only a solid layer of clouds below. All of a sudden the clouds broke, and a long white line of coast appeared. We were over Kahuku Point, the northern tip of the island, and now it was time for our deployment.

There were alternate plans for the attack: If we had surprise, the torpedo planes were to strike first, followed by the level bombers and then the dive bombers, which were to attack the air bases including Hickam and Ford Island near the anchorage. If these bases were first hit by the dive bombers, it was feared that the resultant smoke might hinder torpedo and level-bombing attacks on the ships.

On the other hand, if enemy resistance was expected, the dive bombers would attack first to cause confusion and attract enemy fire. Level bombers, coming next, were to bomb and destroy enemy antiaircraft guns, followed by the torpedo planes, which would attack the ships.

The selection of attack method was for my decision, to be indicated by signal pistol: one "black dragon" for a surprise attack, two "black dragons" if it appeared that surprise was lost. Upon either order the fighters were immediately to dash in as cover.

There was still no news from the reconnaissance planes, but I had made up my mind that we could make a surprise attack, and thereupon ordered the deployment by raising my signal pistol outside the canopy and firing one "black dragon." The time was 0740.

With this order dive bombers rose to 4000 meters, torpedo bombers went down almost to sea level, and level bombers came down just under the clouds. The only group that failed to deploy was the fighters. Flying above the rest of the formation, they seemed to have missed the signal because of the clouds. Realizing this I fired another shot toward the fighter group. This time they noticed the signal immediately and sped toward Oahu.

This second shot, however, was taken by the commander of the dive bomber group as the second of two "black dragons," signifying a non-surprise attack which would mean that his group should attack first, and this error served to confuse some of the pilots who had understood the original signal.

Meanwhile a reconnaissance report came in from *Chikuma*'s plane giving the locations of ten battleships, one heavy cruiser, and ten light cruisers in the harbor. It also reported a 14-meter wind from bearing 080, and clouds over the U. S. Fleet at 1700 meters with a scale 7 density. The *Tone* plane also reported that "the enemy fleet is not in Lahaina Anchorage." Now I knew for sure that there were no carriers in the harbor. The sky cleared as we moved in on the target and Pearl Harbor was plainly visible from the northwest valley of the island. I studied our objective through binoculars. They were there all right, all eight of them. "Notify all planes to launch attacks," I ordered my radio man who immediately began tapping the key. The order went in plain code: *"To, to, to, to. . . . "* The time was 0749.

When Lieutenant Commander Takahashi and his dive-bombing group mistook my signal, and thought we were making a non-surprise attack, his 53 planes lost no time in dashing forward. His command was divided into two groups: one led by himself which headed for Ford Island and Hickam Field, the other, led by Lieutenant Sakamoto, headed for Wheeler Field.

The dive bombers over Hickam Field saw heavy bombers lined up on the apron. Takahashi rolled his plane sharply and went into a dive, followed immediately by the rest of his planes, and the first bombs fell at Hickam. The next places hit were Ford Island and Wheeler Field. In a very short time huge billows of black smoke were rising from these bases. The lead torpedo planes were to have started their run to the Navy Yard from over Hickam, coming from south of the bay entrance. But the sudden burst of bombs at Hickam surprised Lieutenant Commander Murata who had understood that his torpedo planes were to have attacked first. Hence he took a short cut lest the smoke from those bases cover up his targets. Thus the first torpedo was actually launched some five minutes ahead of the scheduled 0800. The time of each attack was as follows:

0755 Dive bombers at Hickam and Wheeler
0757 Torpedo planes at battleships
0800 Fighters strafing air bases
0805 Level bombers at battleships

After issuance of the attack order, my level bomber group kept east of Oahu going past the southern tip of the island. On our left was the Barbers Point airfield, but, as we had been informed, there were no planes. Our information indicated that a powerful anti-aircraft battery was stationed there, but we saw no evidence of it.

I continued to watch the sky over the harbor and activities on the ground. None but Japanese planes were in the air, and there were no indications of air combat. Ships in the harbor still appeared to be asleep, and the Honolulu radio broadcast continued normally. I felt that surprise was now assured, and that my men would succeed in their missions.

Knowing that Admirals Nagumo, Yamamoto, and the General

Staff were anxious about the attack, I decided that they should be informed. I ordered the following message sent to the fleet: "We have succeeded in making a surprise attack. Request you relay this report to Tokyo." The radio man reported shortly that the message had been received by *Akagi*.

The code for a successful surprise attack was *"Tora, tora, tora. . . . "* Before *Akagi's* relay of this message reached Japan, it was received by *Nagato* in Hiroshima Bay and the General Staff in Tokyo, directly from my plane! This was surely a long-distance record for such a low-powered transmission from an airplane, and might be attributed to the use of the word *"Tora"* as our code. There is a Japanese saying, "A tiger (*tora*) goes out 1000 *ri* (2000 miles) and returns without fail."

I saw clouds of black smoke rising from Hickam and soon thereafter from Ford Island. This bothered me and I wondered what had happened. It was not long before I saw waterspouts rising alongside the battleships, followed by more and more waterspouts. It was time to launch our level bombing attacks so I ordered my pilot to bank sharply, which was the attack signal for the planes following us. All ten of my squadrons then formed into a single column with intervals of 200 meters. It was indeed a gorgeous formation.

The lead plane in each squadron was manned by a specially trained pilot and bombardier. The pilot and bombardier of my squadron had won numerous fleet contests and were considered the best in the Japanese Navy. I approved when Lieutenant Matsuzaki asked if the lead plane should trade positions with us, and he lifted our plane a little as a signal. The new leader came forward quickly, and I could see the smiling round face of the bombardier when he saluted. In returning the salute I entrusted the command to them for the bombing mission.

As my group made its bomb run, enemy antiaircraft suddenly came to life. Dark gray bursts blossomed here and there until the sky was clouded with shattering near misses which made our plane tremble. Shipboard guns seemed to open fire before the shore batteries. I was startled by the rapidity of the counterattack which came less than five minutes after the first bomb had fallen. Were it the Japanese Fleet, the reaction would not have been so quick, because although the Japanese character is suitable for offensives, it does not readily adjust to the defensive.

Suddenly the plane bounced as if struck by a huge club. "The fuselage is holed to port," reported the radio man behind me, "and a steering-control wire is damaged." I asked hurriedly if the plane was under control, and the pilot assured me that it was.

No sooner were we feeling relieved than another burst shook the plane. My squadron was headed for *Nevada's* mooring at the northern end of battleship row on the east side of Ford Island. We were just passing over the bay entrance and it was almost time to release our bombs. It was not easy to pass through the concentrated antiaircraft fire. Flying at only 3000 meters, it seemed that this might well be a date with eternity.

I further saw that it was not wise to have deployed in this long single-column formation. The whole level bomber group could be destroyed like ducks in a shooting gallery. It would also have been better if we had approached the targets from the direction of Diamond Head. But here we were at our targets and there was a job to be done.

It was now a matter of utmost importance to stay on course, and the lead plane kept to its line of flight like a homing pigeon. Ignoring the barrage of shells bursting around us, I concentrated on the bomb loaded under the lead plane, pulled the safety bolt from the bomb release lever and grasped the handle. It seemed as if time was standing still.

Again we were shaken terrifically and our planes were buffeted about. When I looked out the third plane of my group was abeam of us and I saw its bomb fall! That pilot had a reputation for being careless. In training his bomb releases were poorly timed, and he had often been cautioned.

I thought, "That damn fellow has done it again!" and shook my fist in his direction. But I soon realized that there was something wrong with his plane and he was losing gasoline. I wrote on a small blackboard, "What happened?" and held it toward his plane. He explained, "Underside of fuselage hit."

Now I saw his bomb cinch lines fluttering wildly, and sorry for having scolded him, I ordered that he return to the carrier. He answered, "Fuel tank destroyed, will follow you," asking permission to stay with the group. Knowing the feelings of the pilot and crew, I gave the permission, although I knew it was useless to try taking that crippled and bombless plane through the enemy fire. It was nearly time for bomb release when we ran into clouds which obscured the target, and I made out the round face of the lead bombardier who was waving his hands back and forth to indicate that we had passed the release point. Banking slightly we turned right toward Honolulu, and I studied the antiaircraft fire, knowing that we would have to run through it again. It was now concentrated on the second squadron.

While circling for another try, I looked toward the area in which the bomb from the third plane had fallen. Just outside the bay entrance I saw a large water ring close by what looked like a destroyer. The ship seemed to be standing in a floating dock, attached to both sides of the entrance like a gate boat. I was suddenly reminded of the midget submarines which were to have entered the bay for a special attack.

At the time of our sortie I was aware of these midget submarines, but knew nothing of their characteristics, operational objectives, force organization, or the reason for their participation in the attack. In *Akagi,* Commander Shibuya, a staff officer in charge of submarine operations, had explained that they were to penetrate the harbor the night before our attack; but, no matter how good an opportunity might arise, they were not to strike until after the planes had done so.

Even now the submarines were probably concealed in the bay, awaiting the air attack. Had the entrance been left open, there would have been some opportunity for them to get out of the harbor. But in light of what I had just seen there seemed little chance of that, and, feeling now the bitterness of war, I vowed to do my best in the assigned mission.

While my group was circling over Honolulu for another bombing attempt, other groups made their runs, some making three tries before succeeding. Suddenly a colossal explosion occurred in battleship row. A huge column of dark red smoke rose to 1000 feet and a stiff shock wave reached our plane. I called the pilot's attention to the spectacle, and he observed, "Yes, Commander, the powder magazine must have exploded. Terrible indeed!" The attack was in full swing, and smoke from fires and explosions filled most of the sky over Pearl Harbor.

My group now entered on a bombing course again. Studying battleship row through binoculars, I saw that the big explosion had been on *Arizona.* She was still flaming fiercely and her smoke was covering *Nevada,* the target of my group. Since the heavy smoke would hinder our bomber accuracy, I looked for some other ship to attack. *Tennessee,* third in the left row, was already on fire; but next in row was *Maryland,* which had not yet been attacked. I gave an order changing our target to this ship, and once again we headed into the antiaircraft fire. Then came the "ready" signal, and I took a firm grip on the bomb release handle, holding my breath and staring at the bomb of the lead plane.

Pilots, observers, and radio men all shouted, "Release!" on seeing the bomb drop from the lead plane, and all the others let go their bombs. I immediately lay flat on the floor to watch the fall of bombs through a peephole. Four bombs in perfect pattern plummeted like devils of doom. The target was so far away that I wondered for a moment if they would reach it. The bombs grew smaller and smaller until I was holding my breath for fear of losing them. I forgot everything in the thrill of watching the fall toward the target. They became small as poppy seeds and finally disappeared just as tiny white flashes of smoke appeared on and near the ship.

From a great altitude near misses are much more obvious than direct hits because they create wave rings in the water which are plain to see. Observing only two such rings plus two tiny flashes I shouted, "Two hits!" and rose from the floor of the plane. These minute flashes were the only evidence we had of hits at that time, but I felt sure that they had done considerable damage. I ordered the bombers which had completed their runs to return to the carriers, but my own plane remained over Pearl Harbor to observe our successes and conduct operations still in progress.

After our bomb run I ordered my pilot to fly over each of the air bases, where our fighters were strafing, before returning over Pearl Harbor to observe the result of our attacks on the warships. Pearl Harbor and vicinity had been turned into complete chaos in a very short time.

Target ship *Utah,* on the western side of Ford Island, had already capsized. On the other side of the island *West Virginia* and *Oklahoma* had received concentrated torpedo attacks as a result of their exposed positions in the outer row. Their sides were almost blasted off, and they listed steeply in a flood of heavy oil. *Arizona* was in miserable shape, her magazine apparently having blown up; she was listing badly and burning furiously.

Two other battleships, *Maryland* and *Tennessee,* were on fire; especially the latter whose smoke emerged in a heavy black column which towered into the sky. *Pennsylvania,* unscathed in the dry-dock, seemed to be the only battleship that had not been attacked.

Most of our torpedo planes, under Lieutenant Commander Murata, flew around the Navy Yard area and concentrated their attacks on the ships moored east of Ford Island. A summary of their reports, made upon return to our carriers, indicated the following hits: one on *Nevada,* nine on *West Virginia,* twelve on *Oklahoma,* and three on *California.*

Elements of the torpedo bombers attacked ships west of the island, but they found only *Utah* and attacked her, claiming six hits. Other torpedo planes headed for *Pennsylvania,* but seeing that she was in drydock they shifted their attack to a cruiser and destroyer tied up at Pier 1010. Five torpedo hits were claimed on these targets, which were *Helena* and *Oglala.*

As I observed the damage done by the first attack wave, the effectiveness of the torpedoes seemed remarkable, and I was struck with the shortsightedness of the United States in being so generally unprepared and in not using torpedo nets. I also thought of our long hard training in Kagoshima Bay and the efforts of those who had labored to accomplish a seemingly impossible task. A warm feeling came with the realization that the reward of those efforts was unfolded here before my eyes.

During the attack many of our pilots noted the brave efforts of the American flyers able to take off who, though greatly outnumbered, flew straight in to engage our planes. Their effect was negligible, but their courage commanded the admiration and respect of our pilots.

It took the planes of the first attack wave about one hour to complete their mission. By the time they were headed back to our carriers, having lost three fighters, one dive bomber, and five torpedo planes, the second wave of 171 planes commanded by Lieutenant Commander Shimazaki was over the target area. Arriving off Kahuku Point at 0840, the attack run was ordered 14 minutes later and they swept in, making every effort to avoid the billowing clouds of smoke as well as the now-intensified antiaircraft fire.

In this second wave there were 36 fighters to control the air over Pearl Harbor, 54 high-level bombers led by Shimazaki to attack Hickam Field and the Naval Air Stations at Kaneohe, while eighty-one dive bombers led by Lieutenant Commander Egusa flew over the mountains to the east and dashed in to hit the warships.

By the time these last arrived, the sky was so covered with clouds and smoke that planes had difficulty in locating their targets. To further complicate the problems of this attack, the ship and ground antiaircraft fire was now very heavy. But Egusa was undaunted in leading his dive bombers through the fierce barrage. The planes chose as their targets the ships which were putting up the stiffest repelling fire. This choice proved effective since these ships had suffered least from the first attack. Thus the second attack achieved a nice spread, hitting the least damaged battleships as well as previously undamaged cruisers and destroyers. This attack also lasted about one hour, but due to the increased return fire, it suffered higher casualties, six fighters and fourteen dive bombers being lost.

After the second wave was headed back to the carriers, I circled Pearl Harbor once more to observe and photograph the results. I counted four battleships definitely sunk and three severely damaged. Still another battleship appeared to be slightly damaged and extensive damage had also been inflicted upon other types of ships. The seaplane base at Ford Island was all in flames, as were the airfields, especially Wheeler Field.

A detailed survey of damage was impossible because of the dense pall of black smoke. Damage to the airfields was not determinable, but it was readily apparent that no planes on the fields were operational. In the three hours that my plane was in the area we did not encounter a single enemy plane. It seemed that at least half the island's air strength must have been destroyed. Several hangars remained untouched, however, and it was possible that some of them held planes which were still operational.

Such were my conclusions as I prepared to return to our carrier. I was startled from these thoughts by the sudden approach of a fighter plane banking from side to side. We were greatly relieved to see the Rising Sun on its wings. As it came closer we saw that it was a *Zuikaku* fighter which must have been here since the first attack wave. I wondered if any other fighters had been left behind, and ordered my pilot to go to the rendezvous point for a final check. Sure enough, there we found a second fighter plane who also followed joyfully after us.

It was extremely difficult for fighter planes to fly long distances at sea. They were not equipped with homing devices and radar as were the larger planes. It was therefore planned to have the bombers, upon completion of their missions, rendezvous with the fighters at a designated point and lead them back to the carriers. Some of the fighters, however, such as these two, must have missed the time of rendezvous, and they were indeed fortunate to find our plane which could lead them safely back to the task force and their carriers.

My plane was just about the last one to get back to *Akagi* where refueled and rearmed planes were being lined up on the busy flight deck in preparation for yet another attack. I was called to the bridge as soon as the plane stopped, and could tell on arriving there that Admiral Nagumo's staff had been engaged in heated discussions about the advisability of launching the next attack. They were waiting for my account of the battle.

"Four battleships definitely sunk," I reported. "One sank instantly, another capsized, the other two settled to the bottom of the bay and may have capsized." This seemed to please Admiral Nagumo, who observed, "We may then conclude that anticipated results have been achieved."

Discussion next centered upon the extent of damage inflicted at airfields and air bases, and I expressed my views saying, "All things considered we have achieved a great amount of destruction, but it would be unwise to assume that we have destroyed everything. There are still many targets remaining which should be hit. Therefore I recommend that another attack be launched."

The factors which influenced Admiral Nagumo's decision—the target of much criticism by naval experts, and an interesting subject for naval historians—have long been unknown, since the man who made it died in the summer of 1944 when United States forces invaded the Marianas. I know of only one document in which Admiral Nagumo's reasons are set forth, and there they are given as follows:

1. The first attack had inflicted all the damage we had hoped for, and another attack could not be expected to greatly increase the extent of that damage.

2. Enemy return fire had been surprisingly prompt even though we took them by surprise; another attack would meet stronger opposition and our losses would certainly be disproportionate to the additional destruction which might be inflicted.

3. Intercepted enemy messages indicated at least 50 large planes still operational; and we did not know the whereabouts of the enemy's carriers, cruisers, and submarines.

4. To remain within range of enemy land-based planes was distinctly to our disadvantage, especially since the effectiveness of our air reconnaissance was extremely limited.

I had done all I could to urge another attack, but the decision rested entirely with Admiral Nagumo, and he chose to retire without launching the next attack. Immediately flag signals were hoisted ordering the course change, and our ships headed northward at high speed.

John A. Rademaker

AMERICANS OF JAPANESE ANCESTRY IN WORLD WAR II

WHEN THE Japanese bombs fell on Pearl Harbor, one group of Americans, those of Japanese ancestry, faced a cruel challenge. The AJA's (Americans of Japanese ancestry) on the mainland became objects of suspicion and even of persecution. In Hawaii some suspicion about them arose, usually among uninformed persons. Some nasty rumors about them spread. Frank Knox, the Secretary of the Navy, made a silly and unfounded statement about widespread fifth-column activity in Hawaii. There was no such activity. Instead, the AJA's responded to the challenge of the Japanese attack with magnificent and selfless courage. In the 100th Battalion and the 442nd Regimental Combat Team, fighting in Italy, as well as in other units, the AJA's won with their blood the right to hold their heads high as American citizens.

The following extract from Dr. John A. Rademaker's *These Are Americans* presents a hard-hitting account of the AJA's in Hawaii on and after December 7, 1941.

THE EVENTS of the morning of December 7, 1941, will long remain indelibly engraved in the memories of the people of Hawaii. It is one thing for people—of Japanese and of every other ancestry—to be aware, as they all were in Hawaii, that there was imminent danger of warfare, and to be aware that such warfare would probably strike one's own home community. It is another to awaken to the sound of bursting shells, racing plane motors, the explosions of anti-aircraft shells, and the other myriad unusual noises which fell upon Honolulu and the rest of Oahu Island on that morning. Most people—whether of Japanese or other ancestry—at first believed it to be a more than usually realistic practice drill of the American 7th Air Force and Pacific Fleet. But the radio soon told them. "This is the real McCoy! The planes have the rising sun emblem on them! It is a real attack!"

Within minutes of the first announcement, requests and orders for mobilization of defense arrangements began to be issued by radio, by telephone, by messenger. From their homes throughout the Territory of Hawaii, the members of the Hawaii National Guard 298th and 299th regiments responded alertly to the call, boys of Japanese parentage, of Chinese origin, of Filipino, of Puerto Rican, of Korean, of Caucasian, and of Hawaiian ancestry. Men who had earlier been inducted into military service were driven to their posts by their fathers, their brothers, sisters, wives, or mothers. One young man of Japanese parentage was aroused by his father with the news that Schofield Barracks was being attacked by the Imperial Japanese Navy. The father drove his son as rapidly as possible to Schofield so that he could join the defenders of Oahu, and urged him to fight his best in defense of his country . . . .

Under all the circumstances, it was to be expected that rumor and imagination should play a large part in the conception of many people concerning what was going on. A report reached the commanding officer of the University of Hawaii R.O.T.C. that two regiments of Japanese troops had been dropped in the hills behind the University from planes by means of parachutes. The R.O.T.C. battalion was ordered to deploy to meet them and delay their advance into the city. The members of the R.O.T.C. were sworn into the newly organized Hawaii Territorial Guard, and after solving the problems of finding firing pins and live ammunition for their guns, deployed as ordered to meet a force reported to outnumber them four to one. Most of the boys in the R.O.T.C. were of Japanese ancestry, but there was no doubt or indecision. They were a determined and alert group of defenders of their Alma Mater and their city. Fortunately, this rumor, like so many others, proved to be unfounded, and soon the boys were called in to take up duties as sentries, guards, and reserve units in preparation for further air attacks and in expectation of a naval attack and an attempted landing by troops of the Japanese government. . . .

The people of Japanese ancestry did their full share of this work, and did it well. Yet there were many people who did not trust them. It was easy to think of them in terms of the likeness of their faces to those of the Japanese airplane pilots and soldiers and sailors, and it was hard to remember that, whatever their faces looked like, inside they were loyal and active citizens and defenders of Hawaii against those same Japanese airplane pilots and Imperial sailors and soldiers. Most people expressed and felt confidence in their loyalty, but there were some who distrusted them and felt that they should not be permitted to participate in the Islands' defense—not to carry guns and exercise authority, at least. Some of these doubting Thomases were in influential positions, and as more and more military men who were unfamiliar with the situation arrived from the mainland, the pendulum of power swung to the point where a decision was made to withdraw all persons of Japanese ancestry from active participation in combatant military duties, in spite of their loyalty and their hard, conscientious work during the days in which the danger was real and when people were dying rather than retreating to positions of safety.

Perhaps it was too much of a shock for the average American from the mainland to debark from a boat in Honolulu as he came to reinforce the defense forces of the Islands, to find a sentry with a Japanese-looking face in an American uniform pacing the docks or directing his movements in the city. Almost certainly it was a decision made in Washington, and not initiated or perhaps even not agreed with by the local military authorities. Perhaps the old feeling of distinctness which every ethnic group tries to hold onto made persons of Caucasian and other ancestry a bit distrustful of Japanese Americans. At any rate, on January 19, 1942, only five or six weeks after these men of Japanese ancestry had given their unstinted energy and unanimous obedience to carrying out all the military orders they received as members of their units of the Hawaii Territorial Guard, they were told that they could no longer be used, and were given honorable discharges. . . .

In spite of the fact that the military and civilian authorities who had direct charge of preventing sabotage and espionage, and who were in the best possible position to know what went on, have constantly said clearly and definitely that there was no sabotage or espionage in Hawaii either before, during, or after the attack on December 7, 1941, some people in the Islands, and most people on the mainland, continued to believe that the Japanese Americans were not trustworthy. Perhaps this was due first of all to a willingness to believe this by some people—a willingness based in large part upon earlier propaganda. But there was also the fact that the press, radio, and movies were not always careful to find out the truth before they published sensational stories compiled from accounts of semi-hysterical witnesses who had their information at third or fourth hand. . . .

Moreover, on the mainland there was apparently little or no effort to deny these unfounded rumors by responsible military and political authorities. In fact, Congressmen on the Tolan Committee cited such rumors as justification for urging the mass evacuation of all Japanese Americans on the Pacific Coast long after they had been specifically and definitely denied by the authorities of the F.B.I., the police, and the Army Intelligence in Hawaii. In Congress they were extensively quoted in support of evacuation of Japanese Americans from the Pacific Coast, though only a few times in support of demands to evacuate the Japanese Americans from Hawaii. On the radio and in the newspapers of the nation they were cited freely, the denials ignored, and their truth taken for granted. They were made the basis for lusty editorials calling for immediate evacuation of Japanese Americans from the Pacific Coast states to prevent sabotage and espionage there "like that at Pearl Harbor." Had they been as promptly and clearly revealed as false by authorities on the mainland as they were in Hawaii, the results would perhaps have been different, not only with regard to the decision to evacuate all Japanese American members of the Hawaii Territorial Guard.

If denials and corrections were issued by the mainland authorities, they apparently did not reach publishers, or at least they failed to reach the readers, listeners, and movie-goers who were exposed to the rumors. Probably the people who left Hawaii hurriedly after the outbreak of hostilities contributed to the distribution of such rumors, for they left under a good deal of emotional strain, and were sometimes poorly informed—and some, of course, could hardly resist the thoroughly human tendency to make a good story just a little better and more exciting, without in the least intending any harmful results to anyone.

The net result was to add to the social forces which were working toward setting the Japanese Americans apart and denying them any role in the defense of the nation. In the mainland, these forces were so strong that it became politically dangerous to speak the truth about the good qualities and loyalty to the United States of the Japanese Americans, and it became highly fashionable politically to criticize them and to say they could not possibly be trusted with freedom to come and go on their regular business. In Hawaii, the rumors were taken care of promptly so that such hysteria could not arise or be fanned into an attitude so strong as to force mass evacuation of all persons of Japanese ancestry from the Islands. The basic racial attitudes were different to begin with, in Hawaii, and the attitudes of acceptance, of racial cooperation, and personal understanding across racial boundaries were strong enough to withstand the pressures which arose with regard to policy toward evacuation or locking up of the Japanese American population as a whole.

Nevertheless, even in Hawaii some people remained suspicious of the loyalty of persons of Japanese ancestry, despite the thorough police and F.B.I. searches of Japanese homes and communities which found no evidence of any deep-dyed plots against the United States government, despite the internment of those who were suspected of disloyalty and despite the clean bill of health given to the persons of Japanese ancestry by the police, the F.B.I., and the Military Intelligence.

But however much suspicion there was, there was an equal amount of knowledge which it was almost impossible to avoid learning about the excellent and faithful service which the Japanese American boys in khaki were giving. To be discharged under such circumstances, with the need for further services evident to everyone, was a heart-breaking experience for the boys who had felt themselves to be wholly a part of their native land, and of the military forces which were defending it. It was also resented by their buddies in the outfits from which they were discharged. Perhaps it was unavoidable under the circumstances, but it was most disheartening that people in authority should listen to tale-mongers and suspicions and ignore the acts and words and feelings which had already spoken most eloquently of the real convictions and loyalty of the Nisei of Hawaii, and of a good many of the Issei too. . . .

The boys who were discharged on January 19, 1942, were far from satisfied to let matters rest, even though they were clearly and honorably freed of all dangers of participation in combat. They felt that if they, as citizens, could not be trusted to serve their country, their critics would doubtless be able to persuade the people of the United States that they should also be denied the privileges of citizenship. The future status of all Japanese Americans hung in the balance. This they could see clearly. They also felt angry because they had been made helpless and stopped from doing what they strongly felt they wanted to do—help in the fight against Fascism and Nazism.

After talking the matter over and discussing it with leading citizens of the Territory, a large portion of the boys who had been relieved of further service decided to petition the military governor for a chance to serve their country again. On January 30, 1942, they called a meeting of former Guardsmen and others interested, and offered to do whatever was asked of them, whether it was military service or not. The military governor, Lieutenant General Delos C. Emmons, enthusiastically accepted their offer, and on February 23, 1942, ordered them to work under the direction of the United States Army Engineers (34th Combat Engineers Regiment) on work details. They were officially called the Corps of Engineers Auxiliary, but the boys, most of whom were students from the University of Hawaii, quickly dubbed themselves the Varsity Victory Volunteers. . . . For eleven months these 169 volunteers built roads, improved highways and bridges, operated shops, built barracks and other buildings needed by the Army, dug ditches, and sweated away with a right good will. Three times each man contributed 350 to 500 cc. of blood to the Blood Bank. On the average, each man bought two hundred dollars' worth of War Bonds out of his regular Army pay. Like all other service organizations, they enjoyed their parties (luaus), celebrations, and ceremonial occasions. Through it all they adhered firmly to a democratic process of membership meetings, committee discussions and decisions, mutual consultation, and cooperation which made of them ever finer Americans and more effective workers for Uncle Sam.

The Varsity Victory Volunteers made a real contribution to the idea and practice of democracy in the world. Many of the leading military and civilian residents of the Territory of Hawaii said so, from Lieutenant General Delos C. Emmons on down—Charles R. Hemenway, president of the Hawaiian Trust Co., Leslie A. Hicks, president of the Hawaiian Electric Co., Gregg M. Sinclair, president of the University of Hawaii, Lieutenant Colonel William Sexton and Captain T. F. Lum, the commanding officers of the VVV's, and many others. . . .

So well did they do their work, and so well did the boys of Japanese ancestry who were already in the uniform of the United States Army throughout the nation fulfill their duties and take advantage of their opportunities to serve their country, that by the middle of the year a far-reaching decision was made in the War Department at Washington, D.C. It was decided to create an All–Japanese American combat unit of regular soldiers already in service, and to call for volunteers to make up a complete Regimental Combat Team composed wholly of Americans of Japanese ancestry.

This decision was hailed by many persons as official recognition of the fact long well-known to sociologists and anthropologists, but not to some of the general public, namely, that loyalty and devotion to one's country are not based upon one's race, parentage, or ancestry, but upon education and the ideals one learns in the school, in the neighborhood, in the church, and in the community, from personal contacts, from books and newspapers, from the radio, and from movies. From all these sources persons of Japanese ancestry had long been learning to live as Americans. They had adopted in their own minds American ideals, American ways of thinking and acting, and they had in almost all cases become, for all practical purposes, Americans at heart.

True, the Issei had not been permitted to become citizens of the United States, and had by Congress been forced to retain their Japanese citizenship if they wanted any at all. But that was something they could not do much about, and they could and did feel at home in Hawaii and the rest of the United States far more than they would have in Japan. Almost every one of the few thousand Issei who had gone back there for a visit before the war said that there were many things in Japan which they could not get used to again, and that they preferred to live in the United States. For the Nisei who had seldom seen Japan, there was still more to bind their feelings and sentiments to the United States, to Hawaii, and little indeed to make them feel any love for Japan, or any feeling other than a mildly sympathetic curiosity about the land from which their father and mother had come. A few Kibei (Nisei who were left in Japan with their relatives, or sent there during their early formative years for a Japanese education) felt otherwise, and many of these were recognized as probably having absorbed the ideas fed to all Japanese school children in Japan by the fascistic military government. But these few hundred Kibei were for the most part interned at once, or carefully watched. A substantial number of them proved to be loyal and devoted to the United States, and served valiantly and valuably in the Army, in industry, and in the government. The other Nisei, who had received their ideas of loyalty and their ideals from American schools proved, in this and many other crises, that they could be expected to live in accordance with the ideas and ideals they had learned in American public schools, in free American communities, in American boyhood gangs, in American theaters, American churches, YMCA's, YWCA's, and other American institutions.

It had taken precious months to have the American people and their administrative authorities recognize this fact, and it was a long, hard struggle, but on June 5, 1942, it was clear that it had been learned at least to some extent, for that was the date when the Hawaii Provisional Battalion was organized. A week later, when this unit of about a thousand Americans of Japanese ancestry reached San Francisco, it was renamed the 100th Infantry Battalion, Separate. From that time on, this first unit proceeded to demonstrate the loyalty, spirit, and devotion of Japanese Americans to the flag, government, and people of the United States. Even then, the people as a whole, particularly those who had been subjected to the well-planned barrage of propaganda on the Pacific Coast, did not yet realize the truth that had driven itself into the minds of the people of Hawaii and of the political and military leaders of our nation.

It was President Roosevelt who said: "The proposal of the War Department to organize a combat team consisting of loyal American citizens of Japanese descent has my full approval. No loyal citizen of the United States should be denied the democratic right to exercise the responsibilities of his citizenship, regardless of his ancestry. The principle on which this country was founded and by which it has always been governed is that Americanism is a matter of mind and heart; Americanism is not, and never was, a matter of race or ancestry. A good American is one who is loyal to this country and to our creed of liberty and democracy. Every loyal American citizen should be given an opportunity to serve this country wherever his skills will make the greatest contribution—whether it be in the ranks of the armed forces, war production, agriculture, government service, or other work essential to the war effort."

It was not until February 1, 1943, that the War Department was able to put into action its plans to create a whole Regimental Combat Team composed only of Japanese Americans, and many voices were heard opposing the acceptance of Japanese Americans as soldiers. Indeed, the Navy Department did not get around to accepting the principle that American loyalty is based upon living the American way in American communities, until June, 1947, when it first announced that it would accept Japanese Americans into the Navy. So, as a matter of fact, restoring American citizens of Japanese ancestry to combat status in our Army was but a major first step in proving the loyalty of the Americans of Japanese ancestry—to give them a chance to do combat service for their country, out in the open, where everyone could see what they did. Of course, much earlier than this, Americans of Japanese ancestry had volunteered and had been accepted to listen to the Tokyo radio, to decipher and translate Japanese broadcasts, documents, books, and maps, and a school for interpreters had been established at San Francisco and moved to Camp Savage, Wisconsin (near Camp McCoy), for further training and for preparing Americans of Japanese ancestry for front-line service as interpreters. There were very few Americans of non-Japanese ancestry who could do these things—and too few Americans of Japanese ancestry who could do them! But outside of using the services of Japanese Americans who had such special language and geographical skills and knowledge, under strict military secrecy, there was little or no public recognition of the trustworthiness of Americans as such if they happened to be Americans of Japanese ancestry, until the creation of the 100th Battalion and the 442nd Regimental Combat Team.

In one sense, the creation of a separate unit along racial lines was contrary to the principle of equality of treatment of all citizens regardless of race for which many Japanese Americans were fighting, and which many Americans of other ancestries believed to be a fundamental principle of our American democracy. For this reason many good Americans urged that the boys of Japanese ancestry should be accepted equally and distributed without distinction among all units of the armed forces. This would have been a means of giving more Americans contact with them, a chance to see and talk with them, and would have in the end resulted in better acquaintanceship with the Japanese Americans in the armed services. On the other hand, the War Department felt that by keeping them together, where the spotlight could be kept upon them, the Americans of Japanese ancestry could demonstrate to all Americans, at home as well as in the services, just what stuff they were made of, and where their loyalties lay. Unfortunately, it also enabled the enemy to throw a disproportionate amount of strength against these boys in an effort to prevent their success in any sector, for the enemy well knew, if many Americans did not, that the loyalty of the Japanese Americans to the United States was clear and conclusive proof that the Nazi propaganda of race prejudice, race discrimination, and race hatred was a pack of lies made up out of whole cloth, and swallowed naively and unthinkingly by many people wherever this poisonous propaganda went. Such clear evidence against this propaganda would defeat the Nazi technique of dividing us by setting our racial and economic and religious groups to fighting each other until it would be possible for the Nazis to defeat us. But this fact, while it did not escape the Germans, also received intelligent attention from the American military and political authorities, and on this basis, the segregated unit was justified and successful. As was to be hoped, when the 442nd and the 100th were reactivated as the first organized army reserves in Hawaii, on July 31, 1947, membership was not restricted on the basis of ancestry, and they will not be segregated units hereafter, but for the time and purpose they were most effective so.

Bob Krauss

STATEHOOD FOR HAWAII

ON MARCH 12, 1959, Congress passed the statehood bill for Hawaii, which officially became the fiftieth state with President Eisenhower's proclamation of August 21. Here was the climax of many years of agitation. Immediately Hawaii's people acquired new dignity and new self-respect as they graduated from territorial status to become first-class American citizens, with the right to vote for the President and their governor (previously appointed) and to send two senators and a representative to Congress.

This account of the statehood celebration and of the events immediately following is by Bob Krauss, Hawaii's beloved newspaper columnist, taken from his deservedly popular book *Here's Hawaii.*

A T EXACTLY 10:04 o'clock on Thursday morning, March 12, 1959, Hawaii poised on the brink of destiny. The weather was balmy. The sun shone warm and pleasantly into downtown office windows. But there was electricity in the air, a tenseness that held half a million people in arrested motion.

At that moment I stood squeezed shoulder to shoulder in a crowd of silent newsmen, staring intently at a blank sheet of yellow paper in a teletype machine on the second floor of the *Advertiser* building. The machine had just signaled an urgent, 10-bell flash. We stood there in a taut circle wating for the message to come through. Suddenly the keys began their methodical clatter. The words jumped at us:

WASHINGTON—HOUSE OFFICIALLY PASSES HAWAIIAN STATEHOOD BILL

A moment later the old bell in Kawaiahao Church, of coral blocks built by missionaries in 1842, began a solemn tolling of thanksgiving that lasted the rest of the day.

Across the street at City Hall, Honolulu's mayor, Neal Blaisdell, listened with tears in his eyes. "God bless the Congress of the United States," he said.

On Queen Emma Street, at Central Intermediate School, the hallways erupted with cheering youngsters who began jitterbugging on the lawn outside.

In the Capital Investment Building downtown, millionaire financier Chinn Ho locked up his desk, broke out half a dozen cases of Scotch, and spent the rest of the morning passing out colored streamers to throw from his office window.

At Iolani Palace, built by Hawaiian kings long before the Islands became part of the United States, the last legislature of the Territory of Hawaii was in session. After an abrupt adjournment, one of the legislators immediately began to campaign for the U.S. Senate.

At the Hawaiian Village Hotel, Henry J. Kaiser set off a string of 20,000 firecrackers.

That night in Waikiki about 100,000 people came to watch the hula girls dance in the street. It created the worst traffic jam in Hawaii's history.

On Sand Island, on the other side of Honolulu Harbor, a statehood bonfire sent flames shooting 75 feet into the air. They were visible ten miles away.

Newsboys waved the headline, CONGRESS SAYS YES!

It was like a gigantic, exuberant wedding party. But not even at a wedding does everybody laugh, for a wedding marks an end as well as a beginning. Each mother must find it hard to believe that the bride in the white wedding veil is really the same little girl who once used to believe in Santa Claus.

In Hawaii, too, that day there were mothers who cried at the wedding. One of them was Aunt Jennie Wilson, Hawaii's grand old woman, who began her career as the favorite hula dancer in the royal court of King Kalakaua in 1886 when Hawaii still belonged to the Hawaiians. She is one of the few living persons who witnessed the annexation of the Islands by the United States.

While the whistles blew downtown and kids out of school raced their jalopies through Waikiki, Aunt Jennie sat alone on her tree-shaded lanai with memories that go back 87 years.

Her house is in a valley on the outskirts of Honolulu at the end of a rutted, winding road that goes through the grounds of a brick factory founded by her late husband and long-time mayor of Honolulu, Johnny Wilson.

The former court beauty was sitting in a rocking chair when I drove up. A cane was on the floor beside her. She wore a faded black duster over her muumuu. Her face was a study in wrinkles. But there was still a saucy snap in her eyes and her old hands were still those of a hula dancer, expressive and graceful.

She shooed two fat pet hens off the porch crowded with old-fashioned furniture. I pulled up a straight-backed, cane-bottomed chair and sat down.

"Aloha, Auntie Jennie," I said, "have you heard about statehood?"

"I heard on the radio that if the whistle blows, it means statehood," she said casually. "I heard the whistle blow."

"You lived in Hawaii before the United States took possession, didn't you."

She smiled like a pleased coquette.. "I was asked to dance by King Kalakaua when I was only fourteen."

"Were you there when Hawaii was annexed by the United States?"

She nodded. "My mother and I sat on our veranda on Queen Street and watched the Hawaiian flag come down on the Iolani Palace grounds. That was on August 12, 1898. There was a big crowd. Haoles in frock coats and Hawaiians, too. But it was very quiet. No laughing, no singing. It was a sad day."

"Did annexation change Hawaii much?"

Aunt Jennie shrugged. "Just more houses, more taxes, more crowded."

"Do you think statehood will change Hawaii much?"

"The same. More people, more hurry, more cars. I'm afraid to go to town now. I'll get run over."

"Did you think Hawaii would ever become a state?"

"No, never."

"Did you think the Hawaiian monarchy would ever be overthrown?"

She chuckled. "I never thought I would live to see the day."

"How has Hawaii changed since the days of King Kalakaua?" I asked.

"I used to know every people on this island. I knew all their cousins and aunties and grandmas. Now I look and I can't find their house. Maybe a store there. And streets right through everywhere. This is not Hawaii any more, only the name. It is America. The people are living like United States."

"Has the spirit of Hawaii changed?"

"Yes, it has changed. Poor old Waikiki. Sometimes I go down and sit on the benches and just look at all the new stores with glass windows. And hotels and apartment houses. When I was a little girl Waikiki was only a beach with coconut trees. In back was a swamp with mosquitoes. There were no houses at all. . . ." Her voice drifted off on the wings of memory. "Once a month King Kalakaua call the people to come for hukilau [community net-fishing]. Plenty fish at Waikiki then. Oh, the people come in families from all over. Dance the hula, sing. No buses to Waikiki then. Not even roads. We walk and carry some poi. Gather limu [sea weed] on the beach.. The King ask each one, 'How many children?' Give them so many fish."

"Do you wish it were still that way?" I asked.

"No can help," Aunt Jennie answered without malice. "Why

complain? I'm not complaining. I'm just telling how it was in Hawaii when I was a girl."

"Do you have any advice to give the new State of Hawaii?"

Then she gave me the characteristically Hawaiian smile that has been the answer to so many similar situations. It is a smile of warmth and openheartedness and, I sometimes think, forgiveness. Aunt Jennie lifted her wrinkled hands in benediction with a hula motion as graceful as a soaring gull and answered, "It will be all right."

So an era ended.

And another began.

It began for nearly 600,000 Americans on a group of fertile, lovely, sun-kissed islands across 2,091 miles of cobalt-blue ocean to the southwest of San Francisco. For these islands it will be an era of fantastic change and spectacular growth.

James H. Shoemaker, director of business research for the Bank of Hawaii, tells me that by 1980 the population of the Islands will have almost tripled. Personal income will be up around $3 billion, creating over twice the buying power available today. About 1,000,000 tourists will visit Hawaii in 1970. That's more than the total resident population now.

By the year 2000 the beach frontage in the residential neighborhood where I live will be a long row of apartment hotels. Lazy Kaanapali Beach on the island of Maui, where I've bathed on a Sunday afternoon with hardly a dozen other swimmers in sight along the quarter-mile crescent of sand, will front a complete complex of chrome and glass tourist hotels, shops, restaurants, and bars. Long before this happens, the flying time between Honolulu and New York will be cut to little more than two hours. A Hawaiian vacation will be within the budgets of school teachers and garage mechanics and store clerks.

Honolulu will sprout factories and freeways and fine art. Workers will be processing frozen tropical foods that a Kansas City hostess will be able to serve two nights later at a dinner party. Hawaiian orchid leis will be on display in Dallas flower shops. Honolulu's professional baseball team will be playing Seattle or Minneapolis or New Orleans.

All of these things belong to the new era that began officially when Hawaii became America's fiftieth state. And something else belongs, too, which is more important. It's expressed in Island population statistics like this:

Japanese	32%
Caucasian	30%
Hawaiian and part Hawaiian	17%
Filipino	11%
Chinese	6%
Others	4%

Let me give you an example of what these figures can mean in a world torn by communism and Little Rock:

It was halfway between downtown Honolulu and Waikiki in a severely modern office, furnished by two contour chairs, a cabinet, a blueprint table, and a mahogany desk, that I met K. D. Park, a structural engineer. His income: about $30,000 a year. He is a small man as are many Orientals, with a bland, school teacher's face and the precise mind of a mathematician. His desk top was completely bare.

Engineer Park's father was a Methodist minister from Korea who came to Hawaii in order to have an opportunity to educate his children in American schools. From the beginning, the preacher's son knew he wanted to become an engineer. He worked his way through high school and the University of Hawaii as a pineapple cannery laborer in the summer and a public library helper in the winter.

Armed with a bachelor's degree, he went into partnership with a young Chinese named Alfred Yee. Gradually they expanded until they now head a staff of eighteen engineers whose names read like a United Nations roll call. But Park was not completely satisfied with his success.

"My father used to tell us over and over, learn, learn, learn all you can. Then go back and help teach those in your homeland who have not had your opportunities."

At last, in 1953, engineer Park decided it was time to pay his debt. He was fifty-three years old. It had been a long time since he'd gone through engineering school. So he enrolled at the Massachusetts Institute of Technology to learn the latest techniques before setting out for Korea to teach.

He spent two years at MIT earning his master's degree. Then he went to Korea, where he took a job teaching engineering at Yonsei University in Seoul, the capital.

"I didn't take my pay," he told me. "It would have come to about $75 a month in American money. This seemed to me a bit ridiculous for a man drawing $2,500 a month from his firm."

When not teaching, he said, he tried to act as an unofficial liaison man between the Americans in Korea and the local officials. He said he found that most of the Americans lived apart and very few spoke Korean. Park, who lived with a Korean family, had the unique position of being accepted by both sides.

"Most of the Korean officials spoke some English," he said, "so the language barrier was not as serious as it is in some Asian countries. But there were constant misunderstandings because the Koreans didn't know the idioms in English. They would use the wrong words.

"I remember once when an American army officer was to lecture before a group of Koreans. A Korean was in charge of rounding up the audience. As it turned out, very few people came.

"After the lecture, the Korean told the American with some heat, 'The meeting was shameful!' The American answered, 'I don't give a damn!' They both went away angry.

"What the Korean had meant to say was, 'I am ashamed the meeting was so poorly attended.' What the American had meant to say was, 'It doesn't bother me.' When I explained this to them they were very relieved and became friends again.

"This little experience in itself is unimportant. But when you multiply it again and again in countries all over Asia wherever Americans must deal with local officials, it is easy to see how relations can become strained.

"It is in this field that Hawaii can help. We have a tremendous reservoir of American Asians in Hawaii who would be accepted completely in Asia. The reservoir includes experts in any field— agriculture, engineering, social studies, medicine, teaching. These people should be tapped for jobs in foreign aid programs. What's wrong with our State Department using more of Hawaii's young men in the consular service?"

"All of this makes a lot of sense to me," I said. "Would you accept if you were appointed American ambassador to Korea?"

For the first time engineer Park was speechless. Obviously the idea had never once entered his head. He thought a long time before answering.

At last he said slowly, "I would be highly honored to serve my country in this way. But, of course, it could never happen."

That conversation took place about a year before Hawaii became a state. At that time I knew dozens of men like Park, and there must have been hundreds more, who were making friends for the United States in Asia without fanfare or reward. But, like so many of us in Hawaii, I had gradually grown discouraged about the possibility that this potential would ever be put to better use.

No matter how you looked at it, Hawaii just didn't seem important to the rest of the nation. And there wasn't anything we could do about it. We didn't even have a congressman to write to!

At that time, Hawaii had been waiting sixty-one years for statehood. Thousands of pages of reports had been filed by junketing congressional committees. In every session of Congress since 1949 a Hawaiian statehood bill had been introduced. Each time, in Hawaii, our hopes rose. And each time, when the bill failed, our hopes fell to a new low.

Some blamed it upon communism in our labor unions. Some said it was because Hawaii is too far from the rest of the United States. But the most powerful reason the statehood bill failed time after time, we all knew, was because over two-thirds of Hawaii's population is Oriental.

"You want to see a Japanese in Congress?"

That was the real reason we weren't a state!

Then, at 10:04 A.M. on March 12, 1959, this suddenly changed. I acquired the right once more to help decide how the government should spend the federal income taxes I paid every year and to complain about our foreign policy, even if I was wrong, and *make* somebody in Washington listen.

I knew that, in the next Presidential election, the candidates for the most important post in the world would be making speeches to seek approval from me, Bob Krauss, 4744 Kahala Avenue, Honolulu, Hawaii. This is a very giddy feeling.

Apparently the other voters in Hawaii felt just as giddy about it as I did. The first state election produced the wildest, free-swinging, ding-dong political rodeo the Islands have ever seen. Governor William F. Quinn's backers dressed in VOTE FOR QUINN muumuus and aloha shirts. Supporters of his opponent, Delegate John

A. Burns, wore VOTE FOR BURNS earrings. One candidate put bumper stickers on his surfboard. There was an avalanche of buttons, pencils, posters, pennants, and VOTE FOR ME neckties. Advertising revenue for Honolulu television stations almost doubled as candidates lined up in front of the cameras.

To wind up the campaign, the Democrats put on an Extravaganza at Ala Moana Park. They offered a free vacation in Kauai as a door prize and put together a program featuring the Royal Hawaiian Band, Tahitian belly dancers, a water skiing demonstration, and a fireworks display plus 10,000 free balloons for the kiddies.

The Republicans countered with a Cavalcade at the Waikiki Shell. They gave away a new car and offered a star-studded program including the talents of top recording artist Martin Denny, a Marine drum-and-bugle corps, and a Dixieland band. They wound it up with 40 solid minutes of fireworks and released 1,000 balloons into the air.

(This put them about 1,000 balloons ahead of the Democrats because the GOP had already given away 10,000 balloons at the State Fair several weeks before.)

By the time the campaign was over, the candidates were gray with exhaustion and, in some cases, serious campaign issues were obscured. But nothing could obscure the fact that for the first time Hawaii was electing a governor, its first two U.S. senators, and its first U.S. representative. Ninety-three per cent of Hawaii's registered voters went to the polls that day.

My most precious memory of that campaign is a heart-to-heart talk I had with U.S. House Candidate Daniel K. Inouye seven hours before the polls opened. It was midnight. Inouye had just come home from an eleventh-hour TV appeal. For him two solid months of handshaking, stump speaking, coffee hours, political rallies, and TV appearances were finally over.

Midnight is an unusual time for an interview. But I was convinced that Dan Inouye, attorney, age thirty-five, was about to become the first American of Japanese ancestry to hold a national political office. By midnight the next day, he would be the first Japanese in Congress!

I wanted to talk to him so that I could pinch myself and make sure this wonderful thing was really happening.

We sat in a living room tastefully done in Japanese modern décor. Over the buffet table hung a silk-screen painting. Half of one wall was sliding doors which led onto a shaded lanai. Past that was the garden enclosed by a hedge. It was all designed to bring the gentle climate of Hawaii's outdoors into the lives of the people in the house.

Dan sprawled on the sofa and loosened his tie. I watched as he fumbled with one hand for a cigarette. He did this by tucking the package under the stump of one arm and drawing out a cigarette with the other. Then, still with one hand, he opened a book of matches and doubled over the paper stick of one match, struck it neatly with his thumb, and lit his cigarette.

Inouye has only one arm because the other was shattered by a rifle grenade in Italy during the Po Valley campaign of April 1945 in World War II as he was leading his platoon of Hawaii Nisei in the destruction of a German observation post. During the action Inouye was shot in the stomach while wiping out a machine-gun nest. Despite his injuries, he refused evacuation and directed the final assault that carried the ridge. He mustered out as a captain in the 442nd Regimental Combat Team with a Distinguished Service Cross and fourteen other decorations for heroism in action. He was the youngest officer in his outfit.

Back home in Hawaii, Inouye attended the University of Hawaii under the GI Bill, then got his law degree from George Washington University in Washington, D.C. He quickly jumped into politics and at age thirty-five, when statehood arrived for Hawaii, he was already a veteran of both houses of the territorial legislature.

I said, "Dan, the chances are good that you'll be elected tomorrow. How do you feel about going to Washington?"

"I'm scared," he answered. "It's such a tremendous thing that's happening. You just can't have any idea how remote this would have seemed to me ten years ago. Or to any of the kids I grew up with.

"What's just as amazing is the concern of people about this election all over the nation. Last February a syndicated series of three articles about this campaign ran in newspapers around the country. Since then, I've received almost 500 letters from people I didn't know and have never heard of. They all wish me good luck. Some have even sent campaign contributions. And only ten of those letters came from other Nisei.

"One woman from Little Rock, Arkansas, wrote, 'In addition to representing the people from Hawaii we hope you can represent us and the rest of the world in a search for the good will and harmony among races you have achieved in Hawaii. We are hungrily searching for your secret.'

"That's the sort of thing that scares me. I hope this message doesn't get lost in the great hubbub and practical maneuvering in Congress. So many times it boils down to just bread and butter and who gets the pork. I hope the message doesn't get lost because there *is* a contribution to be made. In a balance of power as precarious as the one we live under, one ounce of good will may tip the scales for peace.

"I have letters from Europe and Africa and Asia. I know the Japanese in Japan are concerned. One of the letters from Japan came from a class in a school in a little mountain village. The kids wrote that they had made it their class project to get me elected. To do this they were sending me symbols of good fortune.

"They explained that a little paper crane, the kind you fold and hang as an ornament, is good luck. One hundred paper cranes are very good luck and a thousand paper cranes are infallible good luck. With the letter came a box containing one thousand paper cranes. The kids had worked for three days folding them.

"I have been interviewed at least once a week during the campaign by Japanese newspaper reporters. One of them asked me what my family had been in Japan before they moved to Hawaii. I told him my family was of the farming class. He couldn't get over the fact that I, who may sit in the Congress of the United States, was neither of a wealthy nor samurai family. 'Your democracy must be wonderful,' he told me.

"Another Japanese reporter asked, 'Your opponent is a white man. Do you think you will win?' I told him I thought I would. He asked skeptically, 'Tell me honestly, do you really think so in your heart?' I said, 'In my heart I think I will win.' 'Then,' he said, 'you must have great racial understanding here.'

"All of this reminds me of the time I was in the Army hospital in Battle Creek, Michigan, after the war. I was raw and naive and my English was pidgin. But, for some reason, the other guys liked me. They made it a project to give me polish. One fellow had his mother send a complete setting of table silver so that I could practice which fork to use first. They all worked on my English. Another guy would take me, when we had passes, to a fancy restaurant and make me order the meal complete with wine so that I'd learn how. He kept telling me, 'Don't let the waiter push you around.' That was the hardest for me to learn of all.

"There were Negroes and Jews in the bunch and I was the one person who was accepted by everybody. I went on passes with all of them and visited a Negro's family in Chicago. Sometimes the other guys would try to exclude him or the Jewish fellows from the group. I discovered that I could stop it by refusing to go along unless everybody went. 'Okay,' I'd say, 'if Sam isn't going, I won't go either.' So they'd take Sam, too. Wouldn't it be great if Hawaii could play a role like that?"

The next day the voters of Hawaii elected Bill Quinn, an Irishman from St. Louis, as governor, and Jimmy Kealoha, a Hawaiian, as lieutenant governor. Elected as U.S. Senators were Hiram Fong, a Chinese, and Oren Ethelbert Long, a Kansas-born school teacher. Elected to the U.S. House of Representatives was Dan Inouye, Japanese.

That day I felt wonderful. Really! A new era had begun for Hawaii. You could feel it in the air. You could see it all around you. In people's faces. In the new construction going up. In the jets flying overhead. But most important of all you could see it in the roll call of the United States Congress.

There was something else, besides the new era for Hawaii, that made me feel good. That day I had a new and very personal reason for taking pride in my country. It's a wonderful feeling to have your faith in the processes of democracy justified—to know that the United States of America, in spite of mistakes and delay and endless argument, has once more done the right thing.

HAWAIIAN TRADITIONS
AND PLACES

THE FOLLOWING SELECTIONS, which deal with traditions and distinctive places, represent only a small part of the vast body of writings about Hawaii. These selections are intended only as a sample or an appetizer, to reveal a few special aspects of the Hawaiian experience. It is hoped that the inquisitive reader will be lured to go beyond these few fragments and explore Hawaii's literature on his own.

In the following pages, the reader may linger for a time with a Hawaiian legend; watch the hula through the eyes of a scholar (and realize that the hula was much more than an erotic dance); and savor the excitement of a Hawaiian *luau* (feast). In addition, the reader may jog along the bumpy road of Molokai's east end, past white-frame New England churches standing forlornly in *kiawe* groves, then find full reward in a swim in the secluded freshwater pool of Halawa Valley, one of Hawaii's most beautiful and least visited spots.

Understanding is a strange affair. For many, the inner life of Hawaii is in the myths of ancient times or the gestures of a hula dancer's hands, in the quietude of Halawa's pool, rather than in the great events which make up its formal history.

Padraic Colum

A HAWAIIAN MYTH

MYTH IS the heart of ancient tradition. Students of primitive peoples give much attention to myths, as one means of finding out about the inner life of an early society. Students of literature study them too and often discover both subtlety and charm. The casual reader, with less serious purposes, also finds myths rewarding, for the sufficient and simple reason that they entertain.

In 1923, the Hawaiian legislature invited Padraic Colum, a prominent Irish author and specialist in folklore, to study Hawaiian mythology. Colum agreed and produced two delightful books, so simply written that children as well as adults enjoy reading them. One of the myths, which follows, is entitled "How Kana Brought Back the Sun and Moon and Stars After They Had Been Taken Away." It appeared in Colum's *The Bright Islands,* published in 1925.

ONCE THE SUN and the Moon and the Stars were taken away; they were taken away by Ka-hoa-alii, and the people of the world would still be in cold and darkness if Kana and his brother Niheu had not gone to find them and bring them back.

You have been told about Kana, the youth who could stretch himself upwards until his body was as thin as the thread of a spider's web, and you have been told about Niheu, his brother, who carried a war-club so great that by resting one end of it in his canoe and putting the other end against a cliff he could walk from his canoe to the land, and you have been told about Uli, Kana's and Niheu's wise grandmother.

This story begins with Niheu. Once when he was crossing the Island of Hawaii he heard about Ka-hoa-alii's man and how he kept the people fishing and cooking for him; the people were pitying themselves and complaining when Niheu came amongst them.

Then Niheu saw Ka-hoa-alii's man, and he flung his club at him; the stroke of the great club knocked Ka-hoa-alii's man over. And after he had flung his club Niheu went on to his grandmother's house. He told her what he had done. She was made afraid, and she told him that trouble would come because of his mischief. "Go," she said, "and find your brother Kana, and bring him here to us, for we shall need his help."

But before he went Uli made him help her fix a long rope that she had. She took the rope and she tied it to the post of her house, and she brought the end of it down to the seashore, and she tied it to a great stone there. The people wondered, and Niheu wondered at what Uli did. Then Niheu went off to find his brother Kana.

Meanwhile Ka-hoa-alii had heard what Uli's grandson had done to his man. "I will punish Niheu for this, and I will punish all the people of Hawaii," he said. "Now I will take away the Sun and the Moon and the Stars from their sky. I will leave the people in cold and darkness; only where I am will there be warmth and light."

Niheu found his brother, and he started with him for their grandmother's house. While they were on their way the darkness came, for the Sun was taken out of the sky suddenly. But as they went on they struck against the rope that Uli had stretched from the post of her house to the stone on the seashore. Holding the rope, they came to the house. Kana did not go within, for no house was high enough to hold him. The two of them saw their grandmother seated by a blazing fire with lights all around her.

"So you have come," said their grandmother to them. "You are the only two in all the world that can bring the Sun and the Moon and the Stars back into our sky. Ka-hoa-alii has taken them away, and you must go to where Ka-hoa-alii is. Before I tell you what to do, do you, Kana, stretch yourself upwards, and see if there is any light in the sky."

Kana stretched himself upwards until his head was near the sky. He looked around, and he saw a little light in it. He brought himself down again, and he told his grandmother what he had seen.

Then said Uli: "You, Kana, and you, Niheu, will have to go to the country that Ka-hoa-alii rules over. Go straight towards the place that the Sun used to rise in. The fine rain will fall on you and the cold will get into your bones, but go on and on until you come to where an old woman sits at the bottom of a cliff. She is my sister; Luahine-kai-kapu she is named, and she is blind. Tell her that you are Uli's grandchildren, and she will direct you to the country that Ka-hoa-alii rules over."

So Kana and Niheu started off from their grandmother's house. They went in a straight line towards the place that the Sun used to rise in. As they went on the fine rain fell on them and the cold went into their bones. Kana took up Niheu and carried him on. But still the fine rain fell on them and still the cold crept into their bones. Then when they came to the place that is called Kaha-kae-kaea, Niheu lay down to die.

Kana left him wrapped in leaves under a loulu palm and went on. He came to where an old woman sat at the bottom of a cliff; she was blind, and he knew that she was Luahine-kai-kapu, his grandmother's sister.

"Whose child are you?" said Luahine-kai-kapu to Kana. "Your sister's, Uli's grandchild," said Kana. "What have you come for?" said she. "I have come to get the Sun and Moon and Stars that Ka-hoa-alii has taken from our sky; I am the only one who can bring them back. Show me the way to Ka-hoa-alii's country."

"I have no eyes," said Luahine-kai-kapu; "I cannot see to show you the way." "Lie down under this coco-nut tree," said Kana. Luahine-kai-kapu lay down. Kana picked off the young shoots of the coco-nut and called out to her, "Luahine-kai-kapu, turn your face towards the sky." She turned her face up as directed; Kana then threw the two young shoots at her eyes.

Then he struck her in the eyes, and she jumped up and cried out with a loud voice, "Oh, I am killed!" Kana then said to her, "Be quiet and rub your eyes." The old woman began rubbing her eyes. After she had done this she cried out that she was able to see as before.

"Before I send you into the country of Ka-hoa-alii, I shall have to do something to make your hands different," said Luahine-kai-kapu. She took ku-kui-nut and charcoal and she pounded them together and she made a paste. She rubbed the paste she had made on the great hands of Kana. "Now," said she, "you have hands like the hands of Ka-hoa-alii." Then she told him what to do when he came to the place where Ka-hoa-alii lived.

She set a fire before him to guide him, and she set a wind at his back to help him on. And helped on by the wind and guided by the fire, Kana came at last to the borders of Ka-hoa-alii's country. Then the fire died down, and he had no guide to go before him. But still the wind helped him on.

He came to the place where Ka-hoa-alii was. He hid and watched him. Ka-hoa-alii would lift up a great stone that covered a hole in the sky, and take food up in his hands, and feast with his attendants. And when they had feasted they would go into the house and play games. Thus Ka-hoa-alii and his attendants passed the day; they feasted and they played games, and they played games and they feasted.

Kana did what Luahine-kai-kapu told him to do. He watched all they did. When they had gone into the house he went to the great stone. He lifted it up. He propped it up with his feet. Then he put his two hands down into the hole.

Those below put things into his hands. They were things to eat. Kana flung them away, and put his hands down again. Those below put water into his hands. He emptied the water out. Kana put his hands down again. Those below put birds into his hands; he took them up and let them fly around; they were the birds that cry when darkness is going. Now as they flew around they cried, "Kia-wea, Kia-wea."

He put his hands down again. Now his hands were filled with Stars. He took them up and flung them into the sky. There they stayed—the stars that we still see. He lowered his hands again. The Moon was put into his hands. He put the Moon into the blue sky with the Stars, and it stayed there, giving light.

Kana put his hands down again. This time a single bird was put into his hands. He took it up and put it beside him. It was the crowing cock. He put his hands down once more; the warm Sun was put into his hands. He held the bright Sun up. He put it into the sky. The cock beside him crowed.

The cock crew, and Ka-hoa-alii, hearing it crow, came out of his house. He saw Kana standing there, and he saw the Sun shining in the sky. He went towards Kana to kill him, but he saw how tall and how strong Kana was, and he was afraid to touch him. And Kana, seeing that Ka-hoa-alii was afraid of him, demanded from him the Water of Life, the Water of Kane, so that he might restore his brother with it. Ka-hoa-alii gave him the Water of Kane.

Kana then went to Kaha-kae-kaea. His brother Niheu was there, wrapped in leaves under the loulu palm. He gave him the Water of Life, and life came back again to Niheu. Afterwards Ka-hoa-alii came to where they were. He gave them a canoe made out of white chicken feathers, and in that canoe Kana and Niheu returned to Hawaii. They went to their grandmother's house, and they saw the Sun in the heavens, and the Moon following the Sun, and the Stars with the Moon. And never again were these bright lights taken out of our sky.

Nathaniel B. Emerson

THE HULA

HAWAII, like other parts of Polynesia, evokes an image of sunshine, blue waves, white beaches, thick vegetation, and bright flowers. The waves boom, and the trees bend in the trade winds. Next to mind flashes the image of a graceful girl with long hair and dark eyes, swinging her grass skirt from side to side to the sound of hula drums. Here is apparently the perfect erotic prelude.

This image has much truth. But much more than sex was involved in the hula. According to Dr. Nathaniel Emerson, a foremost expert on Hawaiian lore, the hula was the ancient Hawaiian counterpart of concert hall, opera, and theater, a main means of social pleasure, and an important way to preserve the nation's cherished traditions.

Dr. Emerson's scholarly and somewhat technical account of the hula, which follows, was first published in 1909 by the Smithsonian Institution in a book entitled *Unwritten Literature of Hawaii.*

G ESTURE IS A voiceless speech, a shorthand dramatic picture. The Hawaiians were adepts in this sort of art. Hand and foot, face and eye, and those convolutions of gray matter which are linked to the organs of speech, all worked in such harmony that, when the man spoke, he spoke not alone with his vocal organs, but all over, from head to foot, every part adding its emphasis to the utterance. Von Moltke could be reticent in six languages; the Hawaiian found it impossible to be reticent in one.

The hands of the hula dancer are ever going out in gesture, her body swaying and pivoting itself in attitudes of expression. Her whole physique is a living and moving picture of feeling, sentiment, and passion. If the range of thought is not always deep or high, it is not the fault of her art, but the limitations of her original endowment, limitations of hereditary environment, the universal limitations imposed on the translation from spirit into matter.

The art of gestures was one of the most important branches taught by the ƙumu (teacher). When the hula expert, the *olohe,* who has entered the *halau* (school) as a visitor, utters the prayer, "O Laka, give grace to the feet of Pohaku, and to her bracelets and anklets; give comeliness to the figure and skirt of Luukia. To each one give gesture and voice. O Laka, make beautiful the *lei;* inspire the dancers to stand before the assembly," his meaning was clear and unmistakable, and showed his high valuation of this method of expression. We are not, however, to suppose that the ƙumu-hula, whatever his artistic attainments, followed any set of formulated doctrines in his teaching. His science was implicit, unformulated, still enfolded in the silence of unconsciousness, wrapped like a babe in its mother's womb. To apply a scientific name to his method, it might be called inductive, for he led his pupils along the plain

road of practical illustration, adding example, without the con-
fusing aid of preliminary rule or abstract proposition, until his
pupils had traveled over the whole ground covered by his own
experience.

Each teacher went according to the light that was in him, not
forgetting the instructions of his own *kumu,* but using them as a
starting point, a basis on which to build as best he knew. There
were no books, no manuals of instruction, to pass from hand to hand
and thus secure uniformity of instruction. Then, again, it was a long
journey from Hawaii to Kauai, or even from one island to another.
The different islands, as a rule, were not harnessed to one another
under the same political yoke; even districts of the same island
were not infrequently under the independent sway of warring
chiefs; so that for long periods the separation, even the isolation, in
matters of dramatic art and practice was as complete as in politics.

The method pursued by the *kumu* may be summarized as follows:
Having labored to fix the song, the *mele* or *oli,* in the minds of his
pupils, the *haumana,* he appointed some one to recite the words of
the piece, while the class, standing with close attention to the motions of the *kumu* and with ears open at the same time to the words
of the leader, were required to repeat the *kumu's* gestures in pan-
tomime until he judged them to have arrived at a sufficient degree
of perfection. That done, the class took up the double task of recita-
tion joined to that of gesture. In his attempt to translate his concepts
into physical signs the Hawaiian was favored not only by his vivid
power of imagination, but by his implicit philosophy, for the
Hawaiian looked at things from a physical plane—a safe ground to
stand upon—albeit he had glimpses at times far into the depths of
either. When he talked about spirit, he still had in mind a form
of matter. A god was to him but an amplified human being.

It is not the purpose to attempt a scientific classification of gesture as displayed in the *halau.* The most that can be done will be
to give a few familiar generic illustrations which are typical and
representative of a large class.

The *pali,* the precipice, stands for any difficulty or obstacle of
magnitude. The Hawaiian represents this in his dramatic, pictorial
manner with the hand vertically posed on the outstretched arm, the
palm of the hand looking away. If it is desired to represent this wall
of obstacle as being surmounted, the hand is pushed forward, and at
the same time somewhat inclined, perhaps, from its rigid per-

pendicularity, the action being accompanied by a series of slight lifting or waving movements as of climbing.

Another way of dramatically picturing this same concept, that of the *pali* as a wall of obstacle, is by holding the forearm and hand vertically posed with the palmar aspect facing the speaker. This method of expression, while perhaps bolder and more graphic than that before mentioned, seems more purely oratorical and less graceful, less subtly pictorial and elegant than the one previously described, and therefore less adapted to the hula. For it must be borne in mind that the hula demanded the subordination of strength to grace and elegance. We may at the same time be sure that the *halau* showed individuality in its choice of methods, that it varied its technique and manner of expression at different times and places, according to the different conception of one or another *kumu*.

Progression, as in walking or traveling, is represented by means of a forward undulatory movement of the outstretched arm and hand, palm downward, in a horizontal plane. This gesture is rhythmic and beautifully pictorial. If the other hand also is made a partner in the gesture, the significance would seem to be extended, making it include, perhaps, a larger number in the traveling company. The mere extension of the arm, the back-hand advanced, would serve the purpose of indicating removal, travel, but in a manner less gracious and caressing.

To represent an open level space, as of a sand-beach or of the earth-plain, the Hawaiian very naturally extended his arms and open hands—palms downward, of course—the degree of his reaching effort being in a sense a measure of the scope intended.

To represent the act of covering or protecting oneself with clothing, the Hawaiian placed the hollow of each hand over the opposite shoulder with a sort of hugging action. But here, again, one can lay down no hard and fast rule. There was differentiation; the pictorial action might well vary according to the actor's conception of the three or more generic forms that constituted the varieties of Hawaiian dress, which were the *mâlo* of the man, the *pau-u* of the woman, and the decent *kihei,* a togalike robe, which, like the blanket of the North American Indian, was common to both sexes. Still another gesture, a sweeping of the hands from the shoulder down toward the ground, would be used to indicate that costly feather robe, the *ahuula,* which was the regalia and prerogative of kings and chiefs.

The Hawaiian places his hands, palms up, edge to edge, so that the little finger of one hand touches its fellow of the other hand. By this action he means union or similarity. He turns one palm down, so that the little finger and thumb of opposite hands touch each other. The significance of the action is now wholly reversed; he now means disunion, contrariety.

To indicate death, the death of a person, the finger-tips, placed in apposition, are drawn away from each other with a sweeping gesture and at the same time lowered till the palms face the ground. In this case also we find diversity. One old man, well acquainted with hula matters, being asked to signify in pantomimic fashion "the king is sick," went through the following motions: He first pointed upward, to indicate the heaven-born one, the king; then he brought his hands to his body and threw his face into a painful grimace. To indicate the death of the king he threw his hands upward toward the sky, as if to signify a removal by flight. He admitted the accuracy of the gesture, previously described, in which the hands are moved toward the ground.

There are, of course, imitative and mimetic gestures galore, as of paddling, swimming, diving, angling, and the like, which one sees every day of his life and which are to be regarded as parts of that universal shorthand vocabulary of unvocalized speech that is used the world over from Naples to Honolulu, rather than stage-conventions of the *halau*. It will suffice to mention one motion or gesture of this sort which the author has seen used with dramatic effect. An old man was describing the action of Hiiaka (the little sister of Pele) while clearing a passage for herself and her female companion with a great slaughter of the reptilian demon-horde of *mo'o* that came out in swarms to oppose the progress of the goddess through their territory while she was on her way to fetch Prince Lohiau. The goddess, a delicate piece of humanity in her real self, made short work of the little devils who covered the earth and filled the air. Seizing one after another, she bit its life out, or swallowed it as if it had been a shrimp. The old man represented the action most vividly: pressing his thumb, forefinger, and middle finger into a cone, he brought them quickly to his mouth, while he snapped his jaws together like a dog seizing a morsel, an action that pictured the story better than any words.

It might seem at first blush that facial expression, important as it is, owing to its short range of effectiveness, should hardly be put in the same category with what may be called the major stage-gestures that were in vogue in the *halau*. But such a judgment would certainly be mistaken. The Greek use of masks on the stage for their "carrying power" testified to their valuation of the countenance as a semaphore of emotion; at the same time their resort to this artifice was an implicit recognition of the desirability of bringing the window of the soul nearer to the audience. The Hawaiians, though they made no use of masks in the *halau*, valued facial expression no less than the Greeks. The means for the study of this division of the subject, from the nature of the case, is somewhat restricted and the pursuit of illustrations makes it necessary to go outside of the *halau*.

The Hawaiian language was one of hospitality and invitation. The expression *mai*, or *komo mai*, this way, or come in, was the most common of salutations. The Hawaiian sat down to meat before an open door; he ate his food in the sight of all men, and it was only one who dared being denounced as a churl who would fail to invite with word and gesture the passer-by to come in and share with him. This gesture might be a sweeping, downward, or sidewise motion of the hand in which the palm faced and drew toward the speaker. This seems to have been the usual form when the two parties were near to each other; if they were separated by any considerable distance, the fingers would perhaps more likely be turned upward, thus making the signal more distinctly visible and at the same time more emphatic.

In the expression of unvoiced assent and dissent the Hawaiian practised refinements that went beyond our ordinary conventions. To give assent he did not find it necessary so much as to nod the head; a lifting of the eyebrows sufficed. On the other hand, the expression of dissent was no less simple as well as decisive, being attained by a mere grimace of the nose. This manner of indicating dissent was not, perhaps, without some admixture of disdain or even scorn; but that feeling, if predominant, would call for a re-enforcement of the gesture by some additional token, such as a pouting of the lips accompanied by an upward toss of the chin. A more impersonal and coldly businesslike way of manifesting a negative was by an outward sweep of the hand, the back of the hand being turned to the applicant. Such a gesture, when addressed to a huckster or a beggar—a rare bird, by the way, in old Hawaii—was accepted as final.

There was another method of signifying a most emphatic, even contemptuous, no. In this the tongue is protruded and allowed to hang down flat and wide like the flaming banner of a panting hound. A friend states that the Maoris made great use of gestures with the tongue in their dances, especially in the war-dance, sometimes letting it hang down broad, flat, and long, directly in front, sometimes curving it to right or left, and sometimes stuffing it into the hollow of the cheek and puffing out one side of the face. This manner—these methods it might be said—of facial expression, so far as observed and so far as can be learned, were chiefly of feminine practice. The very last gesture—that of the protruded tongue—is not mentioned as one likely to be employed on the stage in the *halau,* certainly not in the performance of what one would call the serious hulas. But it might well have been employed in the *hula ḳi'i* [with puppets], which was devoted . . . to the portrayal of the lighter and more comic aspects of daily life.

It is somewhat difficult to interpret the meaning of the various attitudes and movements of the feet and legs. Their remoteness from the centers of emotional control, their detachment from the vortices of excitement, and their seeming restriction to mechanical functions make them seem but slightly sympathetic with those tides of emotion that speed through the vital parts of the frame. But, though somewhat aloof from, they are still under the dominion of, the same emotional laws that govern the more central parts.

> Man is all sympathy one part with another;
> For head with heart hath joyful amity,
> And both with moon and tides.

The illustrations brought to illuminate this division of the subject will necessarily be of the most general application and will seem to belong rather to the domain of oratory than to that of dramatic or stage expression, by which is meant expression fitted for the purposes of the *halau.*

To begin with a general proposition, the attitude of the feet and legs must be sympathetic with that of the other parts of the body. When standing squarely on both feet and looking directly forward, the action may be called noncommittal, general; but if the address is specialized and directed to a part of the audience, or if attention is called to some particular region, the face will naturally turn in that direction. To attain this end, while the leg and arm of the corresponding side will be drawn back, the leg and arm of the opposite side will be advanced, thus causing the speaker to face the point of address. If the speaker or the actor addresses himself, then, to persons, or to an object, on his right, the left leg will be the one more in advance and the left arm will be the one on which the burden of gesture will fall, and vice versa.

It would be a mistake to suppose that every motion or gesture displayed by the actors on the stage of the *halau* was significant of a purpose. To do that would be to ascribe to them a flawless perfection and strength that no body of artists have ever attained. Many of their gestures, like the rhetoric of a popular orator, were mere flourishes and ornaments. With a language so full of seemingly superfluous parts it could not well be otherwise than that their rhetoric of gesture should be overloaded with flourishes.

The whole subject of gesture, including facial expression, is worthy of profound study, for it is linked to the basic elements of psychology. The illustrations adduced touch only the skirts of the subject; but they must suffice. An exhaustive analysis, the author believes, would show an intimate and causal relation between these facial expressions and the muscular movements that are the necessary accompaniments or resultants of actual speech. To illustrate, the pronunciation of the Hawaiian word *ae* (pronounced like our "aye"), meaning "yes," involves the opening of the mouth to its full extent; and this action, when accomplished, results in a sympathetic lifting of the eyebrows. It is this ultimate and completing part of the action which the Hawaiian woman adopts as her semaphore of assent.

One of the puzzling things about gesture comes when we try to think of it as a science rooted in psychology. It is then we discover variations presented by different peoples in different lands, which force us to the conviction that in only a part of its domain does it base itself on the strict principles of psychology. Gesture, like language, seems to be made up in good measure of an opportunist growth that springs up in answer to man's varying needs and conditions. The writer hopes he will not be charged with begging the question in suggesting that another element which we must reckon with as influential in fashioning and stereotyping gesture is tradition and convention. To illustrate—the actor who took the role of Lord Dundreary in the first performance of the play of the same name accidentally made a fantastic misstep while crossing the stage.

The audience was amused, and the actor, quick to avail himself of any open door, followed the lead thus hinted at. The result is that he won great applause and gave birth to a mannerism which has well-nigh become a stage-convention.

Peter Gilman

A HAWAIIAN LUAU

THE *luau* (feast) has a highly honored place in Hawaiian tradition. The core of the *luau* is *kalua* (roast) pig, cooked whole in *ti* leaves in the *imu* (underground oven). All the rest of the wonderful food takes second place to steaming chunks of tender pork, aromatic with the subtle *ti* flavor. So central is pork to the celebration that a standard way of proposing a *luau* is simply to say, "Let's put a pig in the *imu*." Almost invariably *luaus* take place out of doors. Guests crowd around the *imu* to watch the pig emerge, and then sit at long tables to devour it, along with the many other delicacies, hopefully with strong appetites and light hearts.

Some *luaus* are elaborate. Others are not. The editor recalls with particular delight a country-style *luau* given on Oahu on the "other" (that is, windward) side of the island in December, 1952. The main ingredients were pork, chicken, poi, whiskey, sunshine, and laughter. On this occasion, as geese darted among the guests, a huge Hawaiian politely refused a fourth helping of pork, because, so he explained, he had to go to a turkey dinner within the hour.

What follows is a description of food served at an elaborate *luau*, taken from Peter Gilman's novel *Diamond Head*. Gilman, a former newspaperman and Navy flier, has a particularly keen eye for local color.

W HEN THE SAND was dug away from the imu and they cut away the canvas, smoke wooshed through the night carrying the sweet roasting scent of the meat. The banana leaves and ti leaves were scorched black and the skins of the pigs were steamed a crispy sizzling brown. Each pig was hoisted on to a papapuaa, a huge koa wood platter. . . .

The table was covered with tapa cloth and layers of fern and ti leaves. Jacaranda and shell ginger vines laced about the table. Floral displays of orchid and plumeria sprays wound about bird-of-paradise were spaced at intervals along the table. At each setting was a red hibiscus, the official flower of Hawaii.

The center of the table was piled with fruit: tender, milk-filled coconuts, sweet-meated papayas, avocados from Hana Maui, malala peels of raw sugar cane, slices of watermelon, Isabella grapes bunched in high glassy clusters, mangoes, alligator pears, juicy rose-colored guavas, wild bananas and halakahiki—standing pineapples which appeared whole and uncut but which had been hollowed, corded and cut into long spears and reassembled with the top as a lid. Long slivers of wood had been stuck into the tops of the pine-apples, and on these were speared the pupu—Hawaiian hors d'oeuvres—including succulent pieces of marinated Tera-yaki steak, raw mullet cut in tempting cubes and dusted with paakai salt, chunks of tiny parboiled lobsters fresh out of Kalama Bay, small alemihi crabs with their shells pierced so that the sweet meat could be filled with coconut pudding.

While the men quartered and sliced the three pigs, the young girls brought to the table big calabash bowls of jumbo shrimp, sushi, and saimin, and relish bowls of ake raw liver mixed with chili peppers, kukui nuts crushed and baked with paakai salt, and limu, strips of dried kelp and opihi seaweed. On koa wood platters the girls brought marinated slices of moray eel, and pinkish tidbits of barbecued squid tentacles, and stewed fern stalks served hot and covered with a melted butter and honey sauce and tasting something like asparagus. Coconut half shells filled with Chinese crackseed and roasted macadamia nuts supplanted the pupu. For liquid re-freshment there was pineapple juice, chilled and poured into hol-lowed husks, guava juice, coconut milk straight from the shell, and beer, whisky, okolehao, and Mai Tai, a heady mixture of rums sipped with straws from pineapple husks.

As the pupu was being devoured, the girls brought in platters of lomilomi—fresh raw king salmon mixed with chopped onions and tomatoes and minced with the fingers; moa—tender white meat of chicken mixed with the Hawaiian spinach called taro roots and coconut cream and served in coconut half shells; boned chicken baked in coconut shells with wild rice and pineapple and served in koa wood calabashes floated with mint-flavored spun sugar; bread-fruit roasted over kiawe coals so a crust formed about the succulent inner meat; thick rare slices of pipioma roast beef; heikaukau rock crab with tartar sauce sprinkled with paakai salt, and the all-inclusive welakaukau Hawaiian hot stew.

There was fried butterfish with garlic sauce, i-a paakai salt fish, uahi smoked fish, maloo dried fish, slabs of the wonderfully fresh ahi tuna, boneless chunks of ono which is something like swordfish but tastier, kawelea fish, barracuda, barbecued black sea bass, and finally, as it was taken from the imu and the scorched leaves unwrapped from it, the sizzling lime-white mahimahi dolphin, the most glorious-tasting fish in the sea.

It took six men to carry the three platters of puaa kalua pigs to the table, the meat still steaming, the pink-scrubbed skin turned a crispy brown, the platters surrounded by the yams and wild bananas that had been cooked with the meat for the last five hours in the underground oven.

At every place there was a large goblet carved from a coconut shell that had been thinned and polished and scalloped around the brim, and in the goblet was a quart of that most mystifying of food, the mainstay of the Hawaiian luau—poi.

Constance F. Gordon-Cumming

THE VOLCANOES

VISITORS TO Hawaii, among them Mark Twain and Henry Adams, invariably went to see the two active volcanoes, Mauna Loa and Kilauea, on the island of Hawaii. Visitors to Hawaii still do, especially during an eruption. Writers about Hawaii tried to outdo one another in their descriptions of the volcanoes, much as the missionaries unconsciously vied with one another in describing their dangerous passage around Cape Horn and the hardships of the first years ashore. The Hawaiian Islands are volcanic in origin, and the island of Hawaii is still in process of formation. Many famous landmarks on other islands, such as Diamond Head facing Waikiki Beach, are extinct volcanoes.

The following description of Kilauea was written in 1879 by a British authoress, Constance Frederica Gordon-Cumming, sister of the famous lion hunter and a celebrated world traveler in her own right. She was so fascinated by the volcanoes that she entitled her two-volume work *Fire Fountains: The Kingdom of Hawaii, Its Volcanoes and the History of Its Missions,* from which extracts are reprinted here. The Roback mentioned was, as she explained elsewhere, a "German guide . . . once a sailor, now the owner of a handsome, active Hawaiian wife, with a pretty child." It is possible that Roback exaggerated in describing the Lake of Fire to his impressionable and somewhat naïve employer.

VOLCANO HOUSE, KILAUEA
October 29th 1879

DEAR NELL,—I know you will be relieved to learn that I have returned in safety from the Mouth of the Pit. Truth to say, the reality proved very different from my ideal; and I fear I must confess to some disappointment.

However, I'll tell you all about it in detail.

This morning I made an early start alone with Roback, who carried my sketching-gear and a canteen of drinking-water, for we were bound on a thirsty errand. The first part of the descent was pleasant enough, and clothed with pretty vegetation, chiefly consisting of stunted *ohias* with their feathery crimson blossom, various kinds of fern, a very ornamental silver-grass, quantities of *ohelos* (the flame-coloured whortleberry, sacred in old mythology), and several plants with brilliantly blue berries. Above us, in deep shadow, lay the crag from which we were descending, and before us the great grey lava-bed, formed by countless successive overflows. Its general appearance is that of a billowy ocean, suddenly fossilised, but each several wave has taken a distinct form. . . .

I have already explained to you that, as seen from above, the bed of the outer crater resembles a dark bluish-grey lake, being apparently a level surface. But on a nearer approach, we found it to be a bed of extremely irregular black lava contorted into all manner of forms, such as huge coils of rope, folds of rich black satin drapery, waves of glistening black glass forming a thin iridescent coating to a sort of bubbly red lava.

And here and there the lava had flowed over ridges so steep, that in cooling it had assumed the appearance of a perfectly petrified waterfall. We saw plainly where successive lava-flows overlapped one another—the currents, after flowing in opposite directions, showing where the fires had found temporary vent by some newly formed lake or chimney.

We climbed up and down over undulations which on ordinary ground would be accounted little hills—lava-waves whose crests rose perhaps a hundred feet or more above the general level. A smoothly wrinkled expanse is crossed by a stream of blackest angular blocks, tumbled together anyhow—a chopping sea petrified.

In many places large lava-bubbles blister the surface of the smooth lava. They look like thin bottle-glass, and appear as if blown by escaping gases. Everywhere the lava-crust cracks crisply under foot, breaking into sharp fragments.

Here and there yawn deep splits and fissures. Some are mere narrow cracks, scarcely to be observed but for an occasional puff of white steam. Others are broader, and horribly suggestive, for a hot breath of poisonous sulphurous fumes rises thence, half choking one, and acts as a mirage, making the air tremulous, so that everything around seems to quiver. Through some of these cracks fresh lava has oozed out, and lies in black glossy rolls, as if the old flow were seamed with pitch.

On one high ridge, which seemed to have stood as an island during the more recent flows, the lava had begun to disintegrate, and already a few delicate ferns had—as if by a living instinct—found their way thither, and nestled in this rude cradle, their tender green contrasting strangely with their surroundings. I gathered a few fronds as memorials of the day; and as I looked on this earliest effort of vegetation in the great desert around, I bethought me of such mysterious spots as those strange pits in the Australian Blue Mountains, where, in a deep sunken abyss, untrodden by foot of man, tall tree-ferns and all their beautiful kindred reign undisturbed—and I wondered whether, in some far-back time, those cups into which we now look down on the fern-crowns far below us, were dreary and bare as Kilauea.

At one place we came to what seemed like a pertified waterfall, where a lava-stream had poured over a cliff when almost exhausted, and had quickly cooled, retaining all its distinctive curves and forms. Even the individual particles of spray lay tossed about like congealed rain-drops. It was a most curious and beautiful sight.

Sometimes, as we toiled along, the thin crust of fibrous lava gave way beneath our feet, and we landed in hollows below, at no great depth. These brittle places seem to be surface bubbles or tubes which have contracted in cooling, and they never let us in more than knee-deep. But of course, every such plunge was a startling reminder of what we might do should we chance to sink through a fissure, and made me more ready to obey my guide's injunction, and walk in his footsteps. Sometimes we crossed suspicious-looking tracts, which sounded hollow beneath our feet, and still more vividly suggested possible doom.

Over one steep bank the lava had flowed so gently that it hung in folds like rich drapery—you might have fancied a velvet curtain caught up for effect, in an artist's studio.

Below it lay what looked like many nests of snakes coiled up in intricate convolutions, as if boa-constrictors, and great pythons, and little rattle-snakes, and reptiles of every size, had here congregated.

Just beyond lay an almost level expanse of something which gleamed like a rainbow. As we approached it, the fairy-like play of prismatic colours was altogether dazzling; and on nearer inspection we found that it was produced by myriads of minute flakes of black glass, each iridescent, forming a perfect prism. The thin crust broke beneath our steps, and we perceived that the vitrified lava forming these miniature rainbows was but a scum formed on the surface of a reddish honeycomb—a substance resembling the refuse or slag of iron-works.

Then we came to smooth waves that were really like ocean billows; but beyond these lay a succession of great rollers that had in cooling been forced back, one over the other, so as to form ridges, suggesting huge coils of rope, all twisted and contorted—mighty hawsers laid in long lines ready for use; a likeness which is the more striking, inasmuch as each several rope is seamed with innumerable cracks, leaving raised lines exactly like the twisted strands of hemp—an impression further conveyed by the filaments of stringy brown lava, like spun glass, which lie scattered here and there, having been caught by the wind (when thrown up) in midair in a state of perfect fusion, forming fine lava-drops—a rain of liquid rock, and so drawn out in slender threads, like fine silky hair.

In fact, this filmy, finely-spun glass is known as Pélé's hair—*Rauoho* [*Lauoho*] *o Pélé*. It is of a rich olive-green or yellowish-brown colour—a hint for aesthetic fashions!—and is glossy, like the byssus of certain shells, but very brittle to handle. Sometimes when the great fire fountains toss their spray so high that it flies above the level of the cliffs, the breeze catches it sportively, and carries it far away over the island; and the birds line their nests with this silky volcanic hair. Sometimes you can collect handfuls, clinging to the rocks to which it has drifted, generally with a pear-shaped drop still attached to it. . . .

After traversing three miles of this strangely varied lava-bed, we reached the base of that inner circle of crags which, within the last few months, have been thrown up all round the central crater—*i.e.,* the Halemaumau. So rapidly have they been upheaved, that they now form a ring 600 feet in height; and up this steep ascent we had to climb in order to look into the Lake of Fire.

It was a toilsome ascent, over very brittle lava; but Roback kept cheering me by telling me what a grand sight awaited me, and that he had never seen the lake in finer action than last week. So we climbed over coils of huge hollow vitreous lava-pipes, which constantly broke beneath our weight, and over ridges which looked eagerly for the much-described Lake of Fire.

There was none! at least nothing worth speaking of, in the first instance. I turned to look at my guide, and he stood staring in stupefied, bewildered amazement. He could not believe his own eyes. Only a few days had elapsed since he had led a party of Americans to the very spot where he now stood beside me, in speechless wonder at the change.

They had watched the blood-red waves dashing in scarlet spray against the cliffs on the farther side of the lake of molten fire, then rushing back to form a mad whirlpool in its centre, and thence, as if with a new impulse, flinging themselves headlong into a great cavern which undermined the lava-terrace just below the spot where I was now standing.

My guide pointed to this thin ledge with a shudder, telling me how, on that day, an enthusiastic American girl had been so carried away by the enthralling fascination of the scene, that, forgetting all prudence, she had, notwithstanding his entreaties, contrived to climb down to this very terrace, and thence gain an unimpeded view of the fiery breakers as they dashed with awful roar into the cavern below, and then surged back to meet new waves flowing from the centre, and thus meeting, to form ever-changing ridges and fountains of fire. It was a most frightful risk to run, for no one could foretell at what moment the undermining wave might break down the thin roof of the lava-bubble, and swallow up with it the rash and over-presumptuous human atoms.

Armine von Tempski

RANCHING ON MAUI

ONE OF THE many things that visitors seldom know and usually learn with surprise is that ranching has long been a major feature of Hawaii's life. Vancouver and others brought cattle to the Islands before the eighteenth century ended. Hawaii's cattle industry was well established before ranching became a central part of the life and lore of the American West on the mainland.

Many records exist of cattle raising in Hawaii. But no one has described it better than the Island novelist Armine von Tempski. Her grandfather was a Polish political exile who migrated to Australia. Her father came north to Hawaii, and settled on the island of Maui at the age of 18. She was born there, in 1899. In her autobiography, *Born in Paradise,* part of which follows, she describes her first cattle drive, a particularly dramatic one, when she was only five years old. The experience impressed her deeply. In recalling it, she managed to convey not only what happened but also a child's excitement at being, for a time, part of the mysterious adult world.

MOST OF THE STOCK raised on the ranch was slaughtered locally, but four or five times a year surplus steers were sent to Honolulu to be marketed. Shortly after my fifth birthday Daddy announced that I was old enough to go with him when the next shipment of beeves was made, and not until I went on this expedition did I realize that Daddy and the *paniolos* often risked their lives when they jogged out of my secure world every morning.

For days after I knew I was to go I spent most of my time leaving offerings before *akua* stones, praying to Christ, burning incense before Tatsu's image of Buddha, and lighting candles before the shrines of Portuguese saints to make certain that all the Great Forces would be solidly ranged about me to prevent any possible disaster which might interfere with my going.

The afternoon the steers were due to come down the mountain Makalii took me out to meet them. We spotted the cattle and riders swooping down a green hill. The Herefords reminded me of a swift red river foaming at its edges where their white legs and faces showed. The afternoon shook as they bellowed their fury and bewilderment at being driven from the high grasslands they knew. Makalii opened the gates into the holding pasture. Daddy galloped ahead of the herd, sitting his saddle in the straight-legged fashion of Hawaii—a beautiful, poised seat suggesting a winged centaur about to take flight and sail off into space. As he passed he brandished his coiled lasso and smiled. Owing to the steep pitch of the land it was impossible to prevent the wild mountain cattle from running. Daddy raced through the gates, maneuvering so the stock would not collide with the posts and bruise themselves.

When they were safely through, he pulled out of their way. They surged across the pasture, belly-deep in grass, slowed up, wheeled around, and collected in a tight knot facing the riders. Holomalia followed Daddy into the pasture and they conferred for a few moments. The rest of the men halted at the gates which Makalii was closing, slacked girths, and shook saddles to cool their horses' hot backs.

Wind scurried down from Haleakala; the sharp sweet whistle of plover sounded overhead. Across the green isthmus joining the two halves of the island, the West Maui mountains stood out distinctly, golden mists hanging in their deep valleys. A sort of elemental excitement, brewed by animals, wind, grass, and drifting clouds, flowed toward me. Makalii had trained my ears to hear the minute sounds of rocks, soil, and vegetation worked on by changes in the atmosphere, I could listen in the dark, and by the sound of the wind name the point of the compass from which it was blowing. I could sense the imperceptible change of one season sliding into the other: a sort of vast, muted rustle in earth, sky, and sea—an instant of altered vibrations, then a great peace, like a sigh, when the transition was completed. In a dim instinctive way I was conscious now of the majestic rhythm of Nature's machinery moving behind tangible objects and, reaching out, I grabbed Makalii's hand.

"What is it?" he asked in Hawaiian.

I looked at Haleakala, at the men and cattle, listened to the majestic dissonances of the Pacific. How could I express even to my old Makalii what I was feeling? But with the amazing intuition of his race he knew. Wrinkles gathered up the outer corners of his eyes.

"Today you feel like an *akua* walking on earth," he said, smiling.

I nodded. He had it exactly. In that moment, I felt immortal, I was a lesser god with a small niche in the huge swoop of living.

During the forty-eight hours while the steers were resting I greased my saddle incessantly. At last the time came to go. I was fed supper and put to bed at four as we were to leave at one in the morning. The trip to Makena was always started at night when traveling was cool and the wild steers were less likely to take fright and stampede at strange sights and sounds.

Gan, Mother, and Tatsu dressed me but I was impatient to be rid of them and go. When Dad came I grabbed his hand and we started for the kitchen. The *paniolos* who were going along were eating at one of the tables. Daddy and I sat down at another and I felt enveloped by lusty manhood. When breakfast was over Ah Sin put a package in my hand. "Open after you stop at Makena," he instructed me.

Tatsu bundled me into a sweater and pulled one of Dad's old hats on my head. Mother and Gan came onto the back veranda, where the spurs and lassos always hung, to see us off. The night wind brought the lonely bellowing of uneasy steers scenting changes ahead and the sound lent the dark an awesome quality. Makalii appeared, put a *lei* on my hat, then, forgetting I was no longer a baby, swung me onto his hip. The night smelled of adventure. Horses humped and shivered when girths were drawn tight. Riders mounted warily. Daddy led off at a swinging trot and Ah Sin waved his lantern in a parting salute.

We stopped at the corrals while one of the *paniolos* drove out Keitchi and Pivela, two wise old oxen, used to escort beef cattle to market. Starlight shimmered on their long horns as they set off, businesslike and cool, knowing exactly what they had to do. Hu and Eole unfastened another gate and extra horses, used only for shipping cattle, followed on the heels of the two oxen. When we got clear of the trees the hugeness of the sky burst upon us. Myriads of stars blazed overhead, some winking and sparkling, others sending down a strong steady light. Spurting matches inside cupped hands threw dark faces into brief relief and the fragrance of cigarette smoke drifted back over men's shoulders.

The bawling of the apprehensive steers grew louder. While Daddy and Holomalia went into the pasture to drive them out, the rest of us lined along the road to head them in the right direction. The two old oxen watched and when the beeves raced out of the gate, like a dark tossing river, they slid into the herd. After a few minutes the steers slowed down to a trot, then to a walk. We moved between wire fences that caught gleams of starlight, and if a steer tried to break through them Keitchi or Pivela dug him with their long horns.

After a while we went through another gate and began moving across open pastures. Men rode taut in their saddles, coiled lassos ready in their hands, watching every move of the cattle. *Wanaao,* the Ghost Dawn, stole into the sky. When it died down the darkness intensified. Stars enlarged to golden globes, faded to silver. In the direction of Kahoolawe, the Southern Cross burned above the dark sea.

We began working through cactus and *kiawe*-mesquite—covered wastes, and the fairy fragrance of *ilima* and *indigo* and warm animals filled our nostrils. A fresh chill breeze came out of the east and the pale morning sea girdled the islands with silver. Makalii pointed to a small rosy horseshoe of land lying in the channel between Maui and Kahoolawe. He told me the islet was Molokini, a cone that just got its head above water before the fires building it were extinguished.

The coast below us was covered with a dense growth of *kiawe* trees waving their lacy branches in the wind, and here and there cocoanut groves lifted their glittering green into the sunshine. A purple cone, like a boil, jutted into the sea at the southern end of Haleakala.

"That's Puuolai, the Hill of Earthquakes, where the last activity of the mountain took place," Daddy told me.

A little shiver ran over me. The cone looked so strong and violent that it seemed as if at any minute it might begin spouting lava again. I asked about a three-storied house, miles away, standing on the shore without any other buildings about it.

"That's Kalepolepo, an abandoned store built in the Fifties when the Pacific whaling fleet used to anchor each winter off Maui," Daddy said. "It's a strange old place with tall rooms looking onto the sea. In one of them upstairs is a magnificent piano and below on the shelves of the store you still find bolts of calico and other things which have lain there through the years."

The steers were following the lead-oxen down the rough lava trail, but, every so often, one of the big wild fellows would halt to look back at Haleakala. A gaunt sow, grunting ill-humoredly at her piglets, appeared suddenly out of the cactus and crossed the trail. Without warning the cattle stampeded. Most of them headed upward, making a last mad dash to regain their lost mountain pastures. The still morning echoed with shouts, curses, and the sharp reports of running hoofs striking against loose fragments of lava.

I tore after Makalii. Cactus pads slapped savagely at my bare legs; I ducked my head to escape thorny *kiawe* branches. My horse dodged about to avoid spiny *indigo* bushes. Several times I was almost unseated and had to grab at the pommel, hoping that everyone was too occupied to see. Dad shouted commands, men dashed here and there trying to head the stock off and turn them back to the sea.

A big roan steer with spreading horns tore clear of his massed comrades and streaked away, Hauki racing in pursuit. Because of the high growth of cactus, ropes were useless except in infrequent openings. When the big steer realized that the horse was overtaking it, it swerved and charged. Hauki wrenched his mount onto its hind legs. One horn grazed Hauki's stirrup but the impetus of the beast took it past. With a deft turn of his wrist, Hauki threw his lasso over his shoulder, wheeled around, flung his horse to its haunches and braced back. The steer reached the end of the rope, turned head-over-heels and lay still, the wind partially knocked out of it.

After a furious ten minutes the herd was collected, hot-eyed, panting, with cobwebs of foam drifting from their mouths. Keitchi and Pivela, the old oxen, who had waited in the trail during the uproar, circled disgustedly among the beeves, quieting them, while we sat in a ring waiting until the animals cooled off enough to push on to the sea.

Finally, the herd was put in motion and we picked up a faint road winding under tall cocoanut trees which moved forlornly in the light air coming off the dancing blue water. The bulk of Haleakala above and behind us cut off the cool Trade-wind. Horses' hides were dark with sweat, men mopped their hot faces. My cheeks burned, my ankles were raw, and one bare knee ached dully from a broken-off cactus spine buried in it.

Daddy led the steers into a big stone corral and they crowded and jostled to get at a long dripping water trough. When they were all inside the enclosure, the old oxen came out and drifted off through the grove while two of the *paniolos* lashed a stout gate across the entrance. The spare horses nipped at tufts of *pualeli—*

milkweed—growing at the bases of cocoanut trees and the morning seemed to exhale a sigh of relief and settle back into its peaceful warmness.

Paniolos unsaddled their horses, then went behind the stone wall to get out of their clothes and put on *malos*—breech-clouts. Makalii showed Dad the thorn in my knee and they knelt down to remove it. I shut my eyes. There was a sharp stab and it was out. Makalii took a small bottle of creolin out of his pocket, mixed it with water, and washed the small dark hole.

Eole, Pili, and Kahalewai were humping up long brown trunks, racing each other to reach clusters of green nuts hanging among feathery fronds. Eole got to the top of his tree first and shouted jibes at Pili and Kahalewai. Taking the knife out of his teeth he cut among the drooping leaves and great green nuts came bouncing down. The men on the ground ran to get them like big children on a lark. Makalii brought the finest one to Daddy and got the next best for me.

"Now you look close and I show you how to fix," he said, squatting on the ground. I edged up close. Turning the long green nut up in his hands so the end that grew on the tree faced the ground, he began bruising it against a stone until the fiber was pulverized. Bit by bit he stripped away the green outer covering, then went after the layers of tough white fibers underneath. When the last piece was off he began turning the nut around in his hand, striking it with short sharp taps on the stone, and suddenly the top cracked off like a neat cap.

"Drink," he said, placing the cool, fragrant chalice in my hands.

When I had all I could hold of the sweet fresh water, he broke the soft shell open and we scraped out the jello-like meat with our fingers.

The men fetched small canvas bags filled with salt meat and hard *poi* which, with the cocoanuts, make breakfast. Hauki saddled a fresh horse and went off to see if the steamer was in sight, and the rest of the men began working at a half-finished water trough. They uncovered concrete, mixing buckets, and some dynamite, stored under a tarpaulin.

"I'm going to blast out another well one of these days so there'll always be ample water for the cattle," Daddy told me.

I watched the men working and joking together but the warm

morning made me drowsy and, in spite of my best efforts, people and trees began getting dimmer and farther away. When Hauki rode in I woke up.

"No more steamer," he announced.

Daddy swore, then lighted his pipe. "Last time the blasted boat was two days late and the cattle lost weight. But since nothing can be done about it we might as well have some fun while we're waiting."

The *paniolos'* eyes met his gaily. Dad knew that when Hawaiians have worked hard for a while they want to lay off for some fun. Dad and Holomalia volunteered to watch the cattle while the rest of us went to spear fish and gather *opihis*—edible limpets—for supper.

We drifted along the beach curving toward the Hill of Earthquakes. Through leaning brown cocoanut trunks, waves with crests of emerald and azure crisped toward the shore, or tore their blue into white lace against rough out-juttings of lava. The day had a breathless beauty that made me feel as though I were standing on tiptoe inside. When we reached the base of the big, angry-looking red hill I kept close to Makalii. Its name was frightening and the deep restless Pacific swelling against black lava ledges and falling back from them with sucking noises whispered about eerie things. Small eels hurtled through the air from warm brackish pools among the rocks where they'd been basking, and vanished into the safety of deep water.

Pili got a spear and a long pole out of a crevice where he kept them and went on ahead to look for squid and *ulua*—cavalla fish. The other men began searching among the rocks. Some gathered *wana,* a species of sea-urchin, and Makalii broke a hole in the top of one of the brittle shells and showed me how to suck out the meat which tasted like salty marrow. Other *paniolos* were gathering *limu*—a flat reddish seaweed that crunched crisply and pleasantly between my teeth.

Makalii gave me his legging knife and showed me how to gather *opihis*. I'd eaten them at *luaus* but never had the fun of collecting them. Watching for ones that weren't clamped down tightly, he slid the knife under them and pried them off quickly. After a few tries I got the knack of it and scooped them from their shells, eating them as we drifted along the shore.

Pili beckoned to us. *"He'i!*—squid!"—he shouted excitedly. Makalii and I rushed up to him. In a clear pool at Pili's feet a waving tentacle showed. "You like see close-up?" he asked.

I nodded.

Lowering the pole gently into the water, Pili touched the moving arm and it wrapped about the wood. He jiggled the pole, teasing the octopus, and another long slimy feeler came out and took hold. After a minute all the long arms were wrapped about the stick, then he drew the squid gently toward the edge of the pool so I might see it in detail. Its body, about the size of a small cocoanut, was like a dirty gray sack. Fiery round eyes gazed up hideously. Pili shook the pole; the squid retained its hold but began changing from a slate gray to red with black mottlings.

"He's *huhu*—mad," Pili chuckled, raising his right arm quickly. Feeling the menacing gesture the squid began to unwrithe, but Pili drove the spear into its body and the pool clouded with the sepia it ejected. With incredible swiftness long tentacles rushed up Pili's arm and wrapped tightly about it. I recoiled. Seizing the hideous squirming mass with his free hand, Pili bit the squid between the eyes and its hold began relaxing. Then, nonchalantly, he stripped the tentacles with their horrid sucking cups off his skin.

"In Kakiki and Samoa there are *he'i* with arms twenty and thirty feet long," he told me. "Once in their grip a man is lost. But if you can manage to spear them before they get hold of you you can hear them moan and cry until the hair stands up straight on your head."

Squatting down, he began cutting off the yard-long tentacles. "Tonight I stew in cocoanut milk," he smacked his lips. *"He'i* more good from lobster or crab but *haoles*—white fellas—no like eat because they so ugly."

Stuffing his catch into the bag tied about his brawny middle he straightened up. "Now us go look the place where the big *ulua* feed at half-tide." He measured the water with expert eyes and nodded in a satisfied manner. Securing his spear to his wrist with a long cord he began sneaking along, peering over the black lava ledges. Presently he pointed at a silver streak fathoms below. *"Ulua!"* he whispered excitedly.

The big fish was cruising back and forth, gradually working toward the surface. Peering down through translucent blue depths I saw *wana* like huge orange and vermilion cactus-dahlias blossoming on rough ledges and schools of small brightly-colored fish nibbling at invisible growths on the coral. Presently a flock of tiny black-and-white striped *maninis* came flitting through the water. Pili froze. The big *ulua* sighted the prized delicacy, flashed, and the flock of little fish exploded in all directions. Pili hurled his spear and braced back. The line tied to his wrist whanged taut and the water was thrown into terrific confusion as the yard-long *ulua* raced back and forth, diving and plunging to get free.

Makalii locked his arm through Pili's and they danced and teetered along the edges of the rocks. I was afraid that the *ulua* might pull them in, but after some breath-taking minutes it began losing strength and came to the surface. One moment it was electric blue, the next like a silver-white palm leaf flashing and turning from side to side. Finally it lay over limply and after a tussle Pili and Makalii landed it. It slapped at the rocks viciously with its tail until Pili struck it a blow on the back of its head. It arched over, stiffened, quivered, and the light went out of its scales.

When we rejoined the other *paniolos* who were prowling among the wet rocks, their eyes lighted. "*Ulua! Ulua!* Fine!" they shouted, crowding up to examine the yard-long fish hanging from the spear on Pili's shoulder.

When we got back to the corrals with our bags of plunder and the royal *ulua,* Holomalia had a fire going and Dad was smoking his pipe, a sort of lazy happiness wrapped around him. Some of the men began cooking, others spread a tablecloth of glittering young cocoanut fronds on the clean sand. I undid the package Ah Sin had given me and handed two brightly colored cardboard boxes of Chinese cocoanut candy and a green jar of ginger to Makalii.

"For the *luau*—feast," I said, and his kind face beamed because Hawaiians like to share everything with those around them.

"While supper cooks we'll go for a swim," Dad announced.

Makalii undressed me and made a sort of *malo*—breech-clout— out of his red bandanna. I felt quite grown up and like the brown *paniolos* heading for the sea. As they went into the water they struck it with their cupped hands, sending long hollow echoes traveling across it.

"Why are they doing that?" I asked.

"There's no reef here and the sound scares sharks away," Daddy said.

I drew back.

"No need scare," Makalii said, grinning.

Paniolos were swimming around, laughing and splashing. I hesitated and Daddy squatted down beside me. "First Born, if you want a rich full life you've got to gamble sometimes. As a whole, sharks in these waters are cowards. Now and then a school of *Niiuhis*—Tiger Sharks—cruise in from the South Pacific; then you've got to watch out."

I swallowed.

"*Niiuhis* are real man-eaters and will even attack canoes. At night their eyes are phosphorescent and when fishermen out laying nets see them they paddle like fury for land. I've only run into *Niiuhis* twice during all the years I've lived in Hawaii."

My stomach felt full of butterflies. I wanted to go into the water dancing in from the sky but fear glued my feet to the sand. Daddy looked at me in an odd way and dived in. The *paniolos* shouted, "*Hele mai*—Come, come!"

Shutting my eyes I dashed in, took a few strokes, then turned and swam frantically for shore. Everyone laughed, making my fright just a joke. Soon I was swimming between Daddy and Makalii, and the silken beauty of the ocean washed all other thoughts from my mind.

By the time we came out the afternoon was beginning to die. Clouds waited above the loneliness of the sea like great white birds with their heads hidden under folded wings. With lazy dignity and the unthinking grace of Polynesians, the *paniolos* went about getting supper. I was drugged with sunshine and my body had the fulfilled happy feeling of land after it has been soaked with rain. The grove was filled with shadows but the fire threw ruddy lights on the men crouching around it.

Pili got out his worn accordion, Kahalewai produced a ukulele. Everyone began singing the old cowboy *hula* about the *paniolos* living in the Great House of the Sun. The music had the swagger and swing of our wide careless life, a life with *akuas*—gods—moving in it to give it majesty, and lurking dangers to give it spice. I sat between Dad and Makalii while the song poured richly through me. When it was ended Hauki took the ukulele and sang *Wahine Ui*, Beautiful Woman. His eyes looked hot and wet, and I knew he was thinking about his newest sweetheart as his long slender hands moved lovingly across the small instrument he held to his breast. When he finished, Pili made a remark in Hawaiian, under his breath, that sent everyone into shouts of laughter. Hauki looked pleased and embarrassed, then returned the ukulele to Kahalewai. Moku shouted *"Kaukau!"* and everyone forgot about music and went after food.

I sucked *wana,* crunched seaweed and *opihis,* ate great golden-white flaky pieces of *ulua,* drank cocoanut milk, and last of all passed Ah Sin's ginger and candy around. My skin was hot from sunburn, my eyes heavy. Makalii spread his slicker on the sand.

"I don't want to go to sleep," I protested.

"No need *moemoe,* just lie down," he suggested, smiling.

The slicker felt nice and cool against my burned arms and Makalii's fingers moved soothingly over my hot forehead. No one was anxious to end the fun. I heard Dad and the *paniolos* discussing work and talking about ancient times before white men invaded the scattered island groups of the Pacific. I wanted to share it all but despite my best efforts the thick dark curtain of sleep kept descending, shutting off firelight flickering on bulging muscles and flat backs, and on horses moving like shadows through the grove.

When I opened my eyes again light was stealing across the sea. The morning was as fragile and as sacredly beautiful as the first one of Creation. A pearl-and-silver dawn was lying in the sky and the mountains were steel blue and sharp. Pili was making coffee, Hauki riding off to see if the steamer was in sight. Men were coughing, clearing their throats, stretching and scratching. When the waking-up was over they lighted cigarettes. Moku rounded up the shipping horses and drove them into a rail-enclosure. Eole, Hu, and Kahalewai were coiling up ten-foot lengths of manila rope and placing them on the top of the stone corral where restless steers were shifting back and forth. By the time Hauki returned breakfast was ready.

"No more steamer," he announced.

"Blast it!" Dad said, then held out his cup for coffee.

After we'd eaten, Makalii saddled our two horses and took me to see an old *heiau*—temple—at the base of the Hill of Earthquakes, just beyond the point where Pili had speared the *ulua* the day before. Reverently we inspected the square heap of black stones. "In this temple *kahunas* prayed and offered sacrifices in old times," Makalii said in Hawaiian. "This was the temple of the Shark God where fishermen made offerings before putting out to sea."

Suddenly the mirror-like morning was split by wild shouts from the cocoanut grove. We wheeled and saw the whole herd of steers bolting for the sea. With great splashings they plunged into the water and began swimming off in the direction of Kahoolawe. We raced to our horses, Makalii threw me into my saddle, vaulted onto his horse and we tore along the beach. *Paniolos* on saddleless horses were shooting out of the grove. Daddy's commands sounded like rifle-shots. Makalii's horse flattened into a run and my pony Haki laid back her ears trying to keep up.

"Stop here," Makalii ordered as we neared the grove. "I go *kokua*—help!" and he dashed into the blue water.

The steers were swimming steadily toward the distant red island. The black dots which were their heads had long ripples like V's running out from each side. Men were swimming their horses after them, Daddy on Champagne well in the lead.

A steer's head disappeared. "It's drowning," I thought, my heart pounding. Another head went under. The swimming men began striking the water with their cupped hands. Sharks! The quiet morning which had been so utterly lovely, became a chaos of horror. A third steer vanished. Panic seized the herd. They wheeled, milled, collided, tried to climb on each other's backs. *Paniolos* shouted to each other, striking the sea fiercely with their arched hands, sending long hollow sounds across it.

Breath jammed in my lungs. Daddy, Makalii, all these people and animals I loved, would be torn to pieces by sharks with cruel blunt snouts and wicked wedge-shaped mouths. I wanted to scream but my throat muscles were paralyzed. The panic in the water increased. Horses plunged, fought, reared, their eyes rolling wildly. Men cursed and yelled, steers shook their horns and sent dull unhappy bellows across the sea.

After milling and wheeling, the majority of the herd headed back for land. Makalii came splashing out of the water and raced along the beach, trying to head the cattle toward the corrals. A steer heaved onto the sand, followed by others. Streaming sides flashed in the sun, horns looked wild and strong. The animals collected in knots, debating which way to charge. Enemies in the water, enemies on land! They looked desperate and distracted, ferocious, and forsaken by all their gods.

Daddy raced out of the sea and Makalii galloped back and forth, swinging his lasso to turn the desperate beeves. Moku dashed for the cocoanut grove and reappeared with Keitchi and Pivela. The old oxen looked disgusted but slid among the frantic steers to quiet them.

Eight or ten of the cattle were still swimming around in the bay. Dark muddy spots stained the blue water around some of them. Two disappeared, came to the surface, and were pulled under again. The rangy steer who had started the stampede the previous morning came lurching up the sand. A great hole in his side poured blood and he kept looking at it in a bewildered manner as he ran to rejoin his mates.

Daddy and Holomalia dashed into the water to rescue the five steers whose white faces showed swimming in a circle a short distance from land. Striking the water, yelling in voices which sounded as loud and commanding as *akuas,* Daddy and Holomalia approached them. One steer was pulled under just as Dad got to it, but he and his foreman headed the rest to shore and they finally heaved onto the safety of the land.

I shook in my saddle. My bones felt like jelly and my stomach was empty and tight. The *paniolos* closed in on the animals moving in a restless ring on the trampled beach. I wanted to go to Daddy or Makalii but was afraid that if I moved the steers might stampede again. After what seemed hours, and which was probably only a few minutes, the men, with the old oxen's help, got the herd headed toward the corrals. The steers moved forward, taut and nervous, ready to bolt if a butterfly's shadow crossed their trail. When they were finally inside the stone fence and the gate was fastened, I started forward.

The sand was torn up and a long gory trail showed where the roan steer had been. I kept thinking of the cattle the sharks had eaten and I sobbed. When I rode up, Dad looked as if he didn't know who I was. His eyes were filled with man-thoughts: work and danger. All the other men's faces had the same expression. I felt like a person left out of the world and wailed like a puppy which has been tramped on. Daddy came to me, his strong arm swept me off my horse onto his and, all at once, I had him and everyone back again. When I stopped crying we were on the ground and Daddy held a wet handkerchief to my head.

"Steady, *paniolo,*" he said.

The word jerked me back to my senses. "But the poor steers that got killed—" I said.

"They're with the Great *Akua* now."

"What made them stampede?"

"They were restless from waiting so long. A cocoanut frond fell with a rushing noise into the corral and they jumped the stone wall and bolted."

I held tightly to Dad and swallowed. He never talked to me as though I was a baby, but treated me like a grown-up and it made me want to be steady and brave, as he was.

"What about the roan steer?"

"The boys killed him, he's out of his misery."

Holomalia shouted, *"Hele mai"*—and pointed at the steamer, which was just pulling into sight beyond the Hill of Earthquakes.

"Will you and the boys have to go into the sea again?" I asked shakily.

"Of course, but those blasted sharks aren't going to get any more of my cattle," Daddy said, his jaw getting square. "Usually sharks cruise singly but that was a school of them this morning."

Calling the men together he talked to them in Hawaiian. They looked bothered and pleased and I knew they'd agreed to do something which, though it half scared them, made them glad at the same time. Pili hauled back the tarpaulin covering the dynamite. Daddy glanced at the rapidly approaching steamer, then at the corral full of steers.

"I'm going to risk it," he announced, and taking my hand headed for the beach. Pili went to the last rock jutting into the bay and hurled something far across the water. There was a dull explosion underneath.

"What was that?" I asked.

"Dynamite to stun the sharks and scare them away." Dad's mouth shut into a hard line.

"Why don't you always use it?"

"It's illegal to dynamite fish. Sharks are fish but in this instance dynamiting is justifiable."

Pili hurled in another charge, then we walked back to the corrals and I knew as dogs know such things that Daddy didn't want to talk about it any more. When we reached the corrals the boys were in short dungarees and had their stripped shipping saddles on their horses. The steamer dropped anchor about half a mile offshore and the morning got underway once more.

A whaleboat was lowered and began coming in. Dad went into

the corrals and maneuvered among the steers. The boat anchored about fifty feet from the beach and the sailors called out greetings. Holomalia and Eole guarded the open gate of the corral. When everything was ready Dad roped a steer about the horns and dashed out, Hauki galloping beside the captive. They rushed across the beach at full speed and hit the sea. A great splash went up into the air, then they began swimming for the boat. Flinging the manila rope, which was about the steer's horns, to one of the men in the boat, Daddy wheeled. The man threw a fresh rope to him and he swam back to the beach.

The men worked in pairs, perfectly and without mishap. Dad and Hauki, Pili and Moku, Hu and Kahalewai. Makalii explained details which I didn't understand. The boat had to anchor far enough out so the struggling cattle couldn't get their feet on the bottom and tear free. Eight animals on each side constituted a boat-load. When it had its quota it was drawn back to the ship by a long rope as oars could not be used with the animals floating on each side. When it reached the ship the cattle would have a sling put around them and be hoisted aboard.

The work was rhythmic. Rope, rush, splash, throw, catch, tie . . . then the swim back. Men's shoulder muscles flashed, showers of spray winked in the sunshine, horses came out of the water like wet, sleek seals. As each loaded boat was drawn back to the ship, another took its place. While sailors and *paniolos* worked they held a shouted conversation, punctuated by quick orders when some steer proved troublesome and unruly. There were good-natured insults about the invariable unpunctuality of the steamer. There were explanations. . . . A big surf had been running at Kawaihae and the Parker Ranch had shipped a hundred and fifteen head. Regrets were expressed for the steers which the sharks had got. And so forth . . .

Finally, the last steer was lashed by its horns to the boat. Farewells sounded across the widening strip of water. The steamer blew its whistle. Tired men spilled off tired horses, pulled off their saddles and the horses rolled luxuriously in the moist sand while the men slaked their thirst from green cocoanuts. Sunlight poured down on sparkling blue water. Clouds drifted overhead like white squadrons of ships cruising forever southward to islands lying below the curve of the earth.

Makalii came to me and looked into my eyes. "You like go inside water on a horse like a *paniolo?*" he asked.

I wanted to, it looked beautiful, the horses breasting waves with their tails floating out behind like spreading fans. But I thought of the sharks and hesitated.

"I take you behind me on Nani, if you like to go," Makalii said.

I was torn between doubt and desire, then I remembered what Daddy had said, that if a person wanted a rich full life they had to take risks sometimes.

"Yes," I said finally.

Makalii's eyes lighted. "Good girl!" he announced, and reaching down pulled me up behind him.

Bob Krauss

HALAWA VALLEY, MOLOKAI

IN MANY WAYS the island of Molokai most nearly resembles the Hawaiian Islands as they were in the nineteenth century. The island has dry plains, some used to raise pineapples and some covered with algarroba (*kiawe*) forests, where cattle feed on the algarroba pods. Its north side consists mainly of a high mountain range, part of which overlooks Kalaupapa, the tiny and isolated settlement at sea level where a few sufferers from Hansen's disease (leprosy) live in comfort. Molokai's east end, sparsely inhabited, has several impressive early missionary churches, built in the New England style. At the easternmost tip of the island is Halawa Valley, one of the most beautiful places in the state of Hawaii.

In his informal and highly readable *Bob Krauss' Travel Guide to the Hawaiian Islands* (an extract from which follows), Bob Krauss has described a trip to Molokai's east end. The journey begins at Kaunakakai, a dusty, sprawling village which looks much as Honolulu did in the 1840's. Along the way, the HVB (Hawaii Visitors Bureau) signs indicate some points of interest. The journey ends at Halawa Valley. The Father Damien mentioned was the Roman Catholic missionary who devoted his life to the leper colony across the island.

IF YOU WERE to ask me, "What's the most picturesque, unspoiled part of Hawaii?" I would answer, "The east end of Molokai." This isn't the South Seas as you see it in the movies. This is the

South Seas of Somerset Maugham and Jack London. This is the South Seas with sunburn and mosquito bites. But that's not what you'll remember when you return home. You'll remember those lonely beaches, Ah Ping's Store, the remote valley at the end of the road, and that beautiful waterfall at the end of a jungle trail.

This drive is 25 miles long from Kaunakakai, 33 from the airport. I've done it all in a passenger car, but a jeep is better once you reach the valley. You'll have to take a lunch, or stop for groceries at Ah Ping's Store along the way. A canteen of water is a big help on the trail. So is a bottle of mosquito lotion. Come equipped with a swimsuit, and be prepared to spend the day.

You'll soon discover that the HVB signs on Molokai are meaningless. Most of them point to some invisible Stone Age ruin buried in the *kiawe* off the road on private land where even Daniel Boone couldn't find it. And if he did, he'd be guilty of trespassing. Meanwhile, interesting places you *can* get to aren't marked.

There's a perfect example of this not quite 5½ miles from Kaunakakai. You'll see a sign reading: KAWELA CITY OF REFUGE. But there's no City of Refuge in sight. Next comes: KAWELA BATTLEFIELD. But no battle. However, only .2 of a mile farther on there's a dirt road leading left. If you take this road and then bear left again at the triple fork, you'll come into an expansive, weedy backyard that looks like the Polynesian versian of a hobo jungle.

Here you'll find a communal shanty made of corrugated iron and packing crates covered over with palm fronds. Nearby is the business of the place, a row of kilns where Molokai's thorny *kiawe* is transformed into charcoal. The kilns are underground ovens lined with cement and covered over with mounds of earth. That enormous tree you parked under is a mango.

Another of Father Damien's churches, St. Joseph's, is 5½ miles ahead on the highway. It's a spare, pale green frame building with a tall steeple. The church and a small cemetery are enclosed in a stone wall constructed in the old Hawaiian way, without mortar. Construction date of this church is 1876. During this time the dedicated priest served two congregations "topside" as well as the lepers below at Kalaupapa.

One of Molokai's brief moments of front-page glory occurred in 1927 when two fliers, 25 hours and 2 minutes away from California on a pioneer transpacific flight, ran out of gas and crash-landed in a thicket of *kiawe* trees near here. The pilots are Ernest Smith and

Emory Brontë, and the end of their historic flight is marked by a stone monument beside the highway 1.2 miles ahead.

By a strange coincidence, aviation came to Molokai almost on the spot where contemporaries of Christopher Columbus had left their handiwork. It's the wall of an old fish pond—still in use—.1 of a mile beyond the Smith-Brontë marker on the right. Look for an arm of land jutting from the shore in a half circle. The open end of the natural cove is blocked by a stone wall. This is Keawanui fish pond, known to be over 500 years old.

There's another useless sign 1.2 miles ahead. It points to two *heiaus* on a hillside far to the left of the highway. You can spot them, however, with a pair of binoculars. Look at the foot of a green ridge that ends in a flat slope in the shape of a diamond.

If the *heiaus* aren't much, the view certainly is. You are now traveling along a narrow strip of land between rugged green mountains and the ocean. Cottages along the roadside nestle under palm trees. The grass is luxurious. Flowers bloom beside the cottages.

The next HVB marker reads: MYSTIC SPRING. The spring is on your right at the end of a short, weedy trail. It's enclosed by a circular rock wall that forms a little pool. I don't know the legend of this place, so you can make up your own. Surprisingly enough, though the ocean is only a few feet away, the spring water is fresh.

Like the Mystic Spring, Ah Ping's Store just ahead doesn't look like much. Just a small, frame country store with benches on the front porch, but this time appearances are deceiving. The original Ah Ping set up shop over fifty years ago. Now his grandchildren are on the scene. They are faithfully carrying on the tradition. Once I listed a few of the items for sale here on the road to nowhere. The list included baby blankets, paint, castrating knives, coffeepots, whisky, animal crackers, Clorox, baby food, blue denims, motor oil, sardines, washtubs, *aloha* shirts, brooms, axes, shovels, bamboo goggles, fishhooks, dinner pails and soda pop. Whatever you need, get it here. Ah Ping's is the only store between Kaunakakai and the end of the road.

Kaluaaha Church, the oldest on Molokai, is on the left of the highway less than a mile away. It's a huge stone building with abutments on the corners and a faded red steeple leaning slightly awry. The old Bible on the lectern is in Hawaiian. Father Damien's second church, Our Lady of Sorrows, is just ahead. It's white with a green steeple.

Farther on you'll find several more HVB signs pointing opti-
mistically to practically inaccessible places. One of these is Iliiliopai
Heiau, an impressive old ruin that everyone on Molokai insists you
should see, but if you take their advice don't start looking at the
sign that says ILIILIOPAI HEIAU. Stop, instead, at the one reading:
WAILAU TRAIL.

Here you'll find a swinging wooden gate across a two-track trail
leading into a valley cut into the mountains. Climb through the
gate and walk along the trail. You'll go through a double gate,
then continue on the trail to still another gate. Here you'll find
a stone wall running parallel to the fence. Now follow this fence
to the right. It's a scramble through thorny tangles of lantana and
kiawe. You'll cross a small, dry stream bed, then a larger one
(still following the fence line). At one point you'll have to climb
through a fence that joins the one you're following. Beyond the
second stream, on the right, you'll see the heiau. This was a
sacrificial temple. Since it's on private property, you should call
before you go and ask permission of Mrs. Pearl Friel at her home or
at the Bank of Hawaii branch in Kaunakakai where she works.

King Kamehameha, who has given the HVB signmakers more
work than anyone else, did it again not quite 2½ miles away on
the right at a place called "Paikalani Taro Patch." The conqueror
once camped with his army on Molokai while preparing to invade
Oahu. Like all armies, this one traveled on its stomach. Obviously
the small island of Molokai couldn't support this horde of hungry
strangers. Prudent Kamehameha had his men plant taro in an
enormous patch which is dry now, but you can still see the outline.

By this time you are again traveling on Molokai dirt. Civilization
seems far away. You'll see weather-beaten fishing shacks along the
shore and boats pulled up nearby, fishnets drying in the sun. Almost 3 miles from Kamehameha's taro patch there's a small beach
on a point shaded by a cluster of coconut palms. It's the best swimming beach available to visitors on Molokai.

From there to the end of the road, life is basic. Primitive may be
a better word. The nearest house has no electricity, no telephone.
Water comes from a mountain stream. Deer and wild pigs sometimes wander across the yard at dusk. The closest doctor is 20 miles
away. You'll pass several more beaches out there in the wilderness,
a beach shack or two, and miles of rugged, wave-tossed shore. The

island looming out of the ocean off the point in Maui. The island of Lanai, directly across the channel from Kaunakakai, is now back on your right.

The road winds up upon the bluff, and roller-coasters into and out of ravines and gullies. You'll pass a small deserted village that was once headquarters for a ranch. Then more ravines. Nearly 6 miles from the swimming beach you'll come to a turnout where, across the green plateau to the left, you'll see a thick, circular cluster of trees with gray bark and light green leaves. This is Molokai's sacred *kukui* grove, once the home of the Kahuna Lani-kaula, a feared and powerful priest. Most Hawaiians refuse to go near the place.

Halawa Valley, the dream world at the end of the road, is just ahead. The road begins to snake down and to the left. Then you'll come around a sharp curve and the valley will unfold below, half a mile across, 3 or 4 miles deep, a shady paradise that was once neatly laid out in taro patches and is now being reclaimed by jungle. Long ago this valley supported a large Hawaiian settlement, but the villagers began moving to town where there was more excitement. The tidal wave of 1946 wiped out the homes of those that remained. Today only half a dozen families grow taro beside the stream.

The road hugs the cliff as it switchbacks down to the valley floor. Once at the bottom you'll be engulfed in jungle. A dirt trail for cars leads out to the beach. In the other direction it winds along the base of the cliff toward the head of the valley. There's a little church in the valley near the point where the road comes down out of the cliff. In case you're thirsty and forgot to bring water, you'll find a water tap in the weedy front yard of this church. It's good water, piped in from the stream.

The beach has a romantic, castaway-island appeal. And there's a car track leading from the beach to a grassy spot beside the stream nearby where it's fun to picnic. But the real adventure in Halawa Valley is a hike back to Moaula Falls. In typical Molokai fashion, this gorgeous spot has never been marked, but the trail isn't hard to follow if you know what to look for. The hike will take you about an hour of easy walking. I've done it in less with my two boys, aged nine and ten.

Of course it'll take longer if you stop along the way to explore the ruins, or pick fruit or seeds for making necklaces, or look for fish in the stream, or stop to weave garlands of ferns for headdresses like the Molokai kids do. But that's part of the fun.

This time take the narrow two-tire-track trail leading back up into the valley. There are still a few shacks along this jungle road. If you meet a car coming in the other direction, one of you will have to back up to one of those houses to let the other car by. This trail ends in the backyard of the last house, but the best place to park is in a clearing to the left before you get to the end of the road. From here you will walk. If you're allergic to mosquitoes, this is the place to put on some lotion. Unless you'd rather go skinny-dipping, bring along a suit for swimming in the pool below the waterfall. Picnickers will have to pack their lunches. All set? Here we go!

Walk on past the end of the road, past the last house, and pick up the faint trail that follows a water pipe (put in when the valley was well populated). This water pipe is your compass, signpost and road map. It'll take you right to the falls. You don't have to follow it exactly. Just keep it in sight while you find the easiest route.

You'll cross an old irrigation ditch built by ancient Hawaiians, then the stream that makes Halawa Valley so productive (step across on the rocks), then another old ditch built to irrigate the taro patches you passed on the way up. At this second ditch a faint trail leads up the valley along the stream. Don't go that way. Follow the water pipe up the forested slope to a water tank. Here's where you'll strike the main trail. It's a well-worn path that winds along the base of the cliff on this side of the valley. Just to make it easier, the water pipe also parallels this trail.

There are only two places where the trail is difficult to follow. One is where a thicket of *hau* trees has grown over the path. Circle to your right around the obstacle and pick up the path on the other side. The other place where the trail seems to disappear is where it crosses a stream bed. Here you'll easily pick up the path on the other side if you'll stay on the left of the water pipe.

This is a delightful hike. If you keep your eyes open, you'll find acres of neatly terraced taro patches. At one spot below the trail near the stream an irrigation ditch is still faithfully filtering water through a series of paddies that haven't been used for years.

You'll brush past clumps of fern and vines hanging from the

branches of trees. The farther up you go, the more open the valley becomes. The spot I like the best is deep in the midst of a shadowy, mysterious *kukui* forest. These are the gray-barked trees you see as splotches of light green on forested mountain slopes all over the 50th state. In Halawa Valley you'll find *kukui* nuts scattered along the path. The kernels inside are very oily. The Hawaiians used them for making torches.

They would string half a dozen kernels of the *kukui* nut on the midrib of a coconut frond, then light the topmost kernel. It would burn 3 to 5 minutes, and in turn light the next kernel. Take a few nuts home and try it. They'll work better if you pick nuts in which the kernel is dry enough to rattle when you shake it.

None of this forest beauty is a match for the falls. You'll come upon them suddenly, at the base of towering gray cliffs mottled with black and green. The water seems to plunge out of the clouds into the pool at your feet. And under those towering cliffs it's just spooky enough to make you remember the things the Hawaiians say you should do for safety.

You see, rocks sometimes come tumbling down out of the cliffs. If one of those junior-sized boulders landed on your head, you could be badly hurt. But no Hawaiian on Molokai would admit it was an accident. The stone god did it. To avoid making the god of the cliffs angry, you must take a gift (a penny is adequate), put it on a boulder under a ti leaf, and anchor it with a rock. The symbolism of the gesture is obvious. That penny represents yourself. The ti (which grows thickly at the base of the cliffs), known among the Hawaiians for its power to ward off evil spirits, is your shield. The rock represents the falling stones that can now do you no harm.

Another danger is the pool. It must be 150 feet across, a wonderfully inviting place, and the story goes that it has no bottom. In order to avoid drowning, you must first test the water by throwing in a ti leaf. If the ti leaf floats lazily down the stream (as it usually does), it is safe to go swimming. If it sinks in the pool, the water sprits below are calling for someone; the water is unsafe. I have no idea why the ti leaf sometimes floats and sometimes sinks, but mine have always floated, and the swimming is delicious. I never want to pack up and go.

Like Kauai and Hawaii, Molokai also has a coastline of lovely uninhabited valleys. Halawa is at one end of it. The other valleys are accessible by boat during summer when the water is calm. There you will find complete solitude. But, for the ordinary visitor who'd like to spend an inexpensive day getting acquainted with Hawaii the way it used to be, there is no better pathway than the bumpy road to Halawa Valley.

HAWAII IN LITERATURE

OVER THE YEARS Hawaii has fascinated many distinguished authors. Fortunately, they differed considerably in their interests and attitudes. What intrigued one, the others often ignored. The net result has been highly rewarding. Each author seized upon and emphasized a different facet in Hawaii's abundantly colorful and often contradictory experience.

In the following pages, the reader may explore a variegated literary mosaic about Hawaii. First of all, he will encounter a short yet highly typical note by the Scottish essayist and historian Thomas Carlyle, on the stalwart female chief, Kapiolani, who defied the volcano goddess to vindicate the Christian faith. Next comes pleasant but hardly great verse by the English poet laureate Tennyson, on the same subject. Both Carlyle and Tennyson, in the faraway British Isles, had sympathy for but little real understanding of Hawaii.

But Mark Twain, on a somewhat later visit, brought to Hawaii piercing vision, warm wit, and prose which consistently sings and soars. His travel book *Roughing It* contains some of the best writing ever produced about Hawaii.

This section concludes with two short stories with Hawaiian settings, culled from a long list. One is by Robert Louis Stevenson, and the other is by Jack London. Both men knew Hawaii at first hand. In the opinion of the editor, no fiction produced about Hawaii in later years has surpassed the standard set by these two acknowledged masters.

Thomas Carlyle and Alfred Tennyson
KAPIOLANI

IN DECEMBER, 1824, Kapiolani, a female chief of rank newly converted to Christianity, descended into the live volcano of Kilauea on the island of Hawaii in order to discredit the native fear of the volcano goddess Pele. Along with her numerous attendants, Kapiolani returned unharmed. Her heroic act stimulated many natives to become

Christians. Kapiolani died in 1841 a few weeks after an operation, without anesthetics, which removed her entire right breast because of cancer.

In England, Thomas Carlyle, who was an insatiable reader, mentioned her feat in part four of his edition of Oliver Cromwell's letters, published in 1845. Thirty-seven years later, in the year of his death, the English poet Alfred Tennyson celebrated Kapiolani's exploit in an interesting but far from distinguished lyric poem. One may only add that printed Hawaiiana turns up in many unexpected spots, just as manuscripts dealing with Hawaii are to be found in such unlikely places as the archives of the Hudson's Bay Company in Toronto.

Carlyle on Kapiolani

A CERTAIN QUEEN in some South-Sea Island, I have read in Missionary Books, had been converted to Christianity; did not any longer believe in the old gods. She assembled her people; said to them, "My faithful People, the gods do *not* dwell in that burning-mountain in the centre of our Isle. That is not God; no, that is a common burning-mountain—mere culinary fire burning under peculiar circumstances. See, I will walk before you to that burning-mountain; will empty my wash-bowl into it, cast my slipper over it, defy it to the uttermost, and stand the consequences!"—She walked accordingly, this South-Sea Heroine, nerved to the sticking-place; her people following in pale horror and expectancy: she did her experiment;—and, I am told, they have truer notions of the gods in that Island ever since! Experiment which it is now very easy to *repeat,* and very needless. Honor to the Brave who deliver us from Phantom-dynasties, in South-Sea Islands and in North!

Tennyson on Kapiolani

K APIOLANI WAS a great chieftainess who lived in the Sandwich Islands at the beginning of this century. She won the cause of Christianity by openly defying the priests of the terrible goddess Peelè [Pele]. In spite of their threats of vengeance she ascended the volcano Mauna-Loa, then clambered down over a bank of cinders 400 feet high to the great lake of fire (nine miles round)—Kilauea— the home and haunt of the goddess, and flung into the boiling lava the consecrated berries which it was sacrilege for a woman to handle.

I

When from the terrors of Nature a people have
  fashion'd and worship a Spirit of Evil,
Blest be the Voice of the Teacher who calls to
  them
"Set yourselves free!"

II

Noble the Saxon who hurl'd at his Idol a valorous
  weapon in olden England!
Great and greater, and greatest of women, island
  heroine, Kapiolani
Clomb the mountain, and flung the berries, and
  dared the Goddess, and freed the people
Of Hawa-i-ee!

III

A people believing that Peelè the Goddess would
  wallow in fiery riot and revel
On Kilauea,
Dance in a fountain of flame with her devil, or
  shake with her thunders and shatter her island,
Rolling her anger
Thro' blasted valley and flaring forest in blood-red
  cataracts down to the sea!

IV

Long as the lava-light
Glares from the lava-lake
Dazing the starlight,
Long as the silvery vapour in daylight
Over the mountain
Floats, will the glory of Kapiolani be mingled with
  either on Hawa-i-ee.

V

What said her Priesthood?
"Woe to this island if ever a woman should handle
  or gather the berries of Peelè!
Accursèd were she!

And woe to this island if ever a woman should
    climb to the dwelling of Peelè the Goddess!
Accursèd were she!"

VI

One from the Sunrise
Dawn'd on His people, and slowly before him
Vanish'd shadow-like
Gods and Goddesses,
None but the terrible Peelè remaining as Kapiolani
    ascended her mountain,
Baffled her priesthood,
Broke the Taboo,
Dipt to the crater,
Call'd on the Power adored by the Christian, and
    crying "I dare her, let Peelè avenge herself!"
Into the flame-billow dash'd the berries, and drove
    the demon from Hawa-i-ee.

Mark Twain
MARK TWAIN IN HAWAII

MARK TWAIN visited Hawaii in 1866 and instantly fell in love with
it. After some days in Honolulu, he went to see the volcano of Kilauea
on the island of Hawaii and the extinct crater of Haleakala on Maui.
His witty and gay impressions of the Islands first appeared as articles
in the Sacramento *Union,* and then as part of his *Roughing It.*
    Twenty-nine years later, in 1895, Mark Twain returned to Honolulu
on his lecture tour around the world. This time he had a keen disappointment. There was cholera in Honolulu, and if he went ashore
he would be quarantined and not permitted to continue his voyage.
With regret, he elected to stay on board ship and to view from a distance the shore which for him held special enchantment. He recorded
this frustrating experience in his travel book *Following the Equator.*

From Roughing It

ON A CERTAIN BRIGHT morning the Islands hove in sight, lying
    low on the lonely sea, and everybody climbed to the upper
deck to look. After two thousand miles of watery solitude the vision

was a welcome one. As we approached, the imposing promontory of Diamond Head rose up out of the ocean, its rugged front softened by the hazy distance, and presently the details of the land began to make themselves manifest: first the line of beach; then the plumed cocoanut trees of the tropics; then cabins of the natives; then the white town of Honolulu, said to contain between twelve and fifteen thousand inhabitants spread over a dead level; with streets from twenty to thirty feet wide, solid and level as a floor, most of them straight as a line and few as crooked as a corkscrew.

The further I traveled through the town the better I liked it. Every step revealed a new contrast—disclosed something I was unaccustomed to. In place of the grand mud-colored brown fronts of San Francisco, I saw dwellings built of straw, adobes, and cream-colored pebble-and-shell-conglomerated coral, cut into oblong blocks and laid in cement; also a great number of neat white cottages, with green window-shutters; in place of front yards like billiard-tables with iron fences around them, I saw these homes surrounded by ample yards, thickly clad with green grass, and shaded by tall trees, through whose dense foliage the sun could scarcely penetrate; in place of the customary geranium, calla lily, etc., languishing in dust and general debility, I saw luxurious banks and thickets of flowers, fresh as a meadow after a rain, and glowing with the richest dyes; in place of the dingy horrors of San Francisco's pleasure grove, the "Willows," I saw huge-bodied, wide-spreading forest trees, with strange names and stranger appearance—trees that cast a shadow like a thundercloud, and were able to stand alone without being tied to green poles; in place of gold fish, wiggling around in glass globes, assuming countless shades and degrees of distortion through the magnifying and diminishing qualities of their transparent prison houses, I saw cats—Tomcats, Mary Ann cats, long-tailed cats, bob-tailed cats, blind cats, one-eyed cats, wall-eyed cats, cross-eyed cats, spotted cats, tame cats, wild cats, singed cats, individual cats, groups of cats, platoons of cats, companies of cats, regiments of cats, armies of cats, multitudes of cats, millions of cats, and all of them sleek, fat, lazy, and sound asleep.

I looked on a multitude of people, some white, in white coats, vests, pantaloons, even white cloth shoes, made snowy with chalk duly laid on every morning; but the majority of the people were almost as dark as negroes—women with comely features, fine black eyes, rounded forms, inclining to the voluptuous, clad in a single bright red or white garment that fell free and unconfined from shoulder to heel, long black hair falling loose, gypsy hats, encircled with wreaths of natural flowers of a brilliant carmine tint; plenty of dark men in various costumes, and some with nothing on but a battered stovepipe hat tilted on the nose, and a very scant breechclout;—certain smoke-dried children were clothed in nothing but sunshine—a very neat-fitting and picturesque apparel indeed.

In place of roughs and rowdies staring and blackguarding on the corners, I saw long-haired, saddle-colored Sandwich Island maidens sitting on the ground in the shade of corner houses, gazing indolently at whatever or whoever happened along; instead of wretched cobble-stone pavements, I walked on a firm foundation of coral, built up from the bottom of the sea by the absurd but persevering insect of that name, with a light layer of lava and cinders overlying the coral, belched up out of fathomless perdition long ago through the seared and blackened crater that stands dead and harmless in the distance now; instead of cramped and crowded street-cars, I met dusky native women sweeping by, free as the wind, on fleet horses and astride, with gaudy riding-sashes, streaming like banners behind them; instead of the combined stenches of Chinadom and Brannan street slaughter-houses, I breathed the balmy fragrance of jessamine, oleander, and the Pride of India; in place of the hurry and bustle and noisy confusion of San Francisco, I moved in the midst of a Summer calm as tranquil as dawn in the Garden of Eden; in place of the Golden City's skirting sand hills and the placid bay, I saw on the one side a frame-work of tall, precipitous mountains close at hand, clad in refreshing green, and cleft by deep, cool, chasm-like valleys—and in front the grand sweep of the ocean: a brilliant, transparent green near the shore, bound and bordered by a long white line of foamy spray dashing against the reef, and further out the dead blue water of the deep sea, flecked with "white caps," and in the far horizon a single, lonely sail—a mere accent-mark to emphasize a slumberous calm and a solitude that were without sound or limit. When the sun sunk down—the one intruder from other realms and persistent in suggestions of them—it was tranced luxury to sit in the perfumed air and forget that there was any world but these enchanted islands. . . .

A mile and a half from town, I came to a grove of tall cocoanut trees, with clean, branchless stems reaching straight up sixty or seventy feet and topped with a spray of green foliage sheltering clusters of cocoanuts—not more picturesque than a forest of colossal ragged parasols, with bunches of magnified grapes under them, would be. I once heard a grouty Northern invalid say that a cocoanut tree might be poetical, possibly it was; but it looked like a feather-duster struck by lightning. I think that describes it better than a picture—and yet, without any question, there is something fascinating about a cocoanut tree—and graceful, too.

About a dozen cottages, some frame and the others of native grass, nestled sleepily in the shade here and there. The grass cabins are of a grayish color, are shaped much like our own cottages, only with higher and steeper roofs, usually, and are made of some kind of weed strongly bound together in bundles. The roofs are very thick, and so are the walls; the latter have square holes in them for windows. At a little distance these cabins have a furry appearance, as if they might be made of bear skins. They are very cool and pleasant inside. The King's flag was flying from the roof of one of the cottages, and His Majesty was probably within. He owns the whole concern thereabouts, and passes his time there frequently, on sultry days "laying off." The spot is called "The King's Grove."

Near by is an interesting ruin—the meager remains of an ancient temple—a place where human sacrifices were offered up in those old bygone days when the simple child of nature, yielding momentarily to sin when sorely tempted, acknowledged his error when calm reflection had shown it to him, and came forward with noble frankness and offered up his grandmother as an atoning sacrifice—in those old days when the luckless sinner could keep on cleansing his conscience and achieving periodical happiness as long as his relations held out; long, long before the missionaries braved a thousand privations to come and make them permanently miserable by telling them how beautiful and how blissful a place heaven is, and how nearly impossible it is to get there; and showed the poor native how dreary a place perdition is and what unnecessarily liberal facilities there are for going to it; showed him how, in his ignorance, he had gone and fooled away all his kinsfolk to no purpose; showed him what rapture it is to work all day long for fifty cents to buy food for next day with, as compared with fishing for a pastime and lolling in the shade through eternal summer, and eating of the bounty that nobody labored to provide but Nature. How sad it is to think of the multitudes who have gone to their graves in this beautiful island and never knew there was a hell.

This ancient temple was built of rough blocks of lava, and was simply a roofless enclosure a hundred and thirty feet long and seventy wide—nothing but naked walls, very thick, but not much higher than a man's head. They will last for ages, no doubt, if left unmolested. Its three altars and other sacred appurtenances have crumbled and passed away years ago. It is said that in the old times thousands of human beings were slaughtered here, in the presence of naked and howling savages. If these mute stones could speak, what tales they could tell, what pictures they could describe, of fettered victims writhing under the knife; of massed forms straining forward out of the gloom, with ferocious faces lit up by the sacrificial fires; of the background of ghostly trees; of the dark pyramid of Diamond Head standing sentinel over the uncanny scene, and the peaceful moon looking down upon it through rifts in the cloud-rack!

When Kamehameha (pronunced Ka-may-ha-may-ah) the Great— who was a sort of a Napoleon in military genius and uniform success—invaded this island of Oahu three-quarters of a century ago, and exterminated the army sent to oppose him, and took full and final possession of the country, he searched out the dead body of the King of Oahu, and those of the principal chiefs, and impaled their heads on the walls of this temple.

Those were savage times when this old slaughter-house was in its prime. The King and the chiefs ruled the common herd with a rod of iron; made them gather all the provisions the masters needed; build all the houses and temples; stand all the expenses, of whatever kind; take kicks and cuffs for thanks; drag out lives well flavored with misery, and then suffer death for trifling offenses or yield up their lives on the sacrificial altars to purchase favors from the gods for their hard rulers. The missionaries have clothed them, educated them, broken up the tyrannous authority of their chiefs, and given them freedom and the right to enjoy whatever their hands and brains produce, with equal laws for all, and punishment for all alike who transgress them. The contrast is so strong—the benefit conferred upon this people by the missionaries is so prominent, so palpable, and so unquestionable, that the frankest compliment I can pay them, and the best, is simply to point to the condition of the Sandwich Islanders of Captain Cook's time, and their condition today. Their work speaks for itself. . . .

Passing through the market-place we saw that feature of Honolulu under its most favorable auspices—that is, in the full glory of Saturday afternoon, which is a festive day with the natives. The native girls, by twos and threes and parties of a dozen, and sometimes in whole platoons and companies, went cantering up and down the neighboring streets astride of fleet but homely horses, and with their gaudy riding-habits streaming like banners behind them. Such a troop of free and easy riders, in their natural home, the saddle, makes a gay and graceful spectacle. The riding-habit I speak of is simply a long, broad scarf, like a tavern tablecloth, brilliantly colored, wrapped around the loins once, then apparently passed between the limbs and each end thrown backward over the same, and floating and flapping behind on both sides beyond the horse's tail like a couple of fancy flags; then, slipping the stirrup-irons between her toes, the girl throws her chest forward, sits up like a major-general, and goes sweeping by like the wind.

The girls put on all the finery they can on Saturday afternoon— fine black silk robes; flowing red ones that nearly put your eyes out; others as white as snow; still others that discount the rainbow; and they wear their hair in nets, and trim their jaunty hats with fresh flowers, and encircle their dusky throats with home-made necklaces of the brilliant vermilion-tinted blossom of the *ohia;* and they fill the markets and the adjacent streets with their bright presences, and smell like a rag factory on fire with their offensive cocoanut oil.

Occasionally, you see a heathen from the sunny isles away down in the South Seas, with his face and neck tattooed till he looks like the customary mendicant from Washoe who has been blown up in a mine. Some are tattooed a dead blue color down to the upper lip—masked, as it were—leaving the natural light yellow skin of Micronesia unstained from thence down; some with broad marks drawn down from hair to neck, on both sides of the face, and a strip of the original yellow skin, two inches wide, down the center— a gridiron with a spoke broken out; and some with the entire face discolored with the popular mortification tint, relieved only by one or two thin, wavy threads of natural yellow running across the face from ear to ear, and eyes twinkling out of this darkness, from under shadowing hatbrims, like stars in the dark of the moon.

Moving among the stirring crowds, you come to the poi merchants, squatting in the shade on their hams, in true native fashion, and surrounded by purchasers. (The Sandwich Islanders always squat on their hams, and who knows but they may be the original "ham sandwiches"? The thought is pregnant with interest.) The poi looks like common flour paste, and is kept in large bowls formed of a species of gourd, and capable of holding from one to three or four gallons. Poi is the chief article of food among the natives, and is prepared from the *taro* plant. The taro root looks like a thick, or, if you please, a corpulent sweet potato, in shape, but is of a light purple color when boiled. When boiled it answers as a passable substitute for bread. The buck Kanakas bake it under ground, then mash it up well with a heavy lava pestle, mix water with it until it becomes a paste, set it aside and let it ferment, and then it is poi—and an unseductive mixture it is, almost tasteless before it ferments and too sour for a luxury afterward. But nothing is more nutritious. When solely used, however, it produces acrid humors, a fact which sufficiently accounts for the humorous character of the Kanakas. I think there must be as much of a knack in handling poi as there is in eating with chopsticks. The forefinger is thrust into the mess and stirred quickly round several times and drawn as quickly out, thickly coated, just as if it were poulticed; the head is thrown back, the finger inserted in the mouth and the delicacy stripped off and swallowed—the eye closing gently, meanwhile, in a languid sort of ecstasy. Many a different finger goes into the same bowl and many a different kind of dirt and shade and quality of flavor is added to the virtues of its contents.

Around a small shanty was collected a crowd of natives buying the *awa* root. It is said that but for the use of this root the destruction of the people in former times by certain imported diseases would have been far greater than it was, and by others it is said that this is merely a fancy. All agree that poi will rejuvenate a man who is used up and his vitality almost annihilated by hard drinking, and that in some kinds of diseases it will restore health after all medicines have failed; but all are not willing to allow to the *awa* the virtues claimed for it. The natives manufacture an intoxicating drink from it which is fearful in its effects when persistently indulged in. It covers the body with dry, white scales, inflames the eyes, and causes premature decrepitude. Although the man before whose establishment we stopped has to pay a government license of eight hundred dollars a year for the exclusive right to sell *awa* root, it is said that he makes a small fortune every twelve-month; while saloon-keepers, who pay a thousand dollars a year for the privilege of retailing whisky, etc., only make a bare living.

We found the fish market crowded; for the native is very fond of fish, and *eats the article raw and alive!* Let us change the subject.

In old times here Saturday was a grand gala day indeed. All the native population of the town forsook their labors, and those of the surrounding country journeyed to the city. Then the white folks had to stay indoors, for every street was so packed with charging cavaliers and cavalieresses that it was next to impossible to thread one's way through the cavalcades without getting crippled.

At night they feasted and the girls danced the lascivious *hula hula* —a dance that is said to exhibit the very perfection of educated motion of limb and arm, hand, head, and body, and the exactest uniformity of movement and accuracy of "time." It was performed by a circle of girls with no raiment on them to speak of, who went through an infinite variety of motions and figures without prompting, and yet so true was their "time," and in such perfect concert did they move that when they were placed in a straight line, hands, arms, bodies, limbs, and heads waved, swayed, gesticulated, bowed, stooped, whirled, squirmed, twisted, and undulated as if they were part and parcel of a single individual; and it was difficult to believe they were not moved in a body by some exquisite piece of mechanism.

Of late years however, Saturday has lost most of its quondam gala features. This weekly stampede of the natives interfered too much with labor and the interests of the white folks, and by sticking in a law here, and preaching a sermon there, and by various other means, they gradually broke it up.

The demoralizing *hula hula* was forbidden to be performed, save at night, with closed doors, in presence of few spectators, and only by permission duly procured from the authorities and the payment of ten dollars for the same. There are few girls now-a-days able to dance this ancient national dance in the highest perfection of the art.

The missionaries have christianized and educated all the natives.

They all belong to the church, and there is not one of them, above the age of eight years, but can read and write with facility in the native tongue. It is the most universally educated race of people outside of China. They have any quantity of books, printed in the Kanaka language, and all the natives are fond of reading. They are inveterate churchgoers—nothing can keep them away. All this ameliorating cultivation has at last built up in the native women a profound respect for chastity—in other people. Perhaps that is enough to say on that head. The national sin will die out when the race does, but perhaps not earlier. But doubtless this purifying is not far off, when we reflect that contact with civilization and the whites has reduced the native population from *four hundred thousand* (Captain Cook's estimate), to *fifty-five thousand* in something over eighty years!

Society is a queer medley in this notable missionary, whaling, and governmental center. If you get into conversation with a stranger and experience that natural desire to know what sort of ground you are treading on by finding out what manner of man your stranger is, strike out boldly and address him as "Captain." Watch him narrowly, and if you see by his countenance that you are on the wrong tack, ask him where he preaches. It is a safe bet that he is either a missionary or captain of a whaler. I am now personally acquainted with seventy-two captains and ninety-six missionaries. The captains and ministers form one-half of the population; the third fourth is composed of common Kanakas and mercantile foreigners and their families, and the final fourth is made up of high officers of the Hawaiian government. And there are just about cats enough for three apiece all around. . . .

All the natives are Christians, now, but many of them still desert to the Great Shark God for temporary succor in time of trouble. An irruption of the great volcano of Kilauea, or an earthquake, always brings a deal of latent loyalty to the Great Shark God to the surface. It is common report that the King, educated, cultivated, and refined Christian gentleman as he undoubtedly is, still turns to the idols of his fathers for help when disaster threatens. A planter caught a shark, and one of his christianized natives testified his emancipation from the thrall of ancient superstition by assisting to dissect the shark after a fashion forbidden by his abandoned creed. But remorse shortly began to torture him. He grew moody and sought solitude; brooded over his sin, refused food, and finally said he must die and ought to die, for he had sinned against the Great Shark God and could never know peace any more. He was proof against persuasion and ridicule, and in the course of a day or two took to his bed and died, although he showed no symptom of disease. His young daughter followed his lead and suffered a like fate within the week. Superstition is ingrained in the native blood and bone and it is only natural that it should crop out in time of distress. Wherever one goes in the Islands, he will find small piles of stones by the wayside, covered with leafy offerings, placed there by the natives to appease evil spirits or honor local deities belonging to the mythology of former days.

In the rural districts of any of the Islands, the traveler hourly comes upon parties of dusky maidens bathing in the streams or in the sea without any clothing on and exhibiting no very intemperate zeal in the matter of hiding their nakedness. When the missionaries first took up their residence in Honolulu, the native women would pay their families frequent friendly visits, day by day, not even clothed with a blush. It was found a hard matter to convince them that this was rather indelicate. Finally the missionaries provided them with long, loose calico robes, and that ended the difficulty— for the women would troop through the town, stark naked, with their robes folded under their arms, march to the missionary houses and then proceed to dress!—The natives soon manifested a strong proclivity for clothing, but it was shortly apparent that they only wanted it for grandeur. The missionaries imported a quantity of hats, bonnets, and other male and female wearing apparel, instituted a general distribution, and begged the people not to come to church naked, next Sunday, as usual. And they did not; but the national spirit of unselfishness led them to divide up with neighbors who were not at the distribution, and next Sabbath the poor preachers could hardly keep countenance before their vast congregations. In the midst of the reading of a hymn a brown, stately dame would sweep up the aisle with a world of airs, with nothing in the world on but a "stovepipe" hat and a pair of cheap gloves; another dame would follow, tricked out in a man's shirt, and nothing else; another one would enter with a flourish, with simply the sleeves of a bright calico dress tied around her waist and the rest of the garment dragging behind like a peacock's tail off duty; a stately "buck" Kanaka would stalk in with a woman's bonnet on, wrong side before—only this, and nothing more; after him would stride his fellow, with the legs of a pair of pantaloons tied around his neck, the rest of his person untrammeled; in his rear would come another gentleman simply gotten up in a fiery neck-tie and a striped vest. The poor creatures were beaming with complacency and wholly unconscious of any absurdity in their appearance. They gazed at each other with happy admiration, and it was plain to see that the young girls were taking note of what each other had on, as naturally as if they had always lived in a land of Bibles and knew what churches were made for; here was the evidence of a dawning civilization. The spectacle which the congregation presented was so extraordinary and withal so moving, that the missionaries found it difficult to keep to the text and go on with the services; and by and by when the simple children of the sun began a general swapping of garments in open meeting and produced some irresistibly grotesque effects in the course of re-dressing, there was nothing for it but to cut the thing short with the benediction and dismiss the fantastic assemblage. . . .

At noon I observed a bevy of nude native young ladies bathing in the sea, and went and sat down on their clothes to keep them from being stolen. I begged them to come out, for the sea was rising and I was satisfied that they were running some risk. But they were not afraid, and presently went on with their sport. They were finished swimmers and divers, and enjoyed themselves to the last degree. They swam races, splashed and ducked and tumbled each other about, and filled the air with their laughter. It is said that the first thing an Islander learns is how to swim; learning to walk being a matter of smaller consequence, comes afterward. One hears tales of native men and women swimming ashore from vessels many miles at sea—more miles, indeed, than I dare vouch for or even mention. And they tell of a native diver who went down in thirty or forty-foot waters and brought up an anvil! I think he swallowed the anvil afterward, if my memory serves me. However I will not urge this point. . . .

But the chief pride of Maui is her dead volcano of Haleakala— which means, translated, "the house of the sun." We climbed a thousand feet up the side of this isolated colossus one afternoon; then camped, and next day climbed the remaining nine thousand feet, and anchored on the summit, where we built a fire and froze and roasted by turns, all night. With the first pallor of dawn we got

up and saw things that were new to us. Mounted on a commanding
pinnacle, we watched Nature work her silent wonders. The sea
was spread abroad on every hand, its tumbled surface seeming only
wrinkled and dimpled in the distance. A broad valley below appeared like an ample checker-board, its velvety green sugar plan-
tations alternating with dun squares of barrenness and groves of
trees diminished to mossy tufts. Beyond the valley were mountains
picturesquely grouped together; but bear in mind, we fancied that
we were looking *up* at these things—not down. We seemed to sit
in the bottom of a symmetrical bowl ten thousand feet deep, with
the valley and the skirting sea lifted away into the sky above us!
It was curious; and not only curious, but aggravating; for it was
having our trouble all for nothing, to climb ten thousand feet toward heaven and then have to look *up* at our scenery. However,
we had to be content with it and make the best of it; for all we
could do we could not coax our landscape down out of the clouds.
Formerly, when I had read an article in which Poe treated of this
singular fraud perpetrated upon the eye by isolated great altitudes,
I had looked upon the matter as an invention of his own fancy.

I have spoken of the outside view—but we had an inside one,
too. That was the yawning dead crater, into which we now and
then tumbled rocks, half as large as a barrel, from our perch, and
saw them go careering down the almost perpendicular sides, bound-
ing three hundred feet at a jump; kicking up dust-clouds wherever
they struck; diminishing to our view as they sped farther into distance; growing invisible, finally, and only betraying their course by
faint little puffs of dust; and coming to a halt at last in the bottom
of the abyss, two thousand five hundred feet down from where they
started! It was magnificent sport. We wore ourselves out at it.

The crater of Vesuvius . . . is a modest pit about a thousand feet
deep and three thousand in circumference; that of Kilauea is somewhat deeper, and *ten miles* in circumference. But what are either
of them compared to the vacant stomach of Haleakala? I will not
offer any figures of my own, but give official ones—those of Commander Wilkes, U.S.N., who surveyed it and testifies that it is
twenty-seven miles in circumference! If it had a level bottom it
would make a fine site for a city like London. It must have afforded
a spectacle worth contemplating in the old days when its furnaces
gave full rein to their anger.

Presently, vagrant white clouds came drifting along, high over the sea and the valley; then they came in couples and groups, then in imposing squadrons; gradually joining their forces, they banked themselves solidly together, a thousand feet under us, and *totally shut out land and ocean*—not a vestige of *anything* was left in view but just a little of the rim of the crater, circling away from the pinnacle whereon we sat (for a ghostly procession of wanderers from the filmy hosts without had drifted through a chasm in the crater wall and filed round and round, and gathered and sunk and blended together till the abyss was stored to the brim with a fleecy fog). Thus banked, motion ceased, and silence reigned. Clear to the horizon, league on league, the snowy floor stretched without a break—not level, but in rounded folds, with shallow creases between, and with here and there stately piles of vapory architecture lifting themselves aloft out of the common plain—some near at hand, some in the middle distances, and others relieving the monotony of the remote solitudes. There was little conversation, for the impressive scene overawed speech. I felt like the Last Man, neglected of the judgment, and left pinnacled in mid-heaven, a forgotten relic of a vanished world.

While the hush yet brooded, the messengers of the coming resurrection appeared in the East. A growing warmth suffused the horizon, and soon the sun emerged and looked out over the cloud-waste, flinging bars of ruddy light across it, staining its folds and billow-caps with blushes, purpling the shaded troughs between, and glorifying the massy vapor-palaces and cathedrals with a wasteful splendor of all blendings and combinations of rich coloring.

It was the sublimest spectacle I ever witnessed, and I think the memory of it will remain with me always.

From Following the Equator

ON THE SEVENTH DAY out we saw a dim vast bulk standing up out of the wastes of the Pacific and knew that that spectral promontory was Diamond Head, a piece of this world which I had not seen before for twenty-nine years. So we were nearing Honolulu, the capital city of the Sandwich Islands—those islands which to me were Paradise; a Paradise which I had been longing all those years to see again. Not any other thing in the world could have stirred me as the sight of that great rock did.

In the night we anchored a mile from shore. Through my port

I could see the twinkling lights of Honolulu and the dark bulk of the mountain-range that stretched away right and left. I could not make out the beautiful Nuuanu valley, but I knew where it lay, and remembered how it used to look in the old times. We used to ride up it on horseback in those days—we young people—and branch off and gather bones in a sandy region where one of the first Kamehameha's battles was fought. . . .

When I was in the Islands nearly a generation ago, I was acquainted with a young American couple who had among their belongings an attractive little son of the age of seven—attractive but not practicably companionable with me, because he knew no English. He had played from his birth with the little Kanakas on his father's plantation, and had preferred their language and would learn no other. The family removed to America a month after I arrived in the Islands, and straightway the boy began to lose his Kanaka and pick up English. By the time he was twelve he hadn't a word of Kanaka left; the language had wholly departed from his tongue and from his comprehension. Nine years later, when he was twenty-one, I came upon the family in one of the lake towns of New York, and the mother told me about an adventure which her son had been having. By trade he was now a professional diver. A passenger boat had been caught in a storm on the lake, and had gone down, carrying her people with her. A few days later the young diver descended, with his armor on, and entered the berth-saloon of the boat, and stood at the foot of the companionway, with his hand on the rail, peering through the dim water. Presently something touched him on the shoulder, and he turned and found a dead man swaying and bobbing about him and seemingly inspecting him inquiringly. He was paralyzed with fright. His entry had disturbed the water, and now he discerned a number of dim corpses making for him and wagging their heads and swaying their bodies like sleepy people trying to dance. His senses forsook him, and in that condition he was drawn to the surface. He was put to bed at home, and was soon very ill. During some days he had seasons of delirium which lasted several hours at a time; and while they lasted he talked *Kanaka* incessantly and glibly; and Kanaka only. He was still very ill, and he talked to me in that tongue; but I did not understand it, of course. The doctor-books tell us that cases like this are not uncommon. Then the doctors ought to study the cases and find out how to multiply them. Many languages and things get mislaid in a person's head, and stay mislaid for lack of this remedy.

Many memories of my former visit to the Islands came up in my mind while we lay at anchor in front of Honolulu that night. And pictures—pictures—an enchanting procession of them! I was impatient for the morning to come.

When it came it brought disappointment, of course. Cholera had broken out in the town, and we were not allowed to have any communication with the shore. Thus suddenly did my dream of twenty-nine years go to ruin. Messages came from friends, but the friends themselves I was not to have any sight of. My lecture-hall was ready, but I was not to see that, either.

Several of our passengers belonged in Honolulu, and these were sent ashore; but nobody could go ashore and return. There were people on shore who were booked to go with us to Australia, but we could not receive them; to do it would cost us a quarantine-term in Sydney. They could have escaped the day before, by ship to San Francisco; but the bars had been put up, now, and they might have to wait weeks before any ship could venture to give them a passage any whither. And there were hardships for others. An elderly lady and her son, recreation seekers from Massachusetts, had wandered westward, further and further from home, always intending to take the return track, but always concluding to go still a little further; and now here they were at anchor before Honolulu —positively their last westward-bound indulgence—they had made up their minds to that—but where is the use of making up your mind in this world? It is usually a waste of time to do it. These two would have to stay with us as far as Australia. Then they could go on around the world, or go back the way they had come; the distance and the accommodations and outlay of time would be just the same, whichever of the two routes they might elect to take. Think of it: a projected excursion of five hundred miles gradually enlarged, without any elaborate degree of intention, to a possible twenty-four thousand. However, they were used to extensions by this time, and did not mind this new one much.

And we had with us a lawyer from Victoria, who had been sent out by the Government on an international matter, and he had brought his wife with him and left the children at home with the servants—and now what was to be done? Go ashore amongst the cholera and take the risks? Most certainly not. They decided to

go on to the Fiji islands, wait there a fortnight for the next
ship, and then sail for home. They couldn't foresee that they
wouldn't see a homeward-bound ship again for six weeks, and that
no word could come to them from the children, and no word go
from them to the children in all that time. It is easy to make plans
in this world; even a cat can do it; and when one is out in those
remote oceans it is noticeable that a cat's plans and a man's are
worth about the same. There is much the same shrinkage in both,
in the matter of values.

There was nothing for us to do but sit about the decks in the
shade of the awnings and look at the distant shore. We lay in
luminous blue water; shoreward the water was green—green and
brilliant; at the shore itself it broke in a long white ruffle, and with
no crash, no sound that we could hear. The town was buried
under a mat of foliage that looked like a cushion of moss. The
silky mountains were clothed in soft, rich splendors of melting color,
and some of the cliffs were veiled in slanting mists. I recognized it
all. It was just as I had seen it long before, with nothing of its
beauty lost, nothing of its charm wanting.

Robert Louis Stevenson

THE BOTTLE IMP

In 1888 Robert Louis Stevenson started his celebrated tour of the
Pacific. He reached Hawaii from Tahiti in January, 1889, and left in
June for the Gilbert Islands and Samoa. In Honolulu he became
friendly with King Kalakaua, Liliuokalani (Kalakaua's sister and
Hawaii's last monarch), and the beautiful Princess Kaiulani, whom he
charmed with stories about Scotland. Stevenson visited Hawaii's Kona
Coast and the leper settlement at Molokai. In spite of poor health, he
finished in Hawaii his novel *The Master of Ballantrae* and wrote one
of his famous short stories, "The Bottle Imp," partly inspired by
Hawaiian lore.

Stevenson revisited Honolulu in the fall of 1893. After five weeks he
returned to Samoa, where he died in 1894.

THERE WAS A man of the island of Hawaii, whom I shall call
Keawe; for the truth is, he still lives, and his name must be
kept secret; but the place of his birth was not far from Honaunau,

where the bones of Keawe the Great lie hidden in a cave. This man was poor, brave, and active; he could read and write like a school-master; he was a first-rate mariner besides, sailed for some time in the island steamers, and steered a whale-boat on the Hamakua coast. At length it came in Keawe's mind to have a sight of the great world and foreign cities, and he shipped on a vessel bound to San Francisco.

This is a fine town, with a fine harbour, and rich people un-countable; and, in particular, there is one hill which is covered with palaces. Upon this hill Keawe was one day taking a walk, with his pocket full of money, viewing the great houses upon either hand with pleasure. "What fine houses there are!" he was thinking, "and how happy must these people be who dwell in them, and take no care for the morrow!" The thought was in his mind when he came abreast of a house that was smaller than some others, but all finished and beautified like a toy; the steps of that house shone like silver, and the borders of the garden bloomed like garlands, and the windows were bright like diamonds; and Keawe stopped and wondered at the excellence of all he saw. So stopping, he was aware of a man that looked forth upon him through a window, so clear, that Keawe could see him as you see a fish in a pool upon the reef. The man was elderly, with a bald head and a black beard; and his face was heavy with sorrow, and he bitterly sighed. And the truth of it is, that as Keawe looked in upon the man, and the man looked out upon Keawe, each envied the other.

All of a sudden the man smiled and nodded, and beckoned Keawe to enter, and met him at the door of the house.

"This is a fine house of mine," said the man, and bitterly sighed. "Would you you not care to view the chambers?"

So he led Keawe all over it, from the cellar to the roof, and there was nothing there that was not perfect of its kind, and Keawe was astonished.

"Truly," said Keawe, "this is a beautiful house; if I lived in the like of it, I should be laughing all day long. How comes it, then, that you should be sighing?"

"There is no reason," said the man, "why you should not have a house in all points similar to this, and finer, if you wish. You have some money, I suppose?"

"I have fifty dollars," said Keawe; "but a house like this will cost more than fifty dollars."

The man made a computation. "I am sorry you have no more," said he, "for it may raise you trouble in the future; but it shall be yours at fifty dollars."

"The house?" asked Keawe.

"No, not the house," replied the man; "but the bottle. For, I must tell you, although I appear to you so rich and fortunate, all my fortune, and this house itself and its garden, came out of a bottle not much bigger than a pint. This is it."

And he opened a lockfast place, and took out a round-bellied bottle with a long neck; the glass of it was white like milk, with changing rainbow colours in the grain. Withinsides something obscurely moved, like a shadow and a fire.

"This is the bottle," said the man; and, when Keawe laughed, "You do not believe me?" he added. "Try, then, for yourself. See if you can break it."

So Keawe took the bottle up and dashed it on the floor till he was weary; but it jumped on the floor like a child's ball, and was not injured.

"This is a strange thing," said Keawe. "For by the touch of it, as well as by the look, the bottle should be of glass."

"Of glass it is," replied the man, sighing more heavily than ever; "but the glass of it was tempered in the flames of hell. An imp lives in it, and that is the shadow we behold there moving; or, so I suppose. If any man buy this bottle the imp is at his command; all that he desires—love, fame, money, houses like this house, ay, or a city like this city—all are his at the word uttered. Napoleon had this bottle, and by it he grew to be the king of the world; but he sold it at the last and fell. Captain Cook had this bottle, and by it he found his way to so many islands; but he, too, sold it, and was slain upon Hawaii. For, once it is sold, the power goes and the protection; and unless a man remain content with what he has, ill will befall him."

"And yet you talk of selling it yourself?" Keawe asked.

"I have all I wish, and I am growing elderly," replied the man. "There is one thing the imp cannot do—he cannot prolong life; and, it would not be fair to conceal from you there is a drawback to the bottle; for if a man die before he sells it, he must burn in hell forever."

"To be sure, that is a drawback and no mistake," cried Keawe. "I would not meddle with the thing. I can do without a house, thank God; but there is one thing I could not be doing with one particle, and that is to be damned."

"Dear me, you must not run away with things," returned the man. "All you have to do is to use the power of the imp in moderation, and then sell it to someone else, as I do to you, and finish your life in comfort."

"Well, I observe two things," said Keawe. "All the time you keep sighing like a maid in love, that is one; and, for the other, you sell this bottle very cheap."

"I have told you already why I sigh," said the man. "It is because I fear my health is breaking up; and, as you said yourself, to die and go to the devil is a pity for anyone. As for why I sell so cheap, I must explain to you there is a peculiarity about the bottle. Long ago, when the devil brought it first upon earth, it was extremely expensive, and was sold first of all to Prester John for many millions of dollars; but it cannot be sold at all, unless sold at a loss. If you sell it for as much as you paid for it, back it comes to you again like a homing pigeon. It follows that the price has kept falling in these centuries, and the bottle is now remarkably cheap. I bought it myself from one of my great neighbours on this hill, and the price I paid was only ninety dollars. I could sell it for as high as eighty-nine dollars and ninety-nine cents, but not a penny dearer, or back the thing must come to me. Now, about this there are two bothers. First, when you offer a bottle so singular for eighty odd dollars, people suppose you to be jesting. And second—but there is no hurry about that—and I need not go into it. Only remember it must be coined money that you sell it for."

"How am I to know that this is all true?" asked Keawe.

"Some of it you can try at once," replied the man. "Give me your fifty dollars, take the bottle, and wish your fifty dollars back into your pocket. If that does not happen, I pledge you my honour I will cry off the bargain and restore your money."

"You are not deceiving me?" said Keawe.

The man bound himself with a great oath.

"Well, I will risk that much," said Keawe, "for that can do no harm," and he paid over his money to the man, and the man handed him the bottle.

"Imp of the bottle," said Keawe, "I want my fifty dollars back." And sure enough, he had scarce said the word before his pocket was heavy as ever.

"To be sure this is a wonderful bottle," said Keawe.

"And now good-morning to you, my fine fellow, and the devil go with you for me," said the man.

"Hold on," said Keawe, "I don't want any more of this fun. Here, take your bottle back."

"You have bought it for less than I paid for it," replied the man, rubbing his hands. "It is yours now; and, for my part, I am only concerned to see the back of you." And with that he rang for his Chinese servant, and had Keawe shown out of the house.

Now, when Keawe was in the street, with the bottle under his arm, he began to think. "If all is true about this bottle, I may have made a losing bargain," thinks he. "But, perhaps the man was only fooling me." The first thing he did was to count his money; the sum was exact—forty-nine dollars American money, and one Chile piece. "That looks like the truth," said Keawe. "Now I will try another part."

The streets in that part of the city were as clean as a ship's decks, and though it was noon, there were no passengers. Keawe set the bottle in the gutter and walked away. Twice he looked back, and there was the milky, round-bellied bottle where he left it. A third time he looked back, and turned a corner; but he had scarce done so, when something knocked upon his elbow, and behold! it was the long neck sticking up; and, as for the round belly, it was jammed into the pocket of his pilot-coat.

"And that looks like the truth," said Keawe.

The next thing he did was to buy a corkscrew in a shop, and go apart into a secret place in the fields. And there he tried to draw the cork, but as often as he put the screw in, out it came again, and the cork as whole as ever.

"This is some new sort of cork," said Keawe, and all at once he began to shake and sweat, for he was afraid of that bottle.

On his way back to the port-side he saw a shop where a man sold shells and clubs from the wild islands, old heathen deities, old coined money, pictures from China and Japan, and all manner of things that sailors bring in their sea-chests. And here he had an idea. So he went in and offered the bottle for a hundred dollars. The man of the shop laughed at him at first, and offered him five; but, indeed, it was a curious bottle, such glass was never blown in any human glassworks, so prettily the colours shone under the milky white, and so strangely the shadow hovered in the midst; so, after he had disputed awhile after the manner of his kind, the shopman gave Keawe sixty silver dollars for the thing and set it on a shelf in the midst of his window.

"Now," said Keawe, "I have sold that for sixty which I bought for fifty—or, to say truth, a little less, because one of my dollars was from Chili. Now I shall know the truth upon another point."

So he went back on board his ship, and when he opened his chest, there was the bottle, and had come more quickly than himself. Now Keawe had a mate on board whose name was Lopaka.

'What ails you?" said Lopaka, "that you stare in your chest?"

They were alone in the ship's forecastle, and Keawe bound him to secrecy, and told all.

"This is a very strange affair," said Lopaka; "and I fear you will be in trouble about this bottle. But there is one point very clear— that you are sure of the trouble, and you had better have the profit in the bargain. Make up your mind what you want with it; give the order, and if it is done as you desire, I will buy the bottle myself; for I have an idea of my own to get a schooner, and go trading through the islands."

"That is not my idea," said Keawe; "but to have a beautiful house and garden on the Kona Coast, where I was born, the sun shining in at the door, flowers in the garden, glass in the windows, pictures on the walls, and toys and fine carpets on the tables, for all the world like the house I was in this day—only a story higher, and with balconies all about like the king's palace; and to live there without care and make merry with my friends and relatives."

"Well," said Lopaka, "let us carry it back with us to Hawaii; and if all comes true, as you suppose, I will buy the bottle, as I said, and ask a schooner."

Upon that they were agreed, and it was not long before the ship returned to Honolulu, carrying Keawe and Lopaka, and the bottle. They were scarce come ashore when they met a friend upon the beach, who began at once to condole with Keawe.

"I do not know what I am to be condoled about," said Keawe.

"Is it possible you have not heard," said the friend, "your uncle— that good old man—is dead, and your cousin—that beautiful boy —was drowned at sea?"

Keawe was filled with sorrow, and, beginning to weep and to lament, he forgot about the bottle. But Lopaka was thinking to himself, and presently, when Keawe's grief was a little abated, "I have been thinking," said Lopaka, "had not your uncle lands in Hawaii, in the district of Kau?"

"No," said Keawe, "not in Kau: they are on the mountain-side— a little besouth Hookena."

"These lands will now be yours?" asked Lopaka.

"And so they will," says Keawe, and began again to lament for his relatives.

"No," said Lopaka, "do not lament at present. I have a thought in my mind. How if this should be the doing of the bottle? For here is the place ready for your house."

"If this be so," cried Keawe, "it is a very ill way to serve me by killing my relatives. But it may be, indeed; for it was in just such a station that I saw the house with my mind's eye."

"The house, however, is not yet built," said Lopaka.

"No, nor like to be!" said Keawe; "for though my uncle has some coffee and ava and bananas, it will not be more than will keep me in comfort; and the rest of that land is the black lava."

"Let us go to the lawyer," said Lopaka; "I have still this idea in my mind's eye."

Now, when they came to the lawyer's, it appeared Keawe's uncle had grown monstrous rich in the last days, and there was a fund of money.

"And here is the money for the house!" cried Lopaka.

"If you are thinking of a new house," said the lawyer, "here is the card of a new architect, of whom they tell me great things."

"Better and better!" cried Lopaka. "Here is all made plain for us. Let us continue to obey orders."

So they went to the architect, and he had drawings of houses on his table.

"You want something out of the way," said the architect. "How do you like this?" and he handed a drawing to Keawe.

Now, when Keawe set eyes on the drawing, he cried out aloud, for it was the picture of his thought exactly drawn.

"I am in for this house," thought he. "Little as I like the way it comes to me, I am in for it now, and I may as well take the good along with the evil."

So he told the architect all that he wished, and how he would have that house furnished, and about the pictures on the wall and the knick-knacks on the tables; and he asked the man plainly for how much he would undertake the whole affair.

The architect put many questions, and took his pen and made a computation; and when he had done he named the very sum that Keawe had inherited.

Lopaka and Keawe looked at one another and nodded.

"It is quite clear," thought Keawe, "that I am to have this house, whether or no. It comes from the devil, and I fear I will get little good by that; and of one thing I am sure, I will make no more wishes as long as I have this bottle. But with the house I am saddled, and I may as well take the good along with the evil."

So he made his terms with the architect, and they signed a paper; and Keawe and Lopaka took ship again and sailed to Australia; for it was concluded between them they should not interfere at all, but leave the architect and the bottle-imp to build and to adorn that house at their own pleasure.

The voyage was a good voyage, only all the time Keawe was holding his breath, for he had sworn he would utter no more wishes, and take no more favours, from the devil. The time was up when they got back. The architect told them that the house was ready, and Keawe and Lopaka took a passage in the *Hall,* and went down Kona way to view the house, and see if all had been done fitly according to the thought that was in Keawe's mind.

Now, the house stood on the mountain-side, visible to ships. Above, the forest ran up into the clouds of rain; below, the black lava fell in cliffs, where the kings of old lay buried. A garden bloomed about that house with every hue of flowers; and there was an orchard of papaya on the one hand and an orchard of herdprint on the other, and right in front, toward the sea, a ship's mast had been rigged up and bore a flag. As for the house, it was three stories high, with great chambers and broad balconies on each. The windows were of glass, so excellent that it was as clear as water and as bright as day. All manner of furniture adorned the chambers. Pictures hung upon the wall in golden frames—pictures of ships, and men fighting, and of the most beautiful women, and of singular places; nowhere in the world are there pictures of so bright a colour as those Keawe found hanging in his house. As for the knick-knacks, they were extraordinarily fine: chiming clocks and musical boxes, little men with nodding heads, books filled with pictures, weapons of price from all quarters of the world, and the most elegant puzzles to entertain the leisure of a solitary man. And as no one would care to live in such chambers, only to walk through and view them, the balconies were made so broad that a whole town might have lived upon them in delight; and Keawe knew not which to prefer, whether the back porch, where you got the land breeze, and looked upon the orchards and the flowers, or the front balcony, where you could drink the wind of the sea, and look down the steep wall of the mountain and see the *Hall* going by once a week or so between Hookena and the hills of Pele, or the schooners plying up the coast for wood and ava and bananas.

When they had viewed all, Keawe and Lopaka sat on the porch.

"Well," asked Lopaka, "is it all as you designed?"

"Words cannot utter it," said Keawe. "It is better than I dreamed, and I am sick with satisfaction."

"There is but one thing to consider," said Lopaka, "all this may be quite natural, and the bottle-imp have nothing whatever to say to it. If I were to buy the bottle, and got no schooner after all, I should have put my hand in the fire for nothing. I gave you my word, I know; but yet I think you would not grudge me one more proof."

"I have sworn I would take no more favours," said Keawe. "I have gone already deep enough."

"This is no favour I am thinking of," replied Lopaka. "It is only to see the imp himself. There is nothing to be gained by that, and so nothing to be ashamed of, and yet, if I once saw him, I should be sure of the whole matter. So indulge me so far, and let me see the imp; and, after that, here is the money in my hand, and I will buy it."

"There is only one thing I am afraid of," said Keawe. "The imp may be very ugly to view, and if you once set eyes upon him you might be very undesirous of the bottle."

"I am a man of my word," said Lopaka. "And here is the money betwixt us."

"Very well," replied Keawe, "I have a curiosity myself. So come, let us have one look at you, Mr. Imp."

Now as soon as that was said, the imp looked out of the bottle, and in again, swift as a lizard; and there sat Keawe and Lopaka turned to stone. The night had quite come, before either found a thought to say or voice to say it with; and then Lopaka pushed the money over and took the bottle.

"I am a man of my word," said he, "and had need to be so, or I would not touch this bottle with my foot. Well, I shall get my schooner and a dollar or two for my pocket; and then I will be rid of this devil as fast as I can. For to tell you the plain truth, the look of him has cast me down."

"Lopaka," said Keawe, "do not you think any worse of me than you can help; I know it is night, and the roads bad, and the pass by the tombs an ill place to go by so late, but I declare since I have seen that little face, I cannot eat or sleep or pray till it is gone from me. I will give you a lantern, and a basket to put the bottle in, and any picture or fine thing in all my house that takes your fancy; and be gone at once, and go sleep at Hookena with Nahinu."

"Keawe," said Lopaka, "many a man would take this ill; above all, when I am doing you a turn so friendly, as to keep my word and buy the bottle; and for that matter, the night and the dark, and the way by the tombs, must be all tenfold more dangerous to a man with such a sin upon his conscience, and such a bottle under his arm. But for my part, I am so extremely terrified myself, I have not the heart to blame you. Here I go, then; and I pray God you may be happy in your house, and I fortunate with my schooner, and both get to heaven in the end in spite of the devil and his bottle."

So Lopaka went down the mountain; and Keawe stood in his front balcony, and listened to the clink of the horse's shoes, and watched the lantern go shining down the path, and along the cliff of caves where the old dead are buried; and all the time he trembled and clasped his hands, and prayed for his friend, and gave glory to God that he himself was escaped out of that trouble.

But the next day came very brightly, and that new house of his was so delightful to behold that he forgot his terrors. One day followed another, and Keawe dwelt there in perpetual joy. He had his place on the back porch; it was there he ate and lived, and read the stories in the Honolulu newspapers; but when anyone came by they would go in and view the chambers and pictures. And the fame of the house went far and wide; it was called *Ka-Hale Nui*— the Great House—in all Kona; and sometimes the Bright House, for Keawe kept a Chinaman, who was all day dusting and furbishing; and the glass, and the gilt, and the fine stuffs, and the pictures, shone as bright as the morning. As for Keawe himself, he could not walk in the chambers without singing, his heart was so enlarged; and when ships sailed by upon the sea, he would fly his colours on the mast.

So time went by, until one day Keawe went upon a visit as far as Kailua to certain of his friends. There he was well feasted; and left as soon as he could the next morning, and rode hard, for he was impatient to behold his beautiful house; and, besides, the night then coming on was the night in which the dead of old days go abroad in the sides of Kona; and having already meddled with the devil, he was the more chary of meeting with the dead. A little beyond Honaunau, looking far ahead, he was aware of a woman bathing in the edge of the sea; and she seemed a well-grown girl, but he thought no more of it. Then he saw her white shift flutter as she put it on, and then her red holoku; and by the time he came abreast of her she was done with her toilet, and had come up from the sea, and stood by the track-side in her red holoku, and she was all freshened with the bath, and her eyes shone and were kind. Now Keawe no sooner beheld her than he drew rein.

"I thought I knew everyone in this country," said he. "How comes it that I do not know you?"

"I am Kokua, daughter of Kiano," said the girl, "and I have just returned from Oahu. Who are you?"

"I will tell you who I am in a little," said Keawe, dismounting from his horse, "but not now. For I have a thought in my mind, and if you knew who I was, you might have heard of me, and would not give me a true answer. But tell me, first of all, one thing: are you married?"

At this Kokua laughed out aloud. "It is you who ask questions," she said. "Are you married yourself?"

"Indeed, Kokua, I am not," replied Keawe, "and never thought to be until this hour. But here is the plain truth. I have met you here at the road-side, and I saw your eyes, which are like the stars, and my heart went to you as swift as a bird. And so now, if you want none of me, say so, and I will go on to my own place; but if you think me no worse than any other young man, say so, and I will turn aside to your father's for the night, and to-morrow I will talk with the good man."

Kokua said never a word, but she looked at the sea and laughed.

"Kokua," said Keawe, "if you say nothing, I will take that for the good answer; so let us be stepping to your father's door."

She went on ahead of him, still without speech; only sometimes she glanced back and glanced away again, and she kept the strings of her hat in her mouth.

Now, when they had come to the door, Kiano came out on his veranda, and cried out and welcomed Keawe by name. At that the girl looked over, for the fame of the great house had come to her ears; and, to be sure, it was a great temptation. All that evening they were very merry together; and the girl was as bold as brass under the eyes of her parents, and made a mark of Keawe, for she had a quick wit. The next day he had a word with Kiano, and found the girl alone.

"Kokua," said he, "you made a mark of me all the evening, and it is still time to bid me go. I would not tell you who I was, because I have so fine a house, and I feared you would think too much of that house and too little of the man that loves you. Now you know all, and if you wish to have seen the last of me, say so at once."

"No," said Kokua, but this time she did not laugh, nor did Keawe ask for more.

This was the wooing of Keawe; things had gone quickly; but so an arrow goes, and the ball of a rifle swifter still, and yet both may strike the target. Things had gone fast, but they had gone far also, and the thought of Keawe rang in the maiden's head; she heard his voice in the breach of the surf upon the lava, and for this young man that she had seen but twice she would have left father and mother and her native islands. As for Keawe himself, his horse flew up the path of the mountain under the cliff of tombs, and the sound of the hoofs, and the sound of Keawe singing to himself for pleasure, echoed in the caverns of the dead. He came to the Bright House, and still he was singing. He sat and ate in the broad balcony, and the Chinaman wondered at his master, to hear how he sang between the mouthfuls. The sun went down into the sea, and the night came; and Keawe walked the balconies by lamplight, high on the mountains, and the voice of his singing startled men on ships.

"Here am I now upon my high place," he said to himself. "Life may be no better; this is the mountain top; and all shelves about me toward the worse. For the first time I will light up the chambers, and bathe in my fine bath with the hot water and the cold, and sleep above in the bed of my bridal chamber."

So the Chinaman had word, and he must rise from sleep and light the furnaces; and as he walked below, beside the boilers, he heard his master singing and rejoicing above him in the lighted chambers. When the water began to be hot the Chinaman cried to his master: and Keawe went into the bath-room; and the Chinaman heard him sing as he filled the marble basin; and heard him sing, and the singing broken, as he undressed; until of a sudden, the song ceased. The Chinaman listened, and listened; he called up the house to Keawe to ask if all were well, and Keawe answered him "Yes," and bade him go to bed; but there was no more singing in the Bright House; and all night long the Chinaman heard his master's feet go round and round the balconies without repose.

Now, the truth of it was this: as Keawe undressed for his bath, he spied upon his flesh a patch like a patch of lichen on a rock, and it was then that he stopped singing. For he knew the likeness of that patch, and knew that he was fallen in the Chinese Evil.

Now, it is a sad thing for any man to fall into this sickness. And it would be a sad thing for anyone to leave a house so beautiful and so commodious, and depart from all his friends to the north coast of Molokai, between the mighty cliff and the sea-breakers. But what was that to the case of the man Keawe, he who had met his love but yesterday, and won her but that morning, and now saw all his hopes break, in a moment, like a piece of glass?

Awhile he sat upon the edge of the bath, then sprang, with a cry, and ran outside; and to and fro, to and fro, along the balcony, like one despairing.

"Very willingly could I leave Hawaii, the home of my fathers," Keawe was thinking. "Very lightly could I leave my house, the high-placed, the many windowed, here upon the mountains. Very bravely could I go to Molokai, to Kalaupapa by the cliffs, to live with the smitten and to sleep there, far from my fathers. But what wrong have I done, what sin lies upon my soul, that I should have encountered Kokua coming cool from the sea-water in the evening? Kokua, the soul ensnarer! Kokua, the light of my life! Her may I never wed, her may I look upon no longer, her may I no more handle with my loving hand; and it is for this, it is for you, O Kokua! that I pour my lamentations!"

Now you are to observe what sort of a man Keawe was, for he might have dwelt there in the Bright House for years, and no one been the wiser of his sickness; but he reckoned nothing of that, if he must lose Kokua. And again he might have wed Kokua even as he was; and so many would have done, because they have the souls of pigs; but Keawe loved the maid manfully, and he would do her no hurt and bring her in no danger.

A little beyond the midst of the night, there came in his mind the recollection of that bottle. He went round to the back porch, and called to memory the day when the devil had looked forth; and at the thought ice ran in his veins.

"A dreadful thing is the bottle," thought Keawe, "and dreadful is the imp, and it is a dreadful thing to risk the flames of hell. But what other hope have I to cure my sickness or to wed Kokua? What!" he thought, "would I beard the devil once, only to get me a house, and not face him again to win Kokua?"

Thereupon he called to mind it was the next day the *Hall* went by on her return to Honolulu. "There must I go first," he thought, "and see Lopaka. For the best hope that I have now is to find that same bottle I was so pleased to be rid of."

Never a wink could he sleep; the food stuck in his throat; but he sent a letter to Kiano, and about the time when the steamer would be coming, rode down beside the cliff to the tombs. It rained; his horse went heavily; he looked up at the black mouths of the caves, and he envied the dead that slept there and were done with trouble; and called to mind how he had galloped by the day before, and was astonished. So he came down to Hookena, and there was all the country gathered for the steamer as usual. In the shed before the store they sat and jested and passed the news; but there was no matter of speech in Keawe's bosom, and he sat in their midst and looked without on the rain falling on the houses, and the surf beating among the rocks, and the sighs arose in his throat.

"Keawe of the Bright House is out of spirits," said one to another. Indeed, and so he was, and little wonder.

Then the *Hall* came, and the whaleboat carried him on board. The after-part of the ship was full of Haoles—whites—who had been to visit the volcano, as their custom is; and the midst was crowded with Kanakas, and the fore-part with wild bulls from Hilo and horses from Kau; but Keawe sat apart from all in his sorrow, and watched for the house of Kiano. There it sat low upon the shore in the black rocks, and shaded by the coron palms, and there by the door was a red holoku, no greater than a fly, and going to and fro with a fly's busyness. "Ah, queen of my heart," he cried, "I'll venture my dear soul to win you!"

Soon after darkness fell and the cabins were lit up, and the Haoles sat and played at the cards and drank whiskey as their custom is; but Keawe walked the deck all night; and all the next day, as they streamed under the lee of Maui or of Molokai, he was still pacing to and fro like a wild animal in a menagerie.

Toward evening they passed Diamond Head, and came to the pier of Honolulu. Keawe stepped out among the crowd and began to ask for Lopaka. It seemed he had become the owner of a schooner—none better in the islands—and was gone upon an adventure as far as Pola-Pola or Kahiki; so there was no help to be looked for from Lopaka. Keawe called to mind a friend of his, a lawyer in the town (I must not tell his name), and inquired of him. They said he was grown suddenly rich, and had a fine new house upon Waikiki shore; and this put a thought in Keawe's head, and he called a hack and drove to the lawyer's house.

The house was all brand new, and the trees in the garden no greater than walking-sticks, and the lawyer, when he came, had the air of a man well pleased.

"What can I do to serve you?" said the lawyer.

"You are a friend of Lopaka's," replied Keawe, "and Lopaka purchased from me a certain piece of goods that I thought you might enable me to trace."

The lawyer's face became very dark. "I do not profess to misunderstand you, Mr. Keawe," said he, "though this is an ugly business to be stirring in. You may be sure I know nothing, but yet I have a guess, and if you would apply in a certain quarter I think you might have news."

And he named the name of a man, which, again, I had better not repeat. So it was for days, and Keawe went from one to another, finding everywhere new clothes and carriages, and fine new houses and men everywhere in great contentment, although, to be sure, when he hinted at his business their faces would cloud over.

"No doubt I am upon the track," thought Keawe. "These new clothes and carriages are all the gifts of the little imp, and these glad faces are the faces of men who have taken their profit and got rid of the accursed thing in safety. When I see pale cheeks and hear sighing, I shall know that I am near the bottle."

So it befell at last that he was recommended to a Haole in Beretania Street. When he came to the door, about the hour of the evening meal, there were the usual marks of the new house, and the young garden, and the electric light shining in the windows; but when the owner came, a shock of hope and fear ran through Keawe; for here was a young man, white as a corpse, and black about the eyes, the hair shedding from his head, and such a look in his countenance as a man may have when he is waiting for the gallows.

"Here it is, to be sure," thought Keawe, and so with this man he noways veiled his errand. "I am come to buy the bottle," said he.

At the word, the young Haole of Beretania Street reeled against the wall.

"The bottle!" he gasped. "To buy the bottle!" Then he seemed to choke, and seizing Keawe by the arm, carried him into a room and poured out wine in two glasses.

"Here is my respects," said Keawe, who had been much about with Haoles in his time. "Yes," he added, "I am come to buy the bottle. What is the price by now?"

At that word the young man let his glass slip through his fingers, and looked upon Keawe like a ghost.

"The price," says he; "the price! You do not know the price?"

"It is for that I am asking you," returned Keawe. "But why are you so much concerned? Is there anything wrong about the price?"

"It has dropped a great deal in value since your time, Mr. Keawe," said the young man, stammering.

"Well, well, I shall have the less to pay for it," says Keawe. "How much did it cost you?"

The young man was as white as a sheet. "Two cents," said he.

"What?" cried Keawe, "two cents? Why, then, you can only sell it for one. And he who buys it—" The words died upon Keawe's tongue; he who bought it could never sell it again, the bottle and the bottle imp must abide with him until he died, and when he died must carry him to the red end of hell.

The young man of Beretania Street fell upon his knees. "For God's sake, buy it!" he cried. "You can have all my fortune in the bargain. I was mad when I bought it at that price. I had em-bezzled money at my store; I was lost else; I must have gone to jail."

"Poor creature," said Keawe, "you would risk your soul upon so desperate an adventure, and to avoid the proper punishment of your own disgrace; and you think I could hesitate with love in

front of me. Give me the bottle, and the change which I make sure
you have all ready. Here is a five-cent piece."

It was as Keawe supposed; the young man had the change ready
in a drawer; the bottle changed hands, and Keawe's fingers were
no sooner clasped upon the stalk than he had breathed his wish to
be a clean man. And, sure enough, when he got home to his room,
and stripped himself before a glass, his flesh was whole like an
infant's. And here was the strange thing: he had no sooner seen
this miracle than his mind was changed within him, and he cared
naught for the Chinese Evil, and little enough for Kokua; and had
but the one thought, that here he was bound to the bottle imp for
time and for eternity, and had no better hope but to be a cinder
forever in the flames of hell. Away ahead of him he saw them blaze
with his mind's eye, and his soul shrank, and darkness fell upon
the light.

When Keawe came to himself a little, he was aware it was the
night when the band played at the hotel. Thither he went, because
he feared to be alone; and there, among happy faces, walked to and
fro, and heard the tunes go up and down, and saw Berger beat
the measure, and all the while he heard the flames crackle, and saw
the red fire burning in the bottomless pit. Of a sudden the band
played *Hiki-ao-ao*; that was a song that he had sung with Kokua,
and at the strain courage returned to him.

"It is done now," he thought, "and once more let me take the
good along with the evil."

So it befell that he returned to Hawaii by the first steamer, and
as soon as it could be managed he was wedded to Kokua, and
carried her up the mountain-side to the Bright House.

Now it was so with these two, that when they were together
Keawe's heart was stilled; but as soon as he was alone he fell into
a brooding horror, and heard the flames crackle, and saw the red
fire burn in the bottomless pit. The girl, indeed, had come to him
wholly; her heart leaped in her side at sight of him, her hand clung
to his; and she was so fashioned, from the hair upon her head to
the nails upon her toes, that none could see her without joy. She
was pleasant in her nature. She had the good word always. Full of
song she was, and went to and fro in the Bright House, the brightest
thing in its three stories, carolling like the birds. And Keawe
beheld and heard her with delight, and then must shrink upon one

side, and weep and groan to think upon the price that he had paid for her; and then he must dry his eyes, and wash his face, and go and sit with her on the broad balconies, joining in her songs, and, with a sick spirit, answering her smiles.

There came a day when her feet began to be heavy and her songs more rare; and now it was not Keawe only that would weep apart, but each would sunder from the other and sit in opposite balconies with the whole width of the Bright House betwixt. Keawe was so sunk in his despair, he scarce observed the change, and was only glad he had more hours to sit alone and brood upon his destiny, and was not so frequently condemned to pull a smiling face on a sick heart. But one day, coming softly through the house, he heard the sound of a child sobbing, and there was Kokua rolling her face upon the balcony floor, and weeping like the lost.

"You do well to weep in this house, Kokua," he said. "And yet I would give the head off my body that you (at least) might have been happy."

"Happy!" she cried. "Keawe, when you lived alone in your Bright House you were the word of the island for a happy man; laughter and song were in your mouth, and your face was as bright as the sunrise. Then you wedded poor Kokua; and the good God knows what is amiss in her—but from that day you have not smiled. Oh!" she cried, "what ails me? I thought I was pretty, and I knew I loved him. What ails me, that I throw this cloud upon my husband?"

"Poor Kokua," said Keawe. He sat down by her side, and sought to take her hand; but that she plucked away. "Poor Kokua," he said, again. "My poor child—my pretty. And I had thought all this while to spare you! Well, you shall know all. Then, at least, you will pity poor Keawe; then you will understand how much he loved you in the past—that he dared hell for your possession—and how much he loves you still (the poor condemned one), that he can yet call up a smile when he beholds you."

With that, he told her all, even from the beginning.

"You have done this for me?" she cried. "Ah, well, then what do I care!" and she clasped and wept upon him.

"Ah, child!" said Keawe, "and yet, when I consider the fire of hell, I care a good deal!"

"Never tell me," said she, "no man can be lost because he loved Kokua, and no other fault. I tell you, Keawe, I shall save you with these hands, or perish in your company. What! you loved me and gave your soul, and you think I will not die to save you in return?"

"Ah, my dear, you might die a hundred times, and what difference would that make?" he cried, "except to leave me lonely till the time comes of my damnation?"

"You know nothing," said she. "I was educated in a school in Honolulu; I am no common girl. And I tell you I shall save my lover. What is this you say about a cent? But all the world is not American. In England they have a piece they call a farthing, which is about half a cent. Ah! sorrow!" she cried, "that makes it scarcely better, for the buyer must be lost, and we shall find none so brave as my Keawe! But, then, there is France; they have a small coin there which they call a centime, and these go five to the cent or thereabout. We could not do better. Come, Keawe, let us go to the French islands; let us go to Tahiti, as fast as ships can bear us. There we have four centimes, three centimes, two centimes, one centime; for possible sales to come and go on; and two of us to push the bargain. Come, my Keawe! kiss me, and banish care. Kokua will defend you."

"Gift of God!" he cried. "I cannot think that God will punish me for desiring aught so good! Be it as you will, then, take me where you please: I put my life and my salvation in your hands."

Early the next day Kokua was about her preparations. She took Keawe's chest that he went with sailoring; and first she put the bottle in a corner, and then packed it with the richest of their clothes and the bravest of the knick-knacks in the house. "For," said she, "we must seem to be rich folks, or who will believe in the bottle?" All the time of her preparation she was as gay as a bird; only when she looked upon Keawe the tears would spring in her eye, and she must run and kiss him. As for Keawe, a weight was off his soul; now that he had his secret shared, and some hope in front of him, he seemed like a new man, his feet went lightly on the earth, and his breath was good to him again. Yet was terror still at his elbow; and ever and again, as the wind blows out a taper, hope died in him, and he saw the flames toss and the red fire burn in hell.

It was given out in the country they were gone pleasuring to the States, which was thought a strange thing, and yet not so strange as the truth, if any could have guessed it. So they went to Honolulu in the *Hall,* and thence in the *Umatilla* to San Francisco with a crowd of Haoles, and at San Francisco took their passage by the mail brigantine, the *Tropic Bird,* for Papeete, the chief place of the French in the south islands. Thither they came, after a pleasant voyage, on a fair day of the Trade wind, and saw the reef with the surf breaking and Motuiti with its palms, and the schooner riding withinside, and the white houses of the town low down along the shore among green trees, and overhead the mountains and the clouds of Tahiti, the wise island.

It was judged the most wise to hire a house, which they did accordingly, opposite the British Consul's, to make a great parade of money, and themselves conspicuous with carriages and horses. This it was very easy to do, so long as they had the bottle in their possession; for Kokua was more bold than Keawe, and, whenever she had a mind, called on the imp for twenty or a hundred dollars. At this rate they soon grew to be remarked in the town; and the strangers from Hawaii, their riding and their driving, the fine holokus, and the rich lace of Kokua, became the matter of much talk.

They got on well after the first with the Tahitian language, which is indeed like to the Hawaiian, with a change of certain letters; and as soon as they had any freedom of speech, began to push the bottle. You are to consider it was not an easy subject to introduce; it was not easy to persuade people you are in earnest, when you offer to sell them for four centimes the spring of health and riches inexhaustible. It was necessary besides to explain the dangers of the bottle; and either people disbelieved the whole thing and laughed, or they thought the more of the darker part, became overcast with gravity, and drew away from Keawe and Kokua, as from persons who had dealings with the devil. So far from gaining ground, these two began to find they were avoided in the town; the children ran away from them screaming, a thing intolerable to Kokua; Catholics crossed themselves as they went by; and all persons began with one accord to disengage themselves from their advances.

Depression fell upon their spirits. They would sit at night in their new house, after a day's weariness, and not exchange one word, or the silence would be broken by Kokua bursting suddenly into sobs. Sometimes they would pray together; sometimes they would have the bottle out upon the floor, and sit all evening watching how the shadow hovered in the midst. At such times they would be afraid to go to rest. It was long ere slumber came to them, and, if either dozed off, it would be to wake and find the other silently weeping in the dark, or, perhaps, to wake alone, the other having fled from the house and the neighbourhood of that bottle, to pace under the bananas in the little garden, or to wander on the beach by moonlight.

One night it was so when Kokua awoke. Keawe was gone. She felt in the bed and his place was cold. Then fear fell upon her, and she sat up in bed. A little moonshine filtered through the shutters. The room was bright, and she could spy the bottle on the floor. Outside it blew high, the great trees of the avenue cried aloud, and the fallen leaves rattled in the veranda. In the midst of this Kokua was aware of another sound; whether of a beast or of a man she could scarce tell, but it was as sad as death, and cut her to the soul. Softly she arose, set the door ajar, and looked forth into the moonlit yard. There, under the bananas, lay Keawe, his mouth in the dust, and as he lay he moaned.

It was Kokua's first thought to run forward and console him; her second potently withheld her. Keawe had borne himself before his wife like a brave man; it became her little in the hour of weakness to intrude upon his shame. With the thought she drew back into the house.

"Heaven," she thought, "how careless have I been—how weak! It is he, not I, that stands in this eternal peril; it was he, not I, that took the curse upon his soul. It is for my sake, and for the love of a creature of so little worth and such poor help, that he now beholds so close to him the flames of hell—ay, and smells the smoke of it, lying without there in the wind and moonlight. Am I so dull of spirit that never till now I have surmised my duty, or have I seen it before and turned aside? But now, at lea t, I take up my soul in both the hands of my affection; now I say farewell to the white steps of heaven and the waiting faces of my friends. A love for a love, and let mine be equalled with Keawe's! A soul for a soul, and be it mine to perish!"

She was a deft woman with her hands, and was soon apparelled. She took in her hands the change—the precious centimes they kept ever at their side; for this coin is little used, and they had made provision at the government office. When she was forth in the avenue clouds came on the wind, and the moon was blackened. The town slept, and she knew not whither to turn till she heard one coughing in the shadow of the trees.

"Old man," said Kokua, "what do you here abroad in the cold night?"

The old man could scarce express himself for coughing, but she made out that he was old and poor, and a stranger in the island.

"Will you do me a service?" said Kokua. "As one stranger to another, and as an old man to a young woman, will you help a daughter of Hawaii?"

"Ah," said the old man. "So you are the witch from the eight islands, and even my old soul you seek to entangle. But I have heard of you, and defy your wickedness."

"Sit down here," said Kokua, "and let me tell you a tale." And she told him the story of Keawe from the beginning to the end.

"And now," said she, "I am his wife, whom he bought with his soul's welfare. And what should I do? If I went to him myself and offered to buy it, he will refuse. But if you go, he will sell it eagerly; I will await you here; you will buy it for four centimes, and I will buy it again for three. And the Lord strengthen a poor girl!"

"If you meant falsely," said the old man, "I think God would strike you dead."

"He would!" cried Kokua. "Be sure he would. I could not be so treacherous, God would not suffer it."

"Give me the four centimes and await me here," said the old man.

Now, when Kokua stood alone in the street, her spirit died. The wind roared in the trees, and it seemed to her the rushing of the flames of hell; the shadows towered in the light of the street lamp, and they seemed to her the snatching hands of evil ones. If she had had the strength, she must have run away, and if she had had the breath she must have screamed aloud; but, in truth, she could do neither, and stood and trembled in the avenue, like an affrighted child.

Then she saw the old man returning, and he had the bottle in his hand.

"I have done your bidding," said he, "I left your husband weeping like a child; to-night he will sleep easy." And he held the bottle forth.

"Before you give it me," Kokua panted, "take the good with the evil—ask to be delivered from your cough."

"I am an old man," replied the other, "and too near the gate of the grave to take a favour from the devil. But what is this? Why do you not take the bottle? Do you hesitate?"

"Not hesitate!" cried Kokua. "I am only weak. Give me a moment. It is my hand resists, my flesh shrinks back from the accursed thing. One moment only!"

The old man looked upon Kokua kindly. "Poor child!" said he, "you fear: your soul misgives you. Well, let me keep it. I am old, and can never more be happy in this world, and as for the next—"

"Give it to me!" gasped Kokua. "There is your money. Do you think I am so base as that? Give me the bottle."

"God bless you, child," said the old man.

Kokua concealed the bottle under her holoku, said farewell to the old man, and walked off along the avenue, she cared not whither. For all roads were now the same to her, and led equally to hell. Sometimes she walked, and sometimes ran; sometimes she screamed out loud in the night, and sometimes lay by the wayside in the dust and wept. All that she had heard of hell came back to her; she saw the flames blaze, and she smelled the smoke, and her flesh withered on the coals.

Near day she came to her mind again, and returned to the house. It was even as the old man said—Keawe slumbered like a child. Kokua stood and gazed upon his face.

"Now, my husband," said she, "it is your turn to sleep. When you wake it will be your turn to sing and laugh. But for poor Kokua, alas! that meant no evil—for poor Kokua no more sleep, no more singing, no more delight, whether in earth or Heaven."

With that she lay down in the bed by his side, and her misery was so extreme that she fell in a deep slumber instantly.

Late in the morning her husband woke her and gave her the good news. It seemed he was silly with delight, for he paid no heed to her distress, ill though she dissembled it. The words stuck in her mouth, it mattered not; Keawe did the speaking. She ate not a bite, but who was to observe it? For Keawe cleared the dish. Kokua saw and heard him, like some strange thing in a dream; there were times when she forgot or doubted, and put her hands to her brow; to know herself doomed and hear her husband babble, seemed so monstrous.

All the while Keawe was eating and talking, and planning the time of their return, and thanking her for saving him, and fondling her, and calling her the true helper after all. He laughed at the old man that was fool enough to buy that bottle.

"A worthy old man he seemed," Keawe said. "But no one can

judge by appearances. For why did the old reprobate require the bottle?"

"My husband," said Kokua, humbly, "his purpose may have been good."

Keawe laughed like an angry man.

"Fiddle-de-dee!" cried Keawe. "An old rogue, I tell you; and an old ass to boot. For the bottle was hard enough to sell at four centimes; and at three it will be quite impossible. The margin is not broad enough, the thing begins to smell of scorching—brr!" said he, and shuddered. "It is true I bought it myself at a cent, when I knew not there were smaller coins. I was a fool for my pains; there will never be found another, and whoever has that bottle now will carry it to the pit."

"O my husband!" said Kokua. "Is it not a terrible thing to save oneself by the eternal ruin of another? It seems to me I could not laugh. I would be humbled. I would be filled with melancholy. I would pray for the poor holder."

Then Keawe, because he felt the truth of what she said, grew the more angry. "Heighty-teighty!" cried he. "You may be filled with melancholy if you please. It is not the mind of a good wife. If you thought at all of me, you would sit shamed."

Thereupon he went out, and Kokua was alone.

What chance had she to sell that bottle at two centimes. None, she perceived. And if she had any, here was her husband hurrying her away to a country where there was nothing lower than a cent. And here—on the morrow of her sacrifice—was her husband leaving her and blaming her.

She would not even try to profit by what time she had, but sat in the house, and now had the bottle out and viewed it with unutterable fear, and now, with loathing, hid it out of sight.

By and by, Keawe came back, and would have her take a drive.

"My husband, I am ill," she said. "I am out of heart. Excuse me, I can take no pleasure."

Then was Keawe more wroth than ever. With her, because he thought she was brooding over the case of the old man; and with himself, because he thought she was right, and was ashamed to be so happy.

"This is your truth," cried he, "and this your affection! Your husband is just saved from eternal ruin, which he encountered for the love of you—and you can take no pleasure! Kokua, you have a disloyal heart."

He went forth again furious, and wandered in the town all day. He met friends, and drank with them; they hired a carriage and drove into the country, and there drank again. All the time Keawe was ill at ease, because he was taking this pastime while his wife was sad, and because he knew in his heart that she was more right than he; and the knowledge made him drink the deeper.

Now, there was an old brutal Haole drinking with him, one that had been a boatswain of a whaler—a runaway, a digger in gold mines, a convict in prisons. He had a low mind and a foul mouth; he loved to drink and to see others drunken; and he pressed the glass upon Keawe. Soon there was no more money in the company.

"Here, you!" says the boatswain, "you are rich, you have been always saying. You have a bottle or some foolishness."

"Yes," says Keawe, "I am rich; I will go back and get some money from my wife, who keeps it."

"That's a bad idea, mate," said the boatswain. "Never you trust a petticoat with dollars. They're all as false as water; you keep an eye on her."

Now, this word struck in Keawe's mind; for he was muddled with what he had been drinking.

"I should not wonder but she was false, indeed," thought he. "Why else should she be so cast down at my release? But I will show her I am not the man to be fooled. I will catch her in the act."

Accordingly, when they were back in town, Keawe bade the boatswain wait for him at the corner, by the old calaboose, and went forward up the avenue alone to the door of his house. The night had come again; there was a light within, but never a sound; and Keawe crept about the corner, opened the back door softly, and looked in.

There was Kokua on the floor, the lamp at her side; before her was a milk-white bottle, with a round belly and a long neck; and as she viewed it, Kokua wrung her hands.

A long time Keawe stood and looked in the doorway. At first he was struck stupid; and then fear fell upon him that the bargain had been made amiss, and the bottle had come back to him as it came at San Francisco; and at that his knees were loosened, and the fumes of the wine departed from his head like mists off a river in the morning. And then he had another thought; and it was a strange one, that made his cheeks to burn.

"I must make sure of this," thought he.

So he closed the door, and went softly round the corner again, and then came noisily in, as though he were but now returned. And, lo! by the time he opened the front door no bottle was to be seen; and Kokua sat in a chair and started up like one awakened out of sleep.

"I have been drinking all day and making merry," said Keawe. "I have been with good companions, and now I only came back for money, and return to drink and carouse with them again."

Both his face and voice were as stern as judgment, but Kokua was too troubled to observe.

"You do well to use your own, my husband," said she, and her words trembled.

"Oh, I do well in all things," said Keawe, and he went straight to the chest and took out money. But he looked besides in the corner where they kept the bottle, and there was no bottle there.

At that the chest heaved upon the floor like a sea-billow, and the house span about him like a wreath of smoke, for he saw she was lost now, and there was no escape. "It is what I feared," he thought. "It is she who has bought it."

And then he came to himself a little and rose up; but the sweat streamed on his face as thick as the rain and as cold as the well-water.

"Kokua," said he, "I said to you to-day what ill became me. Now I return to house with my jolly companions," and at that he laughed a little quietly. "I will take more pleasure in the cup if you forgive me."

She clasped his knees in a moment; she kissed his knees with flowing tears.

"Oh," she cried, "I asked but a kind word!"

"Let us never one think hardly of the other," said Keawe, and was gone out of the house.

Now, the money that Keawe had taken was only some of that store of centime pieces they had laid in at their arrival. It was very sure he had no mind to be drinking. His wife had given her soul for him, now he must give his for hers; no other thought was in the world with him.

At the corner, by the old calaboose, there was the boatswain waiting.

"My wife has the bottle," said Keawe, "and, unless you help me to recover it, there can be no more money and no more liquor tonight."

"You do not mean to say you are serious about that bottle?" cried the boatswain.

"There is the lamp," said Keawe. "Do I look as if I was jesting?"

"That is so," said the boatswain. "You look as serious as a ghost."

"Well, then," said Keawe, 'here are two centimes; you must go to my wife in the house, and offer her these for the bottle, which (if I am not much mistaken) she will give you instantly. Bring it to me here, and I will buy it back from you for one; for that is the law with this bottle, that it still must be sold for a less sum. But whatever you do, never breathe a word to her that you have come from me."

"Mate, I wonder are you making a fool of me?" asked the boatswain.

"It will do you no harm if I am," returned Keawe.

"That is so, mate," said the boatswain.

"And if you doubt me," added Keawe, "you can try. As soon as you are clear of the house, wish to have your pocket full of money, or a bottle of the best rum, or what you please, and you will see the virtue of the thing."

"Very well, Kanaka," says the boatswain. "I will try; but if you are having your fun out of me, I will take my fun out of you with a belaying-pin."

So the whaler-man went off up the avenue; and Keawe stood and waited. It was near the same spot where Kokua had waited the night before; but Keawe was more resolved, and never faltered in his purpose; only his soul was bitter with despair.

It seemed a long time he had to wait before he heard a voice singing in the darkness of the avenue. He knew the voice to be the boatswain's; but it was strange how drunken it appeared upon a sudden.

Next the man himself came stumbling into the light of the lamp. He had the devil's bottle buttoned in his coat; another bottle was in his hand; and even as he came in view he raised it to his mouth and drank.

"You have it," said Keawe. "I see that."

"Hands off!" cried the boatswain, jumping back. "Take a step near me, and I'll smash your mouth. You thought you could make a cat's paw of me, did you?"

"What do you mean?" cried Keawe.

"Mean?" cried the boatswain. "This is a pretty good bottle, this is; that's what I mean. How I got it for two centimes I can't make out; but I am sure you sha'n't have it for one."

"You mean you won't sell?" gasped Keawe.

"No, sir," cried the boatswain. "But I'll give you a drink of the rum, if you like."

"I tell you," said Keawe, "the man who has that bottle goes to hell."

"I reckon I'm going anyway," returned the sailor; "and this bottle's the best thing to go with I've struck yet. No, sir!" he cried again, "this is my bottle now, and you can go and fish for another."

"Can this be true?" Keawe cried. "For your own sake, I beseech you, sell it me!"

"I don't value any of your talk," replied the boatswain. "You thought I was a flat, now you see I'm not; and there's an end. If you won't have a swallow of the rum, I'll have one myself. Here's your health, and good-night to you!"

So off he went down the avenue toward town, and there goes the bottle out of the story.

But Keawe ran to Kokua light as the wind; and great was their joy that night; and great, since then, has been the peace of all their days in the Bright House.

Jack London

THE WATER BABY

JACK LONDON first came to Hawaii in 1907, on board his small yacht, the *Snark*, on a projected round-the-world trip which ended in Australia. At that time he was world-famous, particularly for his novels *The Call of the Wild* and *The Sea Wolf*. He stayed in Honolulu for four months. In 1915 he returned to Hawaii and stayed almost a year.

Hawaii fascinated Jack London. One of his most striking short stories, "The Water Baby," which follows, has a Hawaiian setting.

I LENT A WEARY ear to old Kohokumu's interminable chanting of the deeds and adventures of Maui, the Promethean demigod of Polynesia who fished up dry land from ocean depths with hooks made fast to heaven, who lifted up the sky whereunder previously men had gone on all fours, not having space to stand erect, and who made the sun with its sixteen snared legs stand still and agree thereafter to traverse the sky more slowly—the sun being evidently a trade-unionist and believing in the six-hour day, while Maui stood for the open shop and the twelve-hour day.

"Now this," said Kohokumu, "is from Queen Liliuokalani's own family mele:

"Maui became restless and fought the sun
With a noose that he laid.
And winter won the sun,
And summer was won by Maui. . . ."

Born in the Islands myself, I know the Hawaiian myths better than this old fisherman, although I possessed not his memorization that enabled him to recite them endless hours.

"And you believe all this?" I demanded in the sweet Hawaiian tongue.

"It was a long time ago," he pondered. "I never saw Maui with my own eyes. But all our old men from all the way back tell us these things, as I, an old man, tell them to my sons and grandsons, who will tell them to their sons and grandsons all the way ahead to come."

"You believe," I persisted, "that whopper of Maui roping the sun like a wild steer, and that other whopper of heaving up the sky from off the earth?"

"I am of little worth, and am not wise, O Lakana," my fisherman made answer. "Yet have I read the Hawaiian bible the missionaries translated to us, and there have I read that your Big Man of the Beginning made the earth and sky and sun and moon and stars, and all manner of animals from horses to cockroaches and from centipedes and mosquitoes to sea lice and jellyfish, and man and woman and everything, and all in six days. Why, Maui didn't do anything like that much. He didn't *make* anything. He just put things in order, that was all, and it took him a long, long time to make the improvements. And anyway, it is much easier and more reasonable to believe the little whopper than the big whopper."

And what could I reply? He had me on the matter of reasonableness. Besides, my head ached. And the funny thing, as I admitted to myself, was that evolution teaches in no uncertain voice that man did run on all fours ere he came to walk upright, that astronomy states flatly that the speed of the revolution of the earth on its axis has diminished steadily, thus increasing the length of day, and that the seismologists accept that all the islands of Hawaii were elevated from the ocean floor by volcanic action.

Fortunately, I saw a bamboo pole floating on the surface several hundred feet away, suddenly up-end and start a very devil's dance. This was a diversion from the profitless discussion, and Kohokumu and I dipped our paddles and raced the little outrigger canoe to the dancing pole. Kohokumu caught the line that was fast to the butt of the pole and underhanded it in until a two-foot *ukikiki*, battling fiercely to the end, flashed its wet silver in the sun and began beating a tattoo on the inside bottom of the canoe. Kohokumu picked up a squirming, slimy squid, with his teeth bit a chunk of live bait out of it, attached the bait to the hook, and dropped line and sinker overside. The stick floated flat on the surface of the water, and the canoe drifted slowly away. With a survey of the crescent composed of a score of such sticks all lying flat, Kohokumu wiped his hands on his naked sides and lifted the wearisome and centuries-old chant of Kuali:

> "Oh, the great fishhook of Maui!
> *Manai-i-ka-lani*—'made fast to the heavens'!
> An earth-twisted cord ties the hook,
> Engulfed from lofty Kauiki!
> Its bait the red-billed Alae,
> The bird to Hina sacred!
> It sinks far down to Hawaii,
> Struggling and in pain dying!
> Caught is the land beneath the water,
> Floated up, up to the surface,
> But Hina hid a wing of the bird
> And broke the land beneath the water!
> Below was the bait snatched away
> And eaten at once by the fishes,
> The Ulua of the deep muddy places!"

His aged voice was hoarse and scratchy from the drinking of too much swipes at a funeral the night before, nothing of which contributed to make me less irritable. My head ached. The sun glare on the water made my eyes ache, while I was suffering more than half a touch of mal de mer from the antic conduct of the outrigger on the blobby sea. The air was stagnant. In the lee of Waihee, between the white beach and the reef, no whisper of breeze eased the still sultriness. I really think I was too miserable to summon the resolution to give up the fishing and go in to shore.

Lying back with closed eyes, I lost count of time. I even forgot that Kohokumu was chanting till reminded of it by his ceasing. An exclamation made me bare my eyes to the stab of the sun. He was gazing down through the water glass.

"It's a big one," he said, passing me the device and slipping overside feet first into the water.

He went under without splash and ripple, turned over, and swam down. I followed his progress through the water glass, which is merely an oblong box a couple of feet long, open at the top, the bottom sealed water-tight with a sheet of ordinary glass.

Now Kohokumu was a bore, and I was squeamishly out of sorts with him for his volubleness, but I could not help admiring him as I watched him go down. Past seventy years of age, lean as a spear, and shriveled like a mummy, he was doing what few young athletes of my race would do or could do. It was forty feet to bottom. There, partly exposed but mostly hidden under the bulge of a coral lump, I could discern his objective. His keen eyes had caught the projecting tentacle of a squid. Even as he swam, the tentacle was lazily withdrawn, so that there was no sign of the creature. But the brief exposure of the portion of one tentacle had advertised its owner as a squid of size.

The pressure at a depth of forty feet is no joke for a young man, yet it did not seem to inconvenience this oldster. I am certain it never crossed his mind to be inconvenienced. Unarmed, bare of body save for a brief *malo* or loin cloth, he was undeterred by the formidable creature that constituted his prey. I saw him steady himself with his right hand on the coral lump, and thrust his left arm into the hole to the shoulder. Half a minute elapsed, during which time he seemed to be groping and rooting around with his left hand. Then tentacle after tentacle, myriad-suckered and wildly waving, emerged. Laying hold of his arm, they writhed and coiled about his flesh like so many snakes. With a heave and a jerk appeared the entire squid, a proper devilfish or octopus.

But the old man was in no hurry for his natural element, the air above the water. There, forty feet beneath, wrapped about by an octopus that measured nine feet across from tentacle tip to tentacle tip and that could well drown the stoutest swimmer, he cooly and casually did the one thing that gave to him his empery over the monster. He shoved his lean, hawklike face into the very center of the slimy, squirming mass, and with his several ancient fangs bit into the heart and the life of the matter. This accomplished, he came upward slowly, as a swimmer should who is changing atmosphere from the depths. Alongside the canoe, still in the water and peeling off the grisly clinging thing, the incorrigible old sinner burst into the *pule* of triumph which had been chanted by countless squid-catching generations before him:

> "Oh Kanaloa of the taboo nights!
> Stand upright on the solid floor!
>
> Stand upon the floor where lies the squid!
> Stand up to take the squid of the deep sea!
> Rise up, O Kanaloa!
> Stir up! Stir up! Let the squid awake!
> Let the squid that lies flat awake! Let the squid
> that lies spread out. . . ."

I closed my eyes and ears, not offering to lend him a hand, secure in the knowledge that he could climb back unaided into the unstable craft without the slightest risk of upsetting it.

"A very fine squid," he crooned. "It is a wahine squid. I shall now sing to you the song of the cowrie shell, the red cowrie shell that we used as a bait for the squid—"

"You were disgraceful last night at the funeral," I headed him off. "I heard all about it. You made much noise. You sang till everybody was deaf. You insulted the son of the widow. You drank swipes like a pig. Swipes are not good for your extreme age. Some day you will wake up dead. You ought to be a wreck to-day—"

"Ha!" he chuckled. "And you, who drank no swipes, who was a babe unborn when I was already an old man, who went to bed last night with the sun and the chickens—this day you are a wreck.

Explain me that. My ears are as thirsty to listen as was my throat thirsty last night. And here to-day, behold, I am, as that Englishman who came here in his yacht used to say, I am in fine form, in devilish fine form."

"I give you up," I retorted, shrugging my shoulders. "Only one thing is clear, and that is that the devil doesn't want you. Report of your singing has gone before you."

"No," he pondered the idea carefully. "It is not that. The devil will be glad for my coming, for I have some very fine songs for him, and scandals and old gossips of the high *aliis* that will make him scratch his sides. So let me explain to you the secret of my birth. The Sea is my mother. I was born in a double canoe, during a Kona gale, in the channel of Kahoolawe. From her, the Sea, my mother, I received my strength. Whenever I return to her arms, as for a breast clasp, as I have returned this day, I grow strong again and immediately. She, to me, is the milk giver, the life source—"

"Shades of Antaeus!" thought I.

"Some day," old Kohokumu rambled on, "when I am really old, I shall be reported of men as drowned in the sea. This will be an idle thought of men. In truth, I shall have returned into the arms of my mother, there to rest under the heart of her breast until the second birth of me, when I shall emerge into the sun a flashing youth of splendor like Maui himself when he was golden young."

"A queer religion," I commented.

"When I was younger I muddled my poor head over queerer religions," old Kohokumu retorted. "But listen, O Young Wise One, to my elderly wisdom. This I know: as I grow old I seek less for the truth from without me, and find more of the truth from within me. Why have I thought this thought of my return to my mother and of my rebirth from my mother into the sun? You do not know. I do not know, save that, without whisper of man's voice or printed word, without prompting from otherwhere, this thought has arisen from within me, from the deeps of me that are as deep as the sea. I am not a god. I do not make things. Therefore I have not made this thought. I do not know its father or its mother. It is of old time before me, and therefore it is true. Man does not make truth. Man, if he be not blind, only recognizes truth when he sees it. Is this thought that I have thought a dream?"

"Perhaps it is you that are a dream," I laughed. "And that I and sky and sea and the iron-hard land are dreams, all dreams."

"I have often thought that," he assured me soberly. "It may well be so. Last night I dreamed I was a lark bird, a beautiful singing lark of the sky like the larks on the upland pastures of Haleakala. And I flew up, up toward the sun, singing, singing, as old Kohokumu never sang. I tell you now that I dreamed I was a lark bird singing in the sky. But may not I, the real I, be the lark bird? And may not the telling of it be the dream that I, the lark bird, am dreaming now? Who are you to tell me aye or no? Dare you tell me I am not a lark bird asleep and dreaming that I am old Kohokumu?"

I shrugged my shoulders, and he continued triumphantly.

"And how do you know but what you are old Maui himself asleep and dreaming that you are John Lakana talking with me in a canoe? And may you not awake, old Maui yourself, and scratch your sides and say that you had a funny dream in which you dreamed you were a haole?"

"I don't know" I admitted. "Besides, you wouldn't believe me."

"There is much more in dreams than we know," he assured me with great solemnity. "Dreams go deep, all the way down, maybe to before the beginning. May not old Maui have only dreamed he pulled Hawaii up from the bottom of the sea? Then would this Hawaii land be a dream, and you and I and the squid there only parts of Maui's dream? And the lark bird, too?"

He sighed and let his head sink on his breast.

"And I worry my old head about the secrets undiscoverable," he resumed, "until I grow tired and want to forget, and so I drink swipes and go fishing, and sing old songs, and dream I am a lark bird singing in the sky. I like that best of all, and often I dream it when I have drunk much swipes—"

In great dejection of mood he peered down into the lagoon through the water glass.

"There will be no more bites for a while," he announced. "The fish sharks are prowling around, and we shall have to wait until they are gone. And so that the time shall not be heavy, I will sing you the canoe-hauling song to Lono. You remember:

"Give to me the trunk of the tree, O Lono!
Give me the tree's main root, O Lono!
Give me the ear of the tree, O Lono!—"

"For the love of mercy, don't sing!" I cut him short. "I've got a headache, and your singing hurts. You may be in devilish fine form to-day, but your throat is rotten. I'd rather you talked about dreams, or told me whoppers."

"It is too bad that you are sick, and you so young," he conceded cheerily. "And I shall not sing any more. I shall tell you something that is no dream and no whopper, but is what I know to have happened. Not very long ago there lived here, on the beach beside this very lagoon, a young boy whose name was Keikiwai, which, as you know, means Water Baby. He was truly a water baby. His gods were the sea and fish gods, and he was born with knowledge of the language of fishes, which the fishes did not know until the sharks found it out one day when they heard him talk it.

"It happened this way. The word had been brought, and the commands, by swift runners, that the king was making a progress around the island, and that on the next day a *luau* was to be served him by the dwellers here of Waihee. It was always a hardship, when the king made a progress, for the few dwellers in small places to fill his many stomachs with food. For he came always with his wife and her women, with his priests and sorcerers, his dancers and flute players and hula singers, and fighting men and servants, and his high chiefs with their wives, and sorcerers and fighting men and servants.

"Sometimes, in small places like Waihee, the path of his journey was marked afterward by leanness and famine. But a king must be fed, and it is not good to anger a king. So, like warning in advance of disaster, Waihee heard of his coming, and all food-getters of field and pond and mountain and sea were busied with getting food for the feast. And behold, everything was got, from the choicest of royal taro to sugar-cane joints for the roasting, from opihis to limu, from fowl to wild pig and poi-fed puppies—everything save one thing. The fishermen failed to get lobsters.

"Now be it known that the king's favorite food was lobster. He esteemed it above all kao-kao (food), and his runners had made special mention of it. And there were no lobsters, and it is not good to anger a king in the belly of him. Too many sharks had come inside the reef. That was the trouble. A young girl and an old man had been eaten by them. And of the young men who dared dive for lobsters, one was eaten, and one lost an arm, and another lost one hand and one foot.

"But there was Keikiwai, the Water Baby, only eleven years old, but half fish himself and talking the language of fishes. To his father the head men came, begging him to send the Water Baby to get lobsters to fill the king's belly and divert his anger.

"Now this, what happened, was known and observed. For the fishermen and their women, and the taro growers and the bird catchers, and the head men, and all Waihee, came down and stood back from the edge of the rock where the Water Baby stood and looked down at the lobsters far beneath on the bottom.

"And a shark, looking up with its cat's eyes, observed him, and sent out the shark call of 'fresh meat' to assemble all the sharks in the lagoon. For the sharks work thus together, which is why they are strong. And the sharks answered the call till there were forty of them, long ones and short ones and lean ones and round ones, forty of them by count; and they talked to one another, saying: 'Look at that titbit of a child, that morsel delicious of human-flesh sweetness without the salt of the sea in it, of which salt we have too much, savory and good to eat, melting to delight under our hearts as our bellies embrace it and extract from it its sweet.'

"Much more they said, saying: 'He has come for the lobsters. When he dives in he is for one of us. Not like the old man we ate yesterday, tough to dryness with age, nor like the young men whose members were too hard-muscled, but tender, so tender that he will melt in our gullets ere our bellies receive him. When he dives in, we will all rush for him, and the lucky one of us will get him, and, gulp, he will be gone, one bite and one swallow, into the belly of the luckiest one of us.'

"And Keikiwai, the Water Baby, heard the conspiracy, knowing the shark language; and he addressed a prayer, in the shark language, to the shark god Moku-halii, and the sharks heard and waved their tails to one another and winked their cat's eyes in token that they understood his talk. And then he said: 'I shall now dive for a lobster for the king. And no hurt shall befall me, because the shark with the shortest tail is my friend and will protect me.'

"And, so saying, he picked up a chunk of lava rock and tossed it into the water, with a big splash, twenty feet to one side. The forty sharks rushed for the splash, while he dived and by the time they discovered they had missed him, he had gone to the bottom and come back and climbed out, within his hand a fat lobster, a wahine lobster, full of eggs, for the king.

"'Ha!' said the sharks, very angry. 'There is among us a traitor.

The titbit of a child, the morsel of sweetness, has spoken, and has exposed the one among us who has saved him. Let us now measure the length of our tails!'

"Which they did, in a long row, side by side, the shorter-tailed ones cheating and stretching to gain length on themselves, the longer-tailed ones cheating and stretching in order not to be out-cheated and outstretched. They were very angry with the one with the shortest tail, and him they rushed upon from every side and devoured till nothing was left of him.

"Again they listened while they waited for the Water Baby to dive in. And again the Water Baby made his prayer in the shark language to Moku-halii, and said: 'The shark with the shortest tail is my friend and will protect me.' And again the Water Baby tossed in a chunk of lava, this time twenty feet away off to the other side. The sharks rushed for the splash, and in their haste ran into one another, and splashed with their tails till the water was all foam and they could see nothing, each thinking some other was swallowing the titbit. And the Water Baby came up and climbed out with another fat lobster for the king.

"And the thirty-nine sharks measured tails, devouring the one with the shortest tail, so that there were only thirty-eight sharks. And the Water Baby continued to do what I have said, and the sharks to do what I have told you, while for each shark that was eaten by his brothers there was another fat lobster laid on the rock for the king. Of course, there was much quarreling and argument among the sharks when it came to measuring tails; but in the end it worked out in rightness and justice, for, when only two sharks were left, they were the two biggest of the original forty.

"And the Water Baby again claimed the shark with the shortest tail was his friend, fooled the two sharks with another lava chunk, and brought up another lobster. The two sharks each claimed the other had the shorter tail, and each fought to eat the other, and the one with the longer tail won—"

"Hold, O Kohokumu!" I interrupted. "Remember that that shark had already—"

"I know just what you are going to say," he snatched his recital back from me. "And you are right. It took him so long to eat the thirty-ninth shark, for inside the thirty-ninth shark were already the nineteen other sharks he had eaten, and inside the fortieth shark were already the nineteen other sharks he had eaten, and he did not have the appetite he had started with. But do not forget he was a very big shark to begin with.

"It took him so long to eat the other shark, and the nineteen sharks inside the other shark, that he was still eating when darkness fell and the people of Waihee went away home with all the lobsters for the king. And didn't they find the last shark on the beach next morning dead and burst wide open with all he had eaten?"

Kohokumu fetched a full stop and held my eyes with his own shrewd ones.

"Hold, O Lakana!" he checked the speech that rushed to my tongue. "I know what next you would say. You would say that with my own eyes I did not see this, and therefore that I do not know what I have been telling you. But I do know, and I can prove it. My father's father knew the grandson of the Water Baby's father's uncle. Also, there, on the rocky point to which I point my finger now, is where the Water Baby stood and dived. I have dived for lobsters there myself. It is a great place for lobsters. Also, and often, have I seen sharks there. And there on the bottom, as I should know, for I have seen and counted them, are the thirty-nine laval rocks thrown in by the Water Baby as I have described."

"But—" I began.

"Ha!" he baffled me. "Look! While we have talked the fish have begun to bite."

He pointed to three of the bamboo poles erect and devil-dancing in token that fish were hooked and struggling on the lines beneath. As he bent to his paddle, he muttered, for my benefit:

"Of course I know. The thirty-nine lava rocks are still there. You can count them any day for yourself. Of course I know, and I know for a fact."

THE HAWAIIAN LANGUAGE has seven consonants (*h, k, l, m, n, p, w*). The five vowels are pronounced as follows:

a — ah, as in c*a*r   o — oh, as in *o*wn
e — eh, as in v*e*in   u — oo, as in r*u*le
i — ee, as in mar*i*ne

In addition, a number of vowel combinations resemble diphthongs:

ai — eye, as in m*i*le   ei — eh, as in v*e*in
ao and au — ow, as in h*ow*   oe — oy, as in b*o*y

Otherwise every letter is sounded separately. Generally each word is lightly accented on the next to last syllable, but some words have no accent.

The following are some common Hawaiian words, many still in current usage in the Islands, with their English equivalents:

a	of	hei	net
ae	yes	heiau	place of worship
ahi	tuna	holoku	gown often with
ahuula	feather cape		a train)
aina	land	hookupu	donation
alii	chief	hoomalimali	flattery
aloha	love, hello, good-bye	hoomanawanui	take it easy, patience
auwe	alas	huhu	angry
awiwi	hurry, quick	hui	meeting, society
		huki	pull
halakahiki	pineapple	hula	song and dance
halau	long house, school		
hale	house	i	in
hana	work	ia	fish
haole	foreigner, white person	imu	underground oven
haumana	student	imua	forward, in front of
he	a, an		

ka	the	mahimahi	dolphin
kahili	royal standard	mai	this way, hither
kahuna	expert, priest	maile	a vine
kai	sea	makai	seaward
kalo	taro	malihini	stranger,
kalua	roast		newcomer
kamaaina	native-born	malo	loincloth
kamalii	children	maloo	dry
kanaka	man, a native	mauka	inland
kane	man	mauna	mountain
kapa	tapa, dress	mele	chant
kapu	forbidden, sacred	moa	fowl
kauka	doctor	moe	sleep
kaukau	food (colloquial)	moo	reptile
kauwila	spearwood	muumuu	gown, a Mother
keakea	white		Hubbard
keiki	child		
kiawe	algarroba (tree)	nui	big, great
kihei	robe, shawl		
kii	puppet, image	o	of, lest
kokua	help	oe	you
komo mai	come in	ohelo	a mountain berry
kuhina nui	premier	ohia	a tree
kumu	teacher	okole	posterior
		okoleohao	Hawaiian liquor
la	sun	oli	chant
lani	sky, heavens	olohe	hula expert
lauoho	hair	opihi	shellfish
lei	necklace (usually	opu	stomach
	of flowers)		
lele	to fly, jump	paa	stop
limu	kelp	paakai	salt
loa	long, very	paakiki	stubborn
lomilomi	massage	pake	Chinese
luau	feast	pali	cliff
luna	foremost,	paniolo	cowboy,
	overseer		Spaniard
		papa	board
mahalo	thanks	pau	finished
mahele	division	pa'u	skirt

pehea	How? How are you? How is it?	pupu	appetizer
		pupule	crazy
pilau	stench, smelly	tabu	see *kapu*
pilikia	trouble		
pipi	beef, cattle	uahi	smoke
pipioma	roast beef	uku	insect, flea
poha	gooseberry		
poi	taro paste	wahine	woman, female
puaa	pig	wai	water
puka	hole	wela	hot
pule	prayer	wiki	quick, hurry

SOME BASIC BOOKS ABOUT HAWAII

Allen, Gwenfread. *Hawaii's War Years, 1941–1945.* Honolulu: University of Hawaii Press, 1950.
Judd, Gerrit P. *Dr. Judd, Hawaii's Friend.* Honolulu: University of Hawaii Press, 1960.
———. *Hawaii: An Informal History.* New York: Collier Books, 1961.
Krauss, Bob. *Here's Hawaii.* New York: Coward-McCann, Inc., 1960.
———. *Bob Krauss' Travel Guide to the Hawaiian Islands.* New York: Coward-McCann, 1963.
——— (with William P. Alexander). *Grove Farm Plantation. The Biography of a Hawaiian Sugar Plantation.* Palo Alto, Cal.: Pacific Books, 1965.
Kuykendall, Ralph S. *The Hawaiian Kingdom, 1778–1854: Foundation and Transformation.* Honolulu: University of Hawaii Press, 1938.
———. *The Hawaiian Kingdom, 1854–1874: Twenty Critical Years.* Honolulu: University of Hawaii Press, 1953.
Norbeck, Edward. *Pineapple Town: Hawaii.* Berkeley and Los Angeles: University of California Press, 1959.
Rademaker, John A. *These Are Americans: The Japanese Americans in Hawaii in World War II.* Palo Alto, Cal.: Pacific Books, 1951.

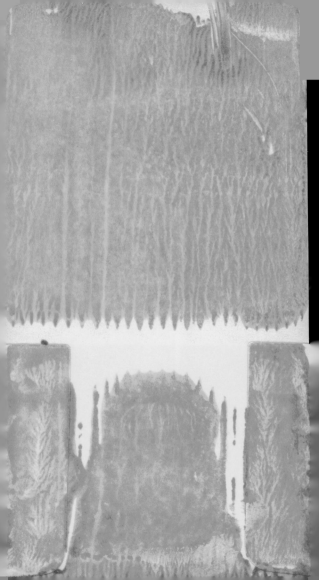

Date Due

Includes prose writings on Hawaiian history and Hawaiian traditions and places and a section of short stories on Hawaii by Robert Louis Stevenson and Jack London, among others.